APPRENTICESHIPS

Construction

Electrotechnical Installation and Maintenance

Handbook

LEVEL 3

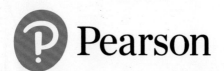

Published by Pearson Education Limited, 80 Strand, London, WC2R 0RL.

www.pearsonschoolsandfecolleges.co.uk

Text © JTL 2018
Edited by Just Content
Typeset by PDQ Digital Media Solutions Ltd.
Original illustrations © Pearson 2018
Picture research by Integra
Cover photo/illustration © TADDEUS, Flegere / Shutterstock.com

The right of JTL to be identified as author of this work has been asserted by them in accordance with the Copyright, Designs and Patents Act 1988.

First published 2018

21 20 19
10 9 8 7 6 5 4 3 2

British Library Cataloguing in Publication Data
A catalogue record for this book is available from the British Library.

ISBN 9 781 292 25984 0

Printed in Slovakia by Neografia

Websites
Pearson Education Limited is not responsible for the content of any external internet sites. It is essential for tutors to preview each website before using it in class so as to ensure that the URL is still accurate, relevant and appropriate. We suggest that tutors bookmark useful websites and consider enabling students to access them through the school/college intranet.

Note from the publisher
Pearson has robust editorial processes, including answer and fact checks, to ensure the accuracy of the content in this publication, and every effort is made to ensure this publication is free of errors. We are, however, only human, and occasionally errors do occur. Pearson is not liable for any misunderstandings that arise as a result of errors in this publication, but it is our priority to ensure that the content is accurate. If you spot an error, please do contact us at resourcescorrections@pearson.com so we can make sure it is corrected.

Contents

Introduction

This book is designed to support the Level 3 Electrotechnical qualification (installation or maintenance). This qualification forms part of the industry recognised Electrotechnical Apprenticeship, developed as part of the trailblazer apprenticeship initiative. It has been developed working with a wide group of employers who developed the standard for the Apprenticeship. This book (alongside Book B) is designed to support the following qualifications:

- 5357-03 City and Guilds Level 3 Electrotechnical qualification (installation or maintenance)
- 601/7345/2 EAL Level 3 Electrotechnical qualification.

Who the qualification is aimed at

The new apprenticeship qualification is aimed at those looking to work as installation or maintenance electricians. It is designed to train and assess you to be recognised as occupationally competent by the industry. You will need to achieve the Level 3 Electrotechnical qualification as part of your apprenticeship.

Electricians will need to display a series of knowledge, skills and behaviours to achieve the apprenticeship.

Knowledge and skills

You must understand and apply the principles, practices and legislation for the:

- termination and connection of conductors, cables and cords in electrical systems
- preparation and installation of wiring systems and electrotechnical equipment
- inspection, testing, commissioning and certification of electrotechnical systems and equipment
- diagnosing and correcting of electrical faults in electrotechnical systems and equipment
- electrical principles associated with the design, building, installation and maintenance of electrical equipment and systems.

You will also need to be able to oversee and organise the work environment and apply health and safety and environmental regulations, guidance notes and relevant codes of practice and understand the requirements of the current edition of the Wiring Regulations.

Behaviours

Electricians will be expected to:

- work reliably and effectively without close supervision
- accept responsibility for the work of themselves and others, allocating and supervising tasks where necessary
- use oral, written and electronic methods of communication

- work effectively with colleagues, other trades, clients, suppliers and the public

- contribute to sustainable development and exercise responsibilities ethically

- maintain and enhance competence in their areas of expertise.

About this book

This book supports three mandatory units (where units have both performance and knowledge versions, this is counted as one unit) of the Level 3 Electrotechnical qualification. It works in combination with Book B, which covers the remaining mandatory units. Between them they will cover all the core mandatory information you need for the qualification, before choosing the pathway you will follow to specialise in either installation or maintenance.

Each chapter of the book relates to a particular unit of the Diploma and provides the information needed to gain the required knowledge and understanding of that area.

This book has been prepared by expert JTL trainers, who have many years of experience of training learners and delivering electrical qualifications. The content of each unit will underpin the various topics which you will be assessed on by your awarding body.

Each chapter has summary features to check your knowledge throughout, as well as a set of multiple-choice questions to allow you to test your knowledge and understanding. Each chapter also features an assessment spread, giving you information and support for preparing for assessment.

This book will also be a useful reference tool for you in your professional life once you have gained your qualifications and are a practicing electrician.

Important note

It is important to note that this book is intended to be used for training. It should not be regarded as being relevant to an actual installation. You should always make specific reference to the British Standards or manufacturer's data when designing electrical installations.

ActiveBook

This book also contains access to an electronic version of this book, known as an ActiveBook, hosted on Pearson's ActiveLearn service. This contains an e-book version of the book, which can be annotated and accessed through the Pearson ActiveLearn platform on a range of devices.

The ActiveBook also contains a number of additional features, including a range of videos and animations designed to complement the content in the book and to help re-inforce knowledge. These videos can be found by clicking the hotspot buttons that can be found on the relevant pages of the ActiveBook and by referring to the resources list of the book.

Features of the book

This book has been fully illustrated with artworks and photographs. These will help to give you more information about a concept or procedure, as well as helping you to follow a step-by-step procedure or identify a particular tool or material.

This book also contains a number of different features to help your learning and development.

JTL tip

This feature highlights key tips and advice from JTL tutors to help remind you of important things to think about when working on this qualification.

Safety

This feature gives you guidance for working safely in the industry when working with electrical installations.

Example

This feature shows you how a calculation is made, talking you through each step with a clear explanation.

Working life

This feature gives you a chance to read about and debate a real life scenario or problem. Why has the situation occurred? What would you do?

Key term

These are new or difficult words. They are picked out in bold in the text and then defined in the margin.

Summary

These are a series of short questions, appearing at key intervals in the book. These give you an opportunity to check and revise your knowledge.

Activity

▶ These are short activities and research opportunities, designed to help you gain further information about and understanding of a topic area.

Getting ready for assessment

▶ This feature provides guidance for preparing for the practical and written assessment. It will give you advice on using the theory you have learned and how to prepare your thinking for the assessment.

The feature also includes a series of multiple-choice questions to help test your knowledge and guide revision and preparation for assessment.

Acknowledgements

JTL would like to express its appreciation to those members of staff who contributed to the development of this book, ensuring that the professional standards expected were delivered and generally overseeing the high quality of the final product. Without their commitment this project would not have been seen through successfully.

Particular thanks to Dave Allan, who revised the content of the previous editions of this book and prepared extensive new materials to cover the new specifications.

The Summary and Getting ready for assessment features were prepared by William Gibbs who also provided many invaluable comments to the development of the book.

Photo acknowledgements

The author and publisher would like to thank the following individuals and organisations for permission to reproduce photographs:

ACKNOWLEDGEMENTS:

Text Credits:

The Health and Safety Executive: Contains public sector information published by the Health and Safety Executive and licensed under the Open Government Licence p27, p36-38, p63;

HM government: The Building Regulations, retrieved from https://assets.publishing. service.gov.uk/government/uploads/system/uploads/attachment_data/file/540326/ BR_PDF_AD__L1A__2013_with_2016_amendments.pdf Contains public sector information published by the Health and Safety Executive and licensed under the Open Government Licence p58;

The Joint Industry Board: Example of an ECS Installation Electrician card, used with permission from JIB p142;

The British Standards Institution: Clauses 559.3.1, 559.4.1, 559.5.1, 559.5.1.201, 559.5.1.204, 559.5.1.207, 559.5.1.208, 559.5.2, 559.5.5 and 559.9 from BS 7671:2008+A3:2015. Requirements for Electrical Installations, IET Wiring Regulations, Eighteenth Edition, BS 7671:2018 (Electrical Regulations), used with permission from BSI p427;

The British Standards Institution: Table 55.3 from BS 7671:2008+A3:2015. Requirements for Electrical Installations, IET Wiring Regulations, Eighteenth Edition, BS 7671:2018 (Electrical Regulations), used with permission from BSI p428;

Photo Credits:

(Key: b-bottom; c-centre; l-left; r-right; t-top)

123RF: Aleksandar Kosev 1, Nosua 51b1, Nopparat Klaewklong 52, Roman023 93, Asier Romero Carballo 108t, Dmitry Kalinovsky 109, Petervick167 121, Carolyn Franks 171, Irochka 214; **Alamy Stock Photo:** Maxstock 71c, Phil Degginger 255, Krys Bailey 259, Helene Rogers/Art Directors & TRIP 285 & 302, David J. Green – electrical 289, 273, 301 & 394, Stu49 293 & 309, Jean Schweitzer 335,

Geoff du Feu 439b, David Gee 424t; © **Dave Allan** 386 & 392**; Getty Images:** Stu49/iStock/Getty Images Plus 314; **Pearson Education Asia Ltd:** Coleman Yuen 205; **Pearson Education Ltd:** Gareth Boden 22, 42, 43t, 43b, 84, 85, 92, 96t, 96b, 97t, 97c, 97b, 154, 272, 284t, 284b, 249t, 298, 344, 402, 415t, Naki Kouyioumtzis 41, 407, 249b & 253, David Sanderson 51t1, 51c1, 51c2, 51t2, 71bl & 74bl, Studio 8 70bl, 71tl, 72, 73bl, 73br & 74tl; Safelincs: 51; **Science Photo Library:** GIPhotoStock 287, 288t & 288b, Andrew Lambert Photography 384; **Shutterstock:** Claudia Otte 21, Paul Daniels 27, Jin young-in 44, Solares 53, Ssuaphotos 55, Bruce Au 70bc, Alexey Nikolaew 70br, Olinchuk 71tr, Edward Westmacott 71br, Elnur 74bc, Phovoir 74br, LoopAll 81, SocoXbreed 83, Israel Hervas Bengochea 108b, Oleksiy Mark 116, **Daniel M Ernst** 142, WestEnd61 165, Julio Embun 181, Frantic00 110, Shutterstock 223, Albert Pego 332, Kalabi Yau 387, Tr3gin 414, Jiri Hera 415c, Ivaschenko Roman 415b, Jouke van Keulen 416t, HomeStudio 416b, Piotr Wardynski 424b, IB Photography 425, Alaettin YILDIRIM 438t, **Skylines** 438b; **Sid Frisby** 439t.

CHAPTER 1

Understand health, safety and environmental considerations

All employers, including the self-employed, have duties under the Health and Safety at Work Act 1974 to ensure the health and safety of themselves and others affected by what they do. This includes people working for employers and the self-employed (for example, part-time workers, trainees and subcontractors), those who use the workplace and equipment they provide, those who visit their premises, and people affected by their work (for example, neighbours or the general public).

This chapter will provide learners with an understanding of the relevant health and safety legislation, practices and procedures when installing and maintaining electrical systems and equipment. The knowledge covered in this chapter underpins the practical application of health and safety legislation, practices and procedures.

This chapter will cover the following learning outcomes.

1. Understand how relevant legislation applies in the workplace.

2. Understand the procedures for dealing with environmental and health and safety situations in the work environment.

3. Be able to demonstrate and understand the procedures for establishing a safe working environment.

4. Understand the requirements for identifying and dealing with hazards in the work environment.

1. Understand how relevant legislation applies in the workplace

There are many different sites and projects, and therefore many acts and regulations. It would be impossible to predict every site that you will ever work on, but this section will look at the most important and commonly applied legislation.

As a worker, these acts and regulations provide a legal framework that protects you. This includes the building in which you are working and the electrical supply that you are working with. They also ensure that you do not cause harm to yourself or others through bad practices.

Health and safety legislation

Qualification mapping

This chapter supports:

- Units 101 and 001 (Understand Health, Safety and Environmental Considerations) from the City & Guilds Level 3 Electrotechnical qualification (5357-03)
- Unit NETK3-01 Understand Health, Safety and Environmental Considerations from the EAL Level 3 Electrotechnical qualification

Health and Safety at Work Act 1974 (HASAWA)

The Health and Safety at Work Act 1974 (HASAWA) is a piece of primary legislation known as an 'enabling Act'. It sets out broad health and safety requirements but also makes provision for the formation and enactment of more specific regulations (also known as Statutory Instruments) – these regulations set out the basic principles by which health and safety at work is regulated.

One way to think about HASAWA is as a general umbrella, under which there are many specific regulations. These regulations are also used by government authorities to control the standard of working conditions throughout industry.

Figure 1.1: The Health and Safety at Work Act is an 'umbrella' act covering many other regulations

The Act is statutory; in other words, it is binding in law and criminal penalties can be imposed on people found guilty of malpractice and misconduct. All employers are covered by HASAWA, but the Act places certain specific duties on both employers and employees, which must be complied with by law.

Each employee – and this includes you – is also required by law to assist and co-operate with their employer and others in making sure that safe working environments are maintained, that all safety equipment is fully and correctly used and that all safety procedures are followed. You should work safely and use common sense at all times.

There are many sections to the Act, but the main ones affecting you – Section 2 (duties of employers to their employees) and Section 7 (duties of employees) – are shown in Table 1.1.

Section 2: Employers	Section 7: Employees
All employers have a duty to:	As an employee you have a duty to:
• care for the welfare, health and safety of their employees where it is practicable for them to do so	• look after your own safety and that of your colleagues and people around them
• provide and maintain safe equipment, tools and plant within the workplace	• not intentionally or recklessly interfere with or misuse anything provided for your health and safety
• ensure working conditions are safe and hygienic	• take reasonable care at work for the health and safety of yourself and others who may be affected by what you do or do not do • bring to your employer's attention any situation you consider dangerous
• provide proper personal protective equipment (PPE) and make sure it is used correctly	• use any PPE provided correctly
• make sure articles and substances are used, handled, stored and transported safely	• help the employer to meet their statutory obligations
• provide any necessary information, instruction, training and supervision to ensure the health and safety of employees • make sure everyone can get in and out of the workplace safely • provide adequate facilities and arrangements for welfare at work.	• co-operate with your employer on health and safety matters • bring to your employer's attention any weakness in their welfare, health and safety arrangements.

Table 1.1: Summary of the duties of employers and employees

The employer must also:

- draw up a written health and safety policy statement if there are five or more employees

- carry out risk assessments for all the company's work activities and review these (and record the assessments if there are five or more employees)

- identify and implement control measures, and tell employees about them
- consult with any official trade union safety representatives
- establish a safety committee if requested in writing by any two or more safety representatives within three months of the request.

In general terms, the Health and Safety at Work Act 1974 (HASAWA) allows employers the freedom to decide how they wish to handle the risks that they identify, using guidance and ACOPs (Approved Codes of Practice) to help them. In cases where the risks are considered too great to be left to employers to handle, more specific regulations (the Statutory Instruments) are used.

Such regulations identify specific actions to be taken, some of which may be absolute (i.e. they *must* be done). Many of these regulations apply to all workplaces (although there are some specialist areas e.g. nuclear power). The most relevant to you are detailed below.

Management of Health and Safety at Work Regulations 1999

The Management of Health and Safety at Work Regulations 1999 explain what employers are required to do to manage health and safety requirements under the HASAWA. They apply to every work activity.

Employers must carry out a risk assessment (and, for companies with five or more employees, record any significant findings), implement any control measures identified (appointing competent people to do this) and arrange for appropriate information and training for employees.

You'll cover risk assessment later in more detail on pages 62–67.

Activity

▶ Consider your own workplace and working practice. What risks do you think might need a formal assessment? For example, is any work done that involves working at height or manual handling? Make a list of six other areas that may need formal assessment.

JTL tips

As far as the EAWR is concerned, a trainee like you is an employee – so you have the same duties and responsibilities as any other employee. It is the duty of every duty holder to comply with the provisions of these Regulations in so far as they relate to matters within their control.

Electricity at Work Regulations 1989 (EAWR)

These Regulations impose general health and safety requirements to do with electricity at work on employers, self-employed people and employees.

- Every employer and self-employed person has a duty to comply with the provisions of the Regulations, as far as they relate to matters within their control.
- Every employee has the duty to co-operate with their employer, as far as necessary to enable the Regulations to be complied with.
- Because these are statutory regulations, penalties can be imposed on people found guilty of malpractice or misconduct.

The EAWR are designed to take account of the responsibilities that many employees in the electrical trades and professions have to take on as part of their job. The level of responsibility you hold to make sure the Regulations are met depends on the amount of control you have over electrical safety in any particular situation.

The Regulations refer to a person as a 'duty holder' in respect of systems, equipment, and conductors. The Regulations clearly define the various duty holders. Table 1.2 shows the definitions of the duty holders.

Employer	Any person or body who employs one or more individuals under a contract of employment or Apprenticeship or provides training under the schemes to which HASAWA applies
Self-employed	An individual who works for gain or reward other than under contract of employment, whether or not he or she employs others
Employee	Regulation 3(2)(b) repeats the duties placed on employees by HASAWA, which are equivalent to those placed on employers and self-employed people where these matters are within their control. This includes trainees like you, who are considered employees under the Regulations

Table 1.2: Duties under the Electricity at Work Regulations 1989

Working life

Tom is working on an electrical system while his colleague Ahmed is preparing to do some work nearby. Tom energises the circuit to do his work but, as Ahmed is doing a different task, he doesn't think it is necessary to tell him exactly what he is doing.

- Why is Tom a duty holder in this situation? You will need to think about whether the circumstances are in Tom's control and what his responsibilities are.
- What are the dangers here?
- What should Tom do immediately?

Absolute/reasonably practicable

Duties in some regulations are regarded as either 'absolute' or 'reasonably practicable'. Table 1.3 offers a guide as to how to interpret these terms.

Absolute	The requirement must be met regardless of cost or any other consideration.
Reasonably practicable	The person doing the work must take in to account: • the amount of risk to health and safety involved • the amount of time, trouble, expense and effort it would take to reduce these risks.

Table 1.3: Definitions of absolute and reasonably practicable

For example, in a home you would expect to find a fireguard in front of a fire to stop young children being injured. This is a cheap and effective way of preventing accidents, so it would be a reasonably practicable situation.

However, if the costs or technical difficulties of taking certain steps to prevent those risks are very high, it might not be reasonably practicable to take those steps. The greater the degree of risk, the less you should be concerned about the cost of measures needed to prevent that risk.

For these Regulations, the risk is often that of death from electrocution, yet the precautions are often simple and cheap to take. Therefore, the level of duty is likely to be an absolute duty in order to reduce the risk.

Safety

Using insulation around cables is one example of a simple, cheap precaution to reduce the danger of electrocution.

Table 1.4 summarises the particular Electricity at Work Regulations you are most likely to have to comply with, showing whether they are regarded as 'absolute' or 'reasonably practicable'.

Regulation	Absolute or reasonably practicable?	What the Regulation says
Regulation 4	reasonably practicable	All electrical systems shall be constructed and maintained to prevent danger. All work activities are to be carried out so as not to give rise to danger.
Regulation 5	absolute	No electrical equipment is to be used where its strength and capability may be exceeded so as to give rise to danger.
Regulation 6	reasonably practicable	Electrical equipment sited in adverse or hazardous environments must be suitable for those conditions.
Regulation 7	reasonably practicable	Permanent safeguarding or suitable positioning of live conductors is required.
Regulation 8	absolute	Equipment must be earthed or other suitable precautions must be taken: for example, the use of residual current devices, double-insulated equipment, reduced voltage equipment, etc.
Regulation 9	absolute	Nothing is to be placed in an earthed circuit conductor that might, without suitable precautions, give rise to danger by breaking the electrical continuity or introducing high impedance.
Regulation 10	absolute	All joints and connections in systems must be mechanically and electrically suitable for use.
Regulation 11	absolute	Suitable protective devices should be installed in each system to ensure all parts of the system and users of the system are safeguarded from the effects of fault conditions.
Regulation 12	absolute	Where necessary to prevent danger, suitable means shall be available for cutting off the electrical supply to any electrical equipment. Note: drawings of the distribution equipment and methods of identifying circuits should be readily available. Ideally, mains-signed isolation switches should be provided in practical work areas.
Regulation 13	absolute	Adequate precautions must be taken to prevent electrical equipment that has been made dead in order to prevent danger from becoming live while any work is carried out.
Regulation 14	absolute	No work can be carried out on live electrical equipment unless this can be properly justified. This means that risk assessments are required. If such work is to be carried out, suitable precautions must be taken to prevent injury.
Regulation 15	absolute	Adequate working space, adequate means of access and adequate lighting shall be provided at all electrical equipment on which or near which work is being done in circumstances that may give rise to danger.
Regulation 16	absolute	No person shall engage in work that requires technical knowledge or experience to prevent danger or injury, unless he or she has that knowledge or experience, or is under appropriate supervision.

Table 1.4: Examples of absolute and reasonably practicable duties in the Electricity at Work Regulations 1989

Workplace (Health, Safety and Welfare) Regulations 1992

The Workplace (Health, Safety and Welfare) Regulations 1992 aim to ensure workplaces meet the health, safety and welfare needs of all members of a workforce, including people with disabilities.

Several of the Regulations require things to be 'suitable'. Regulation 2 (3) makes it clear that things should be suitable for anyone, and this includes people with disabilities. Where necessary, parts of the workplace – especially doors, passageways, stairs, showers, washbasins, lavatories and workstations – should be made accessible for people with disabilities.

Here are some of the definitions used in this legislation.

- **Workplace** – these Regulations apply to a wide range of workplaces: not only factories, shops and offices but also schools, hospitals, hotels and places of entertainment. 'Workplace' includes the common parts of shared buildings, private roads and paths on industrial estates and business parks, and temporary worksites (except workplaces involving construction work on construction sites).

- **Work** – this can be as an employee or self-employed person.

- **Premises** – this includes any place, including an outdoor place.

- **Domestic premises** – this means a private dwelling. These Regulations do not apply to domestic premises, and exclude home-workers. However, they do apply to hotels, to nursing homes and to parts of workplaces where 'domestic' staff are employed, such as the kitchens of hostels.

- **Disabled person** – as defined by Section 1 of the Disability Discrimination Act 1995.

Health in the workplace

This section of the Regulations looks at the general working environment of people in the workplace. Table 1.5 shows the considerations that the Regulations say need to be made in the workplace for some of the key health issues.

> ### Activity
>
> ▶ How does the Disability Discrimination Act 1995 define a disabled person? See if you can find out, on the internet or in your local library.

> ### Safety
>
> Windows or other openings may provide sufficient ventilation but, where necessary, mechanical ventilation systems should be provided and regularly maintained.

Health issue	What to expect/provide
Ventilation	If you are working inside, your workplace should be adequately ventilated with fresh, clean air, but not draughty.
Indoor temperatures	Individuals have different **thermal comfort**, making it hard to create an environment that will satisfy everyone. For workplaces where the activity is mainly seated, such as offices, the temperature should be at least 16°C; for more physical work, it should be at least 13°C (unless other laws require lower temperatures).
	If working in extreme temperatures, your employer should provide the correct clothing and equipment. You should also be medically fit to carry out the work and take precautions to remain so: for example, drinking water regularly in a very hot environment. Work can also be organised to minimise exposure to more extreme environments.
Lighting	Every workplace should have sufficient, suitable lighting and be supplemented by natural light. Automatic emergency lighting, powered by an independent source, should be provided where sudden loss of light would create a risk.
Cleanliness and waste materials	Every workplace and the furniture, furnishings and fittings should be kept clean, and it should be possible to keep the surfaces of floors, walls and ceilings clean. Cleaning and waste removal should be regular and proper facilities should be provided for storing waste.
Space	Workplaces should not be crowded – there should be enough room for you to move around freely and safely, including the height of ceilings. The Regulations suggest that the amount of space for each person should not be less than 11 cubic metres.
Workstations and seating	Workstations should be suitable for the people using them and the work they do. You should be able to leave your workstation swiftly in an emergency, as well as work comfortably at it. Seating should give adequate support for the lower back, and footrests should be provided for workers who cannot place their feet flat on the floor.

Table 1.5: Health issues in the workplace

Key term

Thermal comfort – an individual's preferred temperature. Environmental factors (such as humidity and sources of heat in the workplace) combine with personal factors (such as the clothing a worker is wearing and how physically demanding their work is) to influence this

Safety in the workplace

Table 1.6 shows the considerations that will need to be made in the workplace for some of the key safety issues.

Safety
It is often difficult for drivers to see behind their vehicle when they are reversing. As far as possible, traffic routes should be planned so that drivers do not need to reverse, by using one-way systems and drive-through loading areas.

Safety issue	What to expect/provide
Maintenance	The workplace, certain equipment, devices and systems should be maintained in an efficient working order. Maintenance is required for any equipment and devices that could cause a risk to health, safety or welfare if a fault occurred. The condition of buildings needs to be monitored to ensure they are stable and solid enough to use. There could be risks from the normal running for the work process (for example, vibration or floor loadings) as well as foreseeable risks (such as fire in a cylinder store).
Floors and traffic routes	Workplaces should be organised so that pedestrians and vehicles are separated, so that each can move safely. Appropriate speed limits should be set and route markings clearly set down.
Escalators and staircases	Open sides of staircases should be fenced with an upper rail at 900 mm or higher, and a lower rail. A handrail should be provided on at least one side of every staircase. Escalators and moving walkways should be maintained and equipped with necessary stop controls that are easy to identify and get to.
Windows, doors and gates	These should be cleaned and maintained and capable of being opened, closed and adjusted safely. Doors and gates should open both ways. Power-operated doors and gates should have safety features to prevent people getting stuck or trapped, along with an easily identifiable (and accessible) stop button. If transparent or translucent, these should be made from safety material and protected against breakage. They should be marked to make them visible.

Table 1.6: Safety issues in the workplace

Welfare

Table 1.7 shows the considerations that will need to be made in the workplace for some of the key welfare issues.

Welfare issue	What to expect/provide
Sanitary conveniences and washing facilities	These should be readily accessible, and clean, with running hot and cold water and drying equipment. If required, showers should also be provided. Men and women should have separate facilities, unless each facility is in a separate room with a lockable door and used by only one person at a time.
Drinking water	There should be an adequate supply of high-quality drinking water.
Accommodation for clothing and changing	Adequate, suitable and secure space should be provided to store workers' own clothing and special clothing and provide an opportunity to dry clothes if necessary. There should also be a place to change privately if you need to and store clothing securely.
Rest and eating meals	Suitable, sufficient and readily accessible rest facilities should be provided with seating. Similar facilities should be provided where workers regularly eat meals at work. Facilities should also be provided where food would otherwise be likely to be contaminated. Suitable rest facilities should be provided for pregnant women and nursing mothers. They should be near to sanitary facilities and, where necessary, include the facility to lie down.

Table 1.7: Welfare issues in the workplace

Control of Substances Hazardous to Health Regulations 2002 (COSHH)

COSHH requires employers to control substances hazardous to health. A hazardous substance is anything that can harm your health when you work with it, if it is not properly controlled. Hazardous substances are found in nearly all workplaces, including factories, shops, mines, construction sites and offices. They include:

- substances used directly in work activities, such as glues, paints, cleaning agents
- substances generated during work activities, such as fumes from soldering and welding
- naturally occurring substances, such as grain dust, blood and bacteria.

The COSHH regulations cover the following:

- chemicals, products containing chemicals, fumes, dusts, vapours, mists and gases and biological agents (germs)
- asphyxiating gases
- germs that cause diseases such as leptospirosis or legionnaires' disease, and germs used in laboratories.

COSHH does not cover lead, asbestos or radioactive substances, as these have their own specific regulations.

Figure 1.2 shows the steps employers can take to prevent or reduce workers' exposure to hazardous substances.

Note that for Step 3, if it is reasonably practicable, exposure must be prevented by changing the process so that the hazardous substance is not required or generated. If prevention is not reasonably practicable, exposure should be adequately controlled by one or more of the measures outlined in the Regulations, noting that engineering controls and respiratory protective equipment have to be examined and tested at regular intervals.

Safety

Check the packaging on any substances that you use. If the packaging carries any of the hazard symbols covered later in this chapter (see pages 113–114), the substance is classed as a hazardous substance, so you will need to take extra care.

Work at Height Regulations 2005 (amended 2007)

The Work at Height Regulations 2005 (WAHR) apply to all work at height where there is a risk of a fall which could cause personal injury. The Regulations place a duty on employers, the self-employed, and any person that controls the work of others (for example, facilities managers or building owners who may contract others to work at height). The 2007 Amendment added a duty for those who work at height providing instruction or leadership to one or more people engaged in caving or climbing or any other similar activity.

Here are some of the definitions used in these Regulations.

- **At height** – this means at a height where a person could be injured falling from it, even if it is at or below ground level.

- **Work** – this includes moving around at a place of work (except by a staircase in a permanent workplace), but not travel to or from a place of work.

Step 1: Find out what hazardous substances are used in the workplace and the risks these substances pose to people's health

Step 2: Decide what precautions are needed before any work starts with hazardous substances

Step 3: Prevent people being exposed to hazardous substances or, where this is not reasonably practicable, control the exposure

Step 4: Make sure control measures are used and maintained properly, and that safety procedures are followed

Step 5: If required, monitor exposure of employees to hazardous substances

Step 6: Carry out health surveillance where assessment has shown that this is necessary, or where COSHH makes specific requirements

Step 7: If required, prepare plans and procedures to deal with accidents, incidents and emergencies

Step 8: Make sure employees are properly informed, trained and supervised

Figure 1.2: COSHH safety procedures

Working life

While working on site, another operative from a ceiling company wants to borrow your mobile tower platform. He says your supervisor has said that it was fine to use it. A loud scream is heard later and you hear that the operative has been badly hurt due to falling through the open floor access point.

- What should have been done on receiving that request?
- Whose responsibility is it to check the condition of the platform?
- What training is required before using the platform?

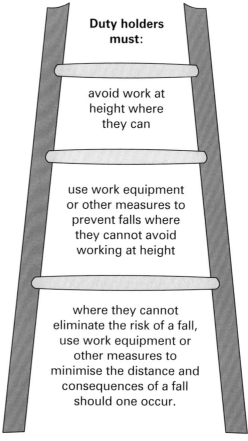

Duty holders must:

avoid work at height where they can

use work equipment or other measures to prevent falls where they cannot avoid working at height

where they cannot eliminate the risk of a fall, use work equipment or other measures to minimise the distance and consequences of a fall should one occur.

Figure 1.3: The role of duty holders

If you are an employee or working under someone else's control, Regulation 14 says you must:

- report any safety hazard to them

- use the equipment supplied (including safety devices) properly, following any training and instructions (unless you think that it would be unsafe to do so, in which case you should seek further instructions before continuing).

Regulation 6(3) states that 'the employer must do all that is reasonably practicable to prevent anyone falling'. The Regulations then set out a simple hierarchy for managing and selecting equipment for work at height (see Figure 1.3).

Duty holders' responsibilities

The Regulations require duty holders to ensure that:

- all work at height is properly planned and organised

- all work at height takes account of weather conditions that could endanger health and safety

- those involved in work at height are trained and competent

- the place where work at height is done is safe

- equipment for work at height is appropriately inspected

- the risks from fragile surfaces are properly controlled

- the risks from falling objects are properly controlled.

Planning

Regulations 4 and 6 require employers to:

- make sure that no work is done at height if it is safe and reasonably practicable to do it other than at height

- make sure that the work is properly planned, appropriately supervised and carried out in as safe a way as is reasonably practicable

- plan for emergencies and rescue

- take account of the risk assessment carried out under Regulation 3 of the Management of Health and Safety at Work Regulations.

Weather

Regulation 4 states employers 'must ensure that the work is postponed while weather conditions endanger health or safety'. This does not apply to emergency services during an emergency.

Staff training

Regulations 5 and 6 require the employer to ensure that:

- everyone involved in the work is competent (or, if being trained, is supervised by a competent person). This includes involvement in organisation, planning, supervision, and the supply and maintenance of equipment

- where other precautions do not entirely eliminate the risk of a fall, those who will be working at height are trained on how to avoid falling (as far as it is reasonably practicable), and how to avoid or minimise injury to themselves if they do fall.

The place where work is done

Regulation 6 states that employers must ensure that the place where work is done at height (including the means of access) is safe and has features to prevent a fall, unless this would mean that the worker was then unable to carry out the work safely. Here you are meant to take into account the demands of the task, the equipment and the working environment.

Equipment, temporary structures, and safety features

Regulations 6, 7, 8 and 12 require an employer who is selecting equipment for work at height to:

- use the most suitable equipment giving collective protection measures (such as guard rails) priority over personal protection measures (such as safety harnesses)

- take account of the working conditions and risks to the safety of all those at the place where the work equipment is to be used

- ensure that all equipment, temporary structures (such as scaffolding) and safety features comply with the detailed requirements of Schedules 2 to 6.

Inspections

'Inspection' is defined by Regulation 12(10) as 'such visual or more rigorous inspection by a competent person as is appropriate for safety purposes … (including) any testing appropriate for those purposes'. Employers must therefore ensure that:

- as far as it is reasonably practicable, each individual place at which work is to be done at height is checked on every occasion before that place is used. This involves checking the surface and every parapet, permanent rail, etc.

- any item of collective fall prevention (for example, guard rails and toe boards), working platforms, collective fall arrest (for example, nets, airbags, etc.), personal fall protection (for example, work restraints, work positioning, fall arrest and rope access), ladders and stepladders, is inspected:
  - after it is assembled or installed (or after it has been assembled and installed if both are required), if its safety depends on how it is assembled or installed
  - as often as is necessary to ensure safety, and in particular to make sure that any deterioration can be detected and remedied in good time

- before using any equipment that has come from another business, and before any equipment leaves your business, it is accompanied by an indication (clear to everyone involved) that the last inspection required by these Regulations has been carried out

- any platform used for (or for access to) construction work and from which a person could fall more than 2 metres is inspected in place before use (and not more than seven days before use). Where it is a mobile platform, inspection at the site is sufficient without re-inspection every time it is moved

- the person inspecting a platform:
  - prepares a report before going off duty
  - gives the report (or a copy) within 24 hours of completing the inspection to the person for whom the inspection was done (for example, the employer or site manager)
  - keeps the report of a platform at the construction site until the work is completed and then at an office for another three months.

Fragile surfaces

Regulation 9 requires employers to:

- ensure no one working under their control goes onto or near a fragile surface unless that is the only reasonably practicable way for the worker to carry out the work safely, having regard to the demands of the task, equipment, or working environment

- ensure (as far as reasonably practicable) that, if anyone does work on or near a fragile surface, suitable platforms, coverings, guard rails and the like are provided (and used) to minimise the risk

- do all that is reasonably practicable, if any risk of a fall remains, to minimise the distance and effect of a fall

- ensure that, if anyone working under their control may go onto or near a fragile surface, they do all that is reasonably practicable to make them aware of the danger, preferably by prominent warning notices fixed at the approaches to the danger zone.

Falling objects

Regulations 10 and 11 require that, where it is necessary to prevent injury, employers must do all that is reasonably practicable to prevent anything falling. If it is not reasonably practicable, they must ensure that no one is injured by anything falling. Employers must ensure:

- nothing is thrown or tipped from height if it is likely to injure anyone, or stored in such a way that its movement is likely to injure anyone

- if the workplace contains an area in which there is a risk of someone being struck by a falling object or person, that the area is clearly indicated and that (as far as reasonably practicable) unauthorised people are unable to reach it.

Personal Protective Equipment at Work Regulations 1992

PPE is defined in these Regulations as 'all equipment (including clothing affording protection against the weather) which is intended to be worn or held by a person at work and which protects them against one or more risks to their health and safety'. Common examples of PPE include safety helmets, gloves, eye protection, high-visibility clothing, safety footwear and safety harnesses.

Table 1.8 shows responsibilities under these Regulations.

Employers	Employees
Must train employees and give information on maintaining, cleaning and replacing damaged PPE	Must use PPE provided by their employer, in accordance with any training in the use of the PPE concerned
Must provide storage for PPE	Must inform employer of any defects in PPE
Must ensure that PPE is maintained in an efficient state and in good repair	Must comply with safety rules
Must ensure that PPE is properly used	Must use safety equipment as directed

Table 1.8: PPE responsibilities of employers and employees

Safety

There are other ways in which a risk can be adequately controlled, such as engineering controls. PPE should be used as a last resort in these situations.

Hearing protection and respiratory protective equipment provided for most work situations are not covered by these Regulations because other regulations apply to them. However, these items need to be compatible with any other PPE provided.

The main point of these Regulations is that PPE is to be supplied by the employer free of charge and used at work wherever there are risks to health and safety that cannot be adequately controlled in other ways. The Regulations also require that PPE is:

• properly assessed before use to ensure it is suitable

• maintained and stored properly

• provided with instructions on how to use it safely

• used correctly by employees.

Manual Handling Operations Regulations 1992 (as amended 2002)

These Regulations aim to reduce the very large number of injuries and ill health caused by the manual handling of loads at work. More than one in four of all reportable injuries are caused by manual handling. These accidents do not include injury done over a longer period, particularly to the back, which can lead to physical impediment or even permanent disablement.

They apply to the transporting or supporting of loads by hand or by bodily force, involving a wide range of manual handling activities, including lifting, lowering, pushing, pulling or carrying either animate (a person) or inanimate (a box etc.) objects.

Under these Regulations employers must:

• avoid the need for hazardous manual handling, so far as is reasonably practicable

• assess the risk of injury from any hazardous manual handling that cannot be avoided

• reduce the risk of injury from hazardous manual handling, so far as is reasonably practicable.

However, employees also have duties too, and must:

• follow appropriate systems of work laid down for their safety

• make proper use of equipment provided for their safety

• co-operate with their employer on health and safety matters

• inform the employer if they identify hazardous handling activities

• take care to ensure that their activities do not put others at risk.

You will find more detail on safe lifting and moving on pages 93–99.

Working life

You arrive at a site in a company vehicle with heavy equipment. There is no one around to help and your supervisor says you must help him. You tell him that you have forgotten your safety boots. He says not to worry, it will be alright. While unloading the equipment it traps your foot causing severe swelling, which necessitates you going to hospital, where the diagnosis reveals a broken foot.

• What should the supervisor have done on arrival at the site?

• What are the PPE requirements relating to this task?

• Who should be notified following this accident?

JTL tips

Manual handling implies that an attempt is being made to move a load. If a girder being moved manually is dropped and fractures an employee's foot, it is a manual handling accident; if the girder is inadvertently knocked over and causes a similar injury, this would not be due to manual handling.

Provision and Use of Work Equipment Regulations 1998 (PUWER)

Under PUWER, equipment provided for use at work must be:

- suitable for the intended use

- safe for use, maintained in a safe condition and, in certain circumstances, inspected to ensure this remains the case

- used only by people who have received adequate information, instruction and training.

JTL tips

As an employee, you do not have duties under PUWER. However, you do have general duties under HASAWA and the Management of Health and Safety at Work Regulations 1999 to take reasonable care of yourself and others who may be affected by your actions, and to co-operate with others.

Generally, any equipment used by an employee at work is covered, including hammers, knives, ladders, drilling machines, power presses, circular saws, lifting equipment (including lifts), dumper trucks and motor vehicles, and even photocopiers. If you are allowed to provide your own equipment, this will also be covered by PUWER, and the employer will need to make sure it complies.

These Regulations cover places where HASAWA applies – including factories, offshore installations, offices, shops, hospitals, hotels and places of entertainment. PUWER also applies in common parts of shared buildings and temporary places of work such as construction sites. While the Regulations cover equipment used by people working from home, they do not apply to domestic work in a private household.

The Regulations do not apply to equipment used by the public, such as compressed-air equipment used in a garage forecourt. However, such circumstances are covered by HASAWA.

Health and Safety (Display Screen Equipment) Regulations 1992

These Regulations require employers to:

- minimise the risks in visual display unit (VDU) work by ensuring that workplaces and jobs are well designed

- analyse workstations to assess and reduce risks

- ensure workstations meet specified minimum requirements

- plan work activities so that they include breaks or changes of activity

- provide eye and eyesight tests on request, and special spectacles if needed

- provide information and training.

The Regulations apply where staff normally use VDUs as a significant part of their normal work. People who use VDUs only occasionally are only covered by the workstation requirements of these Regulations. However, their employers still have general duties to protect them under other health and safety at work legislation.

Construction (Design & Management) Regulations 2015 (CDM)

The aim of the Construction (Design & Management) Regulations 2015 (CDM) is to integrate health and safety into any construction project. Whatever your role, CDM aims to improve health and safety in the industry by helping you to:

- plan the work sensibly so the risks involved are managed from start to finish
- choose the right people for the right job at the right time
- co-operate and co-ordinate your work with others
- have the right information about the risks and how they are being managed
- communicate this information effectively to those who need to know
- consult and engage with workers about the risks and how they are being managed.

Virtually everyone involved in a construction project has legal duties under CDM 2015. The main duty holders are described below.

The client

The client is anyone who has construction work carried out for them. The main duty for clients is to make sure their project is suitably managed, ensuring the health and safety of all who might be affected by the work, including members of the public. CDM 2015 recognises two types of client.

Commercial clients have construction work carried out as part of their business. These clients could be individuals, partnerships or companies, and include property developers and companies managing domestic properties.

Domestic clients have construction work carried out for them but not in connection with any business – this is usually work done on their own home or the home of a family member. CDM 2015 does not require domestic clients to carry out client duties as these normally pass to other duty-holders.

The designer

The designer is an organisation or individual whose work involves preparing or modifying designs, drawings, specifications, bills of quantity or design calculations. Designers can be architects, consulting engineers and quantity surveyors, or anyone who specifies and alters designs as part of their work. They can also include trades people if they carry out design work.

The designer's main duty is to eliminate, reduce or control foreseeable risks that may arise during construction work, or in the use and maintenance of the building once built. Designers work under the control of a principal designer on projects with more than one contractor.

The contractor

The contractor is an individual or business in charge of carrying out construction work (e.g. building, altering, maintaining or demolishing). Anyone who manages this work or directly employs or engages construction workers is a contractor.

A contractor's main duty is to plan, manage and monitor the work under their control in a way that ensures the health and safety of anyone it might affect (including members of the public).

Contractors work under the control of the principal contractor on projects with more than one contractor.

The worker

The worker is an individual who carries out the work involved in building, altering, maintaining or demolishing buildings or structures. Workers include: plumbers, electricians, scaffolders, painters, decorators, steel erectors and labourers, as well as supervisors like foremen and chargehands.

Their duties include co-operating with their employer and other duty holders, and reporting anything they see that might endanger the health and safety of themselves or others. Workers must also be consulted on matters affecting their health, safety and welfare.

Workers have an important role and should take an active part in helping to manage health and safety risks. In particular, workers must:

- only carry out construction work if they have the relevant skills, knowledge, training and experience – or if they are provided with the training and supervision that enables them to do it safely and without risk to health

- make themselves aware of the health and safety risks involved in work on every site and the ways in which those risks are managed

- always follow site rules and procedures

- co-operate with other duty holders, such as the contractor in control of their work and the principal contractor (who controls the overall project when there is more than one contractor)

- report any risks they find to whoever controls the work on site, whether the risks affect their own health and safety or anyone else, including other workers and members of the public.

>>>> **Environmental legislation**

Before you look at this topic, you should first understand what is meant by the term 'the environment'. The word 'environment' relates to our surroundings and includes:

- the built environment – man-made items such as houses, roads and electricity supplies

- the natural environment – natural items such as plants, birds, forests, rivers and rocks

- the social and cultural environment – the culture that someone has been educated in or lives in, and the people and institutions with whom that person interacts.

In this section, the focus is the effect of the built environment on the world we live in.

The Environmental Protection Act 1990

The Environmental Protection Act 1990 (EPA) aims to protect the environment from the results of 'the release into any environmental medium (e.g. air, land, water) from any process, of substances which are capable of causing harm to man or any other living organisms supported by the environment'.

This Act brought together a wide range of environmental legislation and replaced most of the Control of Pollution Act 1974 (COPA). EPA defines the fundamental structure and authority for waste management and control of emissions into the environment.

There are effectively nine parts to the legislation, covering these topics:

- Part 1: Integrated pollution control and air pollution control by local authorities

- Part 2: Waste on land

- Part 2a: Contaminated land

- Part 3: Statutory nuisances and clean air (such as smoke, fumes, insects, noise and artificial light)

- Part 4: Litter, etc.

- Part 5: Amendment of the Radioactive Substances Act 1960

- Part 6: Genetically modified organisms

- Part 7: Nature conservation in Great Britain and Countryside Matters in Wales

- Part 8: Miscellaneous (including sea pollution, control of dogs and burning of hay)

- Part 9: General (including corporate offences).

Control of Asbestos Regulations 2012

These Regulations prohibit the importation, supply and use of all forms of asbestos. They continue the ban introduced for blue and brown asbestos in 1985 and for white asbestos in 1999. They also continue to ban the second-hand use of asbestos products, such as asbestos cement sheets and asbestos boards and tiles; this includes panels that have been covered with paint or textured plaster-containing asbestos.

The Regulations require mandatory training for anyone liable to be exposed to asbestos fibres at work. This includes maintenance workers and others who may come into contact with or who may disturb asbestos (such as cable installers) as well as those involved in asbestos removal work.

For more on asbestos, see pages 116–117.

Figure 1.4: Smog is just one of many ways in which our environment is being damaged

The Pollution Prevention and Control Act 1999 (PPC)

The Environmental Protection Act controlled industries that emit significant levels of pollution to the environment (air, land and water). This has now been replaced by the Pollution Prevention and Control Act 1999, which allowed creation of the Environmental Permitting Regulations 2010 (EPR), which bring together the PPC, Waste Management and groundwater and discharge consents licensing and permitting into one new regulatory system.

Under this new system, local authorities are required to regulate the smaller industries, termed Part A2 and Part B installations; the Environment Agency regulates the larger industries, which are known as Part A1 installations.

Emissions to the environment (air, land and water) must be controlled from Part A1 and A2 installations and such installations are also required to account for energy-efficiency and to control against **noise pollution**. Part B installations on the other hand are only regulated for emissions to air.

For A1 installations, the system of control is called Integrated Pollution Prevention and Control (IPPC), with the Environment Agency as the regulator; for A2 installations, it is called Local Authority Integrated Pollution Prevention and Control (LA-IPPC), with local authorities as the regulators.

The Control of Pollution Act 1989

This legislation requires carriers of controlled waste to register with the Environment Agency (EA) or Scottish Environment Protection Agency (SEPA) and outlines the penalties (including seizure and disposal) for vehicles shown to have been used for illegal waste disposal. The Controlled Waste (Registration of Carriers and Seizure of Vehicles) Regulations 1991 then introduced a registration system for carriers of such controlled waste.

Safety

The ban applies to new use of asbestos. If existing asbestos-containing materials are in good condition, they may be left in place, with their condition monitored and managed to ensure they are not disturbed.

Key term

Noise pollution – excessive noise from any source, but particularly industrial sources, that spoils people's experience of the environment; examples could be noise from machinery, plant or power tools

The Environment Act 1995

The Environment Act 1995 allowed the creation of the Environment Agency (EA) in England and the Scottish Environment Protection Agency (SEPA). Both these organisations protect the environment and manage resources, as well as setting new standards for environmental management.

The Act gave the EA and SEPA responsibility for regulating pollution control, water, general environmental and recreational duties, environmental duties relating to sites of special scientific interest (SSSIs), regional and local fisheries, flood prevention and control. It also sets out a system for identifying and repairing contaminated land and requires local councils to prepare reviews of air quality.

The Hazardous Waste Regulations 2005 and The List of Waste Regulations 2005

The Hazardous Waste Regulations (HWR) and the List of Waste Regulations (LoWR) control waste that can harm human health or the environment, or is difficult to handle. They aim to make sure that hazardous waste is properly managed at all times.

The use of EWC (European Waste Catalogue) codes is a legal requirement of the Duty of Care (DoC) legislation across the UK. The DoC requires that a waste holder (producer, carrier or disposer) takes all reasonable steps to ensure that waste is described in a way that permits its safe handling and management, and that any transfer of waste is accompanied by a written description of the waste including a LoWR code.

The HWR:

- define hazardous waste in England and Wales

- require producers or consignors of hazardous waste to register their premises

- restrict mixing of wastes and require separation of wastes where appropriate

- make sure that companies document the movement of hazardous waste

- require consignees receiving hazardous waste to keep thorough records and provide the EA with information on the disposal and recovery of hazardous waste every three months.

The LoWR:

- introduced the 'List of Wastes' linked to the European Waste Catalogue

- explain the List, giving help on choosing the code for a specific waste

- show how waste is classified as either hazardous or non-hazardous

- show limits for certain hazardous properties.

Figure 1.5: Would this become hazardous waste?

Waste needs to be assessed to see if it contains dangerous substances such as fluorescent tubes or batteries.

The Control of Noise at Work Regulations 2005

The Control of Noise at Work Regulations 2005 (the Noise Regulations) aim to ensure workers' hearing is protected from excessive noise at their place of work, as this could cause them to lose their hearing or to suffer from **tinnitus**.

People often experience temporary deafness after leaving a noisy place. Although hearing recovers within a few hours, you should never ignore these things: it is a sign that, if you continue to be exposed to the noise, your hearing could be permanently damaged.

Hearing loss is usually gradual and happens because of prolonged exposure to noise. It may only be when damage caused by noise combines with hearing loss due to ageing that people realise how deaf they have become. However, young people can be affected by noise just as badly as older people.

Noise can also be a safety hazard at work, interfering with communication and making warnings harder to hear. Employers are obliged by law to carry out risk assessments and identify measures to eliminate or reduce risks from exposure to noise, to protect the hearing of their employees.

As a rough guide, employers will probably need to do something about the noise if any of these questions gets a 'yes'.

- Is the noise intrusive (such as a busy street, a vacuum cleaner or a crowded restaurant) for most of the working day?

- Do employees have to raise their voices to carry out a normal conversation when about 2 metres apart for at least part of the day?

- Do employees use noisy powered tools or machinery for more than half an hour each day?

- Do you work in a noisy industry such as: construction, demolition or road repair; woodworking; plastics processing; engineering; textile manufacture; general fabrication; forging, pressing or stamping; paper or board making; canning or bottling; foundries?

- Are there noises due to impacts (such as hammering, drop-forging or pneumatic impact tools), explosive sources such as cartridge-operated tools or detonators, or guns?

Noise levels

The Noise Regulations require you to take specific action at certain action values, relating to:

- the levels of exposure to noise of your employees averaged over a working day or week

- the maximum noise (peak sound pressure) to which employees are exposed in a working day.

Key term

Tinnitus – a permanent ringing in the ears

Safety

Bear in mind that permanent hearing damage can be caused immediately by a sudden, extremely loud, explosive noise, such as from a gun or cartridge-operated machine.

The values are:

- lower exposure action values:
  - daily or weekly exposure of 80 **dB**
  - peak sound pressure of 135 dB
- upper exposure action values:
  - daily or weekly exposure of 85 dB
  - peak sound pressure of 137 dB.

There are also levels of noise exposure that must not be exceeded:

- exposure limit values:
  - daily or weekly exposure of 87 dB
  - peak sound pressure of 140 dB.

These exposure limit values take account of any reduction in exposure provided by hearing protection.

Noise and statutory nuisance

Part 3 of the Environmental Protection Act 1990 (as amended) creates various statutory nuisances, including noise emitted from premises. The Act further defines statutory nuisance in relation to noise as being 'noise emitted from premises that is prejudicial to health or a nuisance'.

A statutory nuisance could arise from the poor state of your premises or any noise, smoke, fumes, gases, dust, steam, smell, effluvia, the keeping of animals, deposits and accumulations of refuse and/or other material.

For action to be taken, the nuisance complained of must be, or be likely to be, 'prejudicial to people's health or interfere with a person's legitimate use and enjoyment of land'. This particularly applies to nuisance to neighbours in their homes and gardens.

Here are some examples of good practice concerning noise for any business.

- Establish whether your business might cause a nuisance by checking noise, odours and other emissions near the boundary of your site during different operating conditions and at different times of the day. Take all reasonable steps to prevent or minimise a nuisance or a potential nuisance.

- Make sure there is a good level of housekeeping on your site and that your site manager and staff are aware of the need to avoid nuisances. Regularly check your site for any waste accumulations, evidence of vermin, noise or smell as applicable.

- Even if a complaint does not amount to a statutory nuisance you should consider if there are simple, practical things that you can do to keep the peace.

- Try to establish a good relationship with your neighbours, particularly in relation to transient events likely to affect them. Advise neighbours in advance if you believe that a particular operation such as building work or an installation process for new plant could cause an adverse effect. If neighbours are kept informed they will perceive the business as more considerate and are less likely to make a complaint.

- At noise-sensitive locations, monitor background noise before your works begin, and include in your method statement any actions you can take to reduce noise levels.

- Reduce noise levels outside or escaping your buildings by increasing insulation to the building fabric and keeping doors and windows closed.

- Make sure any burglar alarms on your premises have a maintenance contract and a callout agreement.

- Avoid or minimise noisy activities, especially at night; pay particular attention to traffic movements, reversing sirens, deliveries, external public-address systems and radios.

- Where practical, schedule or restrict noisy activities to the normal working day (for example, 08.00 to 18.00, Monday to Friday and 08.00 to 13.00 on Saturday).

- If noisy operations take place near site boundaries, relocate them if you can, perhaps further away, or make use of existing buildings/stockpiles/topography as noise barriers.

- Consider replacing any noisy equipment and take account of noise emissions when buying new or replacement equipment.

- Maintain fans and refrigeration equipment to help keep noise levels as low as possible.

- Do not have any bonfires; find other ways to reuse or recover wastes – see the Clean Air and Waste Management Guidelines.

- Keep abatement equipment, such as filters and cyclones, in good working order. Ensure boilers, especially oil or solid-fuel units, are operating efficiently and do not emit dark smoke during start-up.

The Waste Electrical and Electronic Equipment (WEEE) Regulations 2013

Electrical and electronic waste (such as TVs, monitors and computers) has become the fastest growing waste in the UK, with nearly two million tonnes of it generated every year. The Waste Electrical and Electronic Equipment (WEEE) Regulations 2013 aim to reduce the amount of this waste going to landfill and improve recovery and recycling rates.

You need to comply with the WEEE Regulations if you:

- manufacture or import electrical or electronic equipment

- distribute electrical or electronic equipment

- generate any electrical or electronic waste

- collect electrical or electronic waste from your customers for treatment or disposal

- operate a waste treatment facility

- export electrical or electronic waste.

The WEEE Regulations apply to electrical and electronic equipment (EEE) in the categories listed below with a voltage of up to 1000 V for AC or up to 1500 V for DC. You need to comply with the WEEE Regulations if you generate, handle or dispose of waste that falls under one of these ten categories listed as Schedule 1 of the Regulations:

1. large household appliances

2. small household appliances

3. IT and telecommunications equipment

4. consumer equipment

5. lighting equipment

6. electrical and electronic tools

7. toys, leisure and sports equipment

8. medical devices

9. monitoring and control equipment

10. automatic dispensers.

JTL tips

Since 1 January 2014, non-household luminaires and lamps that incorporate an integrated (i.e. non-removable) LED light source previously classified under category 5 'Lighting Equipment' should be reported in category 13 'Gas discharge lamps and LED light sources'. An 'LED light source' is a product that falls within category 5 of Schedule 1 of the Regulations and which uses an integrated light emitting diode as its light source. There is no change to the classification of products in other categories that contain an LED light source.

All businesses that use EEE must comply with these Regulations. This includes all domestic or household EEE that you may use on your premises. For all non-household EEE, either the producer or end user is responsible for the disposal of the products.

You must obtain and keep proof that your waste EEE was given to a waste management business and was subsequently treated and disposed of in an environmentally sound way.

Summary

1. Briefly explain what an employer's responsibility is under the Health and Safety at Work Act?

2. In relation to the Electricity at Work Regulations, does the employer have the same or different duties? Give a reason for your answer.

3. Under the Personal Protective Equipment at Work Regulations what four checks must be made to ensure that PPE is effective?

2. Procedures for dealing with Environmental and Health and Safety situations in the work environment

You have just seen that there is a lot of legislation to read and interpret correctly if the workplace is to be as safe as possible. Keeping up to date with and understanding the implications of this legislation can be daunting; so how do you and your employers manage it?

It may seem odd, but there is no set method for distributing new or amended health and safety requirements to employers. It is up to every employer to ensure that they are meeting legal requirements, with lack of knowledge not regarded as an excuse in a court of law.

Figure 1.6: Displaying a health and safety notice in the workplace is compulsory.

Companies keep up to date in different ways, often depending on their size and structure. In smaller companies the owner or manager is likely to have responsibility, but pressure on their time might be very high.

Many smaller companies hire an external health and safety consultant. The consultant will normally visit the employer and carry out an inspection of the main premises and types of site and activities undertaken. They will then produce the necessary paperwork – for example, risk assessments, safety policy, Control of Substances Hazardous to Health Regulations (COSHH) assessments – and provide a manual for the employer to refer to and implement.

Some employers use a consultant on a one-off basis and then maintain the information and systems provided themselves. However, they must ensure that this manual remains up to date with all developments. Some employers use consultants on an ongoing basis, with the consultant monitoring all legislation, codes of practice and relevant information, and continually providing the employer with updated information, documentation and services.

Large companies often have their own specialist staff with responsibility for health and safety.

Activity

▶ Check your own health and safety manuals. Are they up to date? How can you tell if they are? If they are not up to date, what could you do about this?

Safety

In 2016/17, 139 people were killed in workplace accidents in Britain. There were also 64,000 non-fatal injuries and 80,000 workers suffering from work-related ill health. (Source: The Health and Safety Executive)

Responsible bodies and persons

The Health and Safety Executive (HSE)

The Health and Safety Executive (HSE) is responsible for the regulation of almost all the risks to health and safety from work activity in Britain. Its mission is to protect people's health and safety by making sure that risks in the workplace are controlled.

Among other things, the HSE looks after health and safety in nuclear installations and mines, factories, farms, hospitals and schools, offshore gas and oil installations, the gas grid and railways, as well as with the movement of dangerous goods and substances.

JTL tips   **JTL**

As well as via the HSE itself, you can get information on health and safety from your local authority and the emergency services. Local authorities are actually responsible to the HSE for enforcement in offices, shops and other parts of the services sector.

HSE Inspectors

To help enforce the law, HSE Inspectors have a range of statutory powers. They can, and sometimes do, visit and enter premises without warning. Actions an Inspector can take are outlined below.

- **Issuing an improvement notice** – this will say what needs to be done, why and by when. The time period within which to take the remedial action will be at least 21 days to allow the duty holder time to appeal to an Employment Tribunal. The notice also contains a statement of the Inspector's opinion that an offence has been committed.

- **Issuing a prohibition notice** – where an activity involves, or will involve, a risk of serious personal injury, the Inspector can serve a prohibition notice to stop the activity immediately or after a specified time period, and not allow it to be resumed until remedial action has been taken. The notice will explain why the action is necessary.

- **Taking legal action** – the Inspector may also wish to start legal proceedings. Improvement and prohibition notices and written advice may be used in court proceedings.

HSE Inspectors apply 'proportionality' before deciding on a course of action. This means they make sure that the degree of enforcement to be taken will be in proportion to the degree of risks they have discovered.

Approved Codes of Practice (ACOPs)

ACOPs give practical advice on how to comply with the law and are approved by the HSE, with the consent of the Secretary of State. Failing to follow an ACOP is not an offence in itself. However, in any criminal or civil proceedings, the court will use an employer's non-compliance or contravention of any relevant ACOP to show an offence. Here the employer's only defence would be to prove that he or she was using another appropriate method or system.

Penalties for health and safety offences

Section 85 of the Legal Aid, Sentencing and Punishment of Offenders Act 2012 (which came into force on 12 March 2015) effectively increased the level of most fines available for magistrates' courts to an unlimited fine. It was previously £20,000 for most health and safety offences.

This means unlimited fines can be set that are proportional to the offence and they also have the power to offer imprisonment of up to 6 months; hopefully this will act as a better deterrent for companies that breach health and safety law.

Insurance

Employers are responsible for the health and safety of their employees while they are at work. An employee may be injured at work, or a former employee may become ill as a result of their work while in employment. The employee might try to claim compensation from the employer if they believe the employer is responsible. The Employers' Liability (Compulsory Insurance) Act 1969 ensures employers have at least a minimum level of £5 million insurance to cover against any such claims.

Public liability insurance is different. It covers an employer for claims made against it by members of the public or other businesses, but not for claims by the employer's employees. The amount of this cover is not mandatory and should be assessed against the business, but it is likely that £5 million would be a requirement.

When an employer takes out employers' liability insurance, it will have an agreement with the insurer about the circumstances in which the latter will pay compensation. For example, the policy will cover the specific activities that relate to the business. There are certain conditions that could restrict the amount of money an insurer might have to pay. Employers must make sure their contract with the insurer does not contain any of these conditions.

However, the insurer cannot refuse to pay compensation purely because the employer:

- has not provided reasonable protection for employees against injury or disease
- cannot provide certain information to the insurer
- did something the insurer told it not to do (for example, said it was at fault)
- has not done something the insurer told it to do (for example, report the incident)
- has not met any legal requirement connected with the protection of the employees.

However, this does not mean employers can forget about their legal responsibilities to protect the health and safety of their employees. If an insurer believes that an employer has failed to meet its legal responsibilities for the health and safety of its employees and that this failure has led to the claim, the policy may enable the insurer to sue the employer to reclaim the cost of the compensation.

> > > >

Appropriate responsible persons to report health and safety issues

Responsibility begins with senior management. Strong leadership is vital in delivering effective health and safety risk control. Everyone should know and believe that management is committed to continuous improvement in health and safety performance.

Management should explain its expectations, and how the organisation and procedures will deliver them. Although health and safety functions can (and should) be delegated, legal responsibility for health and safety rests with the employer.

These general duties are expanded and explained in the Management of Health and Safety at Work Regulations 1999. Employers must:

- assess work-related risks for both employees and those not in their employment

- have effective arrangements in place for planning, organising, controlling, monitoring and reviewing preventive and protective measures

- appoint one or more competent people to help undertake the measures needed to comply with health and safety law

- provide employees with good, clear information on the risks they face and the preventive and protective measures that control those risks.

Health and safety policy statement

As you saw in the section on the HASAWA, by law, anyone employing five or more people must have a written health and safety policy, including arrangements for putting that policy into practice.

This should be the key to achieving acceptable standards, reducing accidents and reducing the incidence of work-related ill health. A good health and safety policy also shows employees that their employer cares about them.

Activity

▶ A health and safety policy should be more than just a legal requirement – it should show the commitment of an employer to planning and managing health and safety well. Find out about your employer's approach to health and safety. Can you see any ways in which it could be improved?

Employee rights, responsibilities and limitations

As an employee, you have rights. However, you also have responsibilities for your own well-being and that of your colleagues. Many of these rights and responsibilities fall under the HASAWA or CDM. However, some additional rights and responsibilities are outlined as follows.

- If you have reasonable concerns about your safety, you can stop work and leave your work area, without being disciplined.

- You can get in touch with the HSE or your local authority if your employer won't listen to your concerns, without being disciplined.

- You have the right to take rest breaks during the working day, to have time off from work during the working week, and to have annual paid holiday.

- You must report any injuries, strains or illnesses you suffer as a result of doing your job (your employer may need to change the way you work).

- You must tell your employer if something happens that might affect your ability to work (for example, becoming pregnant or suffering an injury). Your employer has a legal responsibility for your health and safety, so they may need to suspend you while they find a solution to the problem, but you will normally be paid if this happens.

- If you drive or operate machinery, you have a responsibility to tell your employer if you take medication that makes you drowsy. They should temporarily move you to another job if they have one for you to do.

Limitations on your responsibilities

There may also be limitations on your responsibilities – things you should not do or try to do, because really, they are somebody else's responsibility. You should therefore be aware of the appropriate responsible persons to whom you should report any health and safety or welfare matters.

As an apprentice electrician, the most obvious starting point will be your site supervisor, but there are other people who could be involved, depending on the situation. Some of them are listed below.

The safety officer

The safety officer is a suitably qualified member of staff with responsibility for all things related to health and safety, and is answerable to the company managers. A safety officer's role and responsibilities are likely to include:

- arranging internal and external training for employees on safety issues

- monitoring and implementing codes of practice and regulations

- updating and displaying information

- liaising with external agencies, such as the HSE

- carrying out and recording regular health and safety inspections and risk assessments

- advising on selection, training, use and maintenance of PPE

- maintenance of accident reports and records.

If there were an accident, the safety officer would lead the investigations, identify the causes and advise on any improvements in safety standards that need to be made.

Safety

What is written in a health and safety policy has to be put into practice. The true test of the policy is the actual conditions in the workplace, not how well the statement has been written.

The safety representative

The safety representative is often a trade union member. The representative's role is similar to that of the safety officer, and includes:

- making representations to the employer on behalf of members on any health, safety and welfare matter

- representing members in consultation with the HSE Inspectors or other enforcing authorities

- inspecting designated workplace areas at least every three months

- investigating any potential hazards, complaints by members and causes of accidents, dangerous occurrences and diseases

- requesting facilities and support from the employer to carry out inspections and receive legal and technical information

- paid time off to carry out the role and do union-approved training.

The Health and Safety Executive has issued guidance for employers who do not recognise independent trade unions. For all but the smallest companies, it recommends setting up a safety committee of members drawn from both management and employees. This will help employers to meet the conditions of Section 2 (Part 4) of HASAWA and the Health and Safety (Consultation with Employees) Regulations 1996.

Environmental health officers

Environmental health officers are employed by local authorities to inspect commercial businesses such as warehouses, offices, shops, pubs and restaurants within a borough area.

They have the right to enter any workplace without giving notice, though in practice they often do give notice. Normally, the officer looks at the workplace, work activities and management of health and safety, and checks the business is complying with health and safety law.

Environmental health officers may offer guidance or advice to help businesses. They may also talk to employees and their representatives, take photographs and samples, serve improvement notices and take action if there is a risk to health and safety that needs to be dealt with immediately.

Safety

Under the Consultation with Employees Regulations, any employee not covered by a trade union safety representative must be consulted by their employer. The employer can choose to consult with them directly or through their elected representatives.

What to do if there's an accident or emergency

Everyone hopes that, with careful planning, there will never be an accident or emergency. However, you need to be prepared for dealing with such an event.

Reporting of Injuries, Diseases and Dangerous Occurrences Regulations 2013 (RIDDOR)

The Reporting of Injuries, Diseases and Dangerous Occurrences Regulations 2013 (RIDDOR) place a legal duty on employers, the self-employed and those in control of premises (the responsible person) to report work-related accidents, diseases and dangerous occurrences to the relevant enforcing authority (the HSE or local authority). This can help enforcing authorities to identify where and how risks arise, as well as to investigate serious accidents.

If you are an employee and have suffered a work-related injury, or have been diagnosed as suffering from a work-related reportable disease, you should inform your employer. If you are concerned that your employer or other Responsible Person has not made a required report you should:

- ask them if they have reported the incident

- and/or approach your employer or trade union representative.

If you still feel that your accident or work-related disease has not been properly reported, you may then raise your concern with the HSE.

Safety

Gas Safe registered gas fitters must report any dangerous gas fittings or appliances that they find.

Additionally, the UK gas supply network (Cadent Gas Ltd – West Midlands, North West, East of England and North London; Northern Gas Networks Limited – North East England, including Yorkshire and Northern Cumbria; Wales and West Utilities Limited – Wales and South West England; SGN – Scotland and Southern England, including South London) must report where they learn, either directly or indirectly that someone has died, been found unconscious or taken to hospital in connection with the gas they distributed, filled, imported or supplied.

Regulations 4–6 of RIDDOR cover the reporting of work-related deaths and injuries (other than for certain gas incidents). RIDDOR only requires deaths and injuries to be reported when:

- there has been an accident, which caused the injury

- the accident was work-related

- the injury is of a type that is reportable.

What is an 'accident'?

Relative to RIDDOR, an accident is 'a separate, identifiable, unintended incident, which causes physical injury'. This specifically includes acts of non-consensual violence to people at work.

Be aware that injuries themselves are not accidents – there must be an identifiable external event that causes the injury. Also, cumulative exposures to hazards, which eventually cause injury (e.g. repetitive lifting), are not classed as 'accidents' under RIDDOR.

What is meant by 'work-related'?

RIDDOR only requires the reporting of accidents that happen as a result of, or in connection with, work. If an accident occurs on work premises, it does not automatically mean that the accident was work-related – the work activity itself must contribute to the accident. An accident is 'work-related' if any of the following played a significant role:

- the way the work was carried out

- machinery, plant, substances or equipment used for the work

- the condition of the site or premises where the accident happened.

What are 'reportable' injuries?

The following injuries are reportable under RIDDOR when they result from a work-related accident:

- the death of any person (Regulation 6)

- specified injuries to workers (Regulation 4)

- injuries to workers that result in their incapacitation for more than seven days (Regulation 4)

- injuries to non-workers that result in them being taken directly to hospital for treatment, or specified injuries to non-workers that occur on hospital premises (Regulation 5).

The death of any person

All deaths to both workers and non-workers, with the exception of suicides, must be reported immediately if they arise from a work-related accident, including an act of physical violence to a worker.

Specified injuries to workers

The list of 'specified injuries' in RIDDOR 2013 replaces the previous list of 'major injuries' in RIDDOR 1995. Specified injuries are (Regulation 4):

- fractures, other than to fingers, thumbs and toes

- amputations

- any injury likely to lead to permanent loss of sight or a reduction in sight

- any crush injury to the head or torso causing damage to the brain or internal organs

- serious burns (including scalding) which:
  - cover more than 10 per cent of the body
  - cause significant damage to the eyes, respiratory system or other vital organs

- any scalping requiring hospital treatment

- any loss of consciousness caused by head injury or asphyxia

- any other injury arising from working in an enclosed space which:
  - leads to hypothermia or heat-induced illness
  - requires resuscitation or admittance to hospital for more than 24 hours.

Over-three-day incapacitation of a worker

Accidents must be recorded, but need not be reported where they result in a worker being incapacitated for more than three consecutive days (and less than seven). If you are an employer, who must keep an accident book under the Social Security (Claims and Payments) Regulations 1979, that record will be sufficient.

Over-seven-day incapacitation of a worker

Accidents must be reported where the injury incurred results in an employee or self-employed person being away from work, or unable to perform their normal work duties, for more than seven consecutive days. This seven-day period does not include the day of the accident, but does include weekends and rest days. The report must be made within 15 days of the accident.

Non-fatal accidents to non-workers (e.g. members of the public)

Accidents to members of the public, or others who are not at work, must be reported if they result in an injury and the person is taken directly from the scene of the accident to hospital for treatment for that injury. Examinations and diagnostic tests do not constitute 'treatment' in such circumstances.

There is no need to report incidents where people are taken to hospital purely as a precaution and when no injury is apparent.

Occupational diseases

Employers and self-employed people must report diagnoses of certain occupational diseases where these are likely to have been caused or made worse by their work. These include (Regulations 8 and 9):

- carpal tunnel syndrome

- severe cramp of the hand or forearm

- occupational dermatitis

- hand-arm vibration syndrome

- occupational asthma

- tendonitis or tenosynovitis of the hand or forearm

- any occupational cancer

- any disease attributed to an occupational exposure to a biological agent.

HSE

Health and Safety Executive

Health and Safety at Work etc Act 1974
The Reporting of Injuries, Diseases and Dangerous Occurrences Regulations 2013

Zoom [120%] KS i ?

Report of an injury

About you and your organisation

*Title

*Forename

*Family Name

*Job Title

*Your Phone No

*Organisation Name

Address Line 1   (eg building name)

Address Line 2   (eg street)

Address Line 3   (eg district)

*Town

County

*Post Code   Fax Number

*E-Mail

☐ Remember me ?

*Did the incident happen at the above address? ☐ Yes ☐ No

[Next] [Form Preview]

HSE

Health and Safety Executive

Health and Safety at Work etc Act 1974
The Reporting of Injuries, Diseases and Dangerous Occurrences Regulations 2013

Zoom [120%] KS i ?

Report of a dangerous occurrence

This form is for duty-holders only to report defined Dangerous Occurrences under RIDDOR. It is not for making a complaint about or reporting a workplace issue. Advice on this is available on the HSE website.

About you and your organisation

*Title

*Forename

*Family Name

*Job Title

*Your Phone No

*Organisation Name

Address Line 1   (eg building name)

Address Line 2   (eg street)

Address Line 3   (eg district)

*Town

County

*Post Code   Fax Number

*E-Mail

☐ Remember me ?

*Did the incident happen at the above address? ☐ Yes ☐ No

[Next] [Form Preview]

Figure 1.7: HSE online reporting form

Dangerous occurrences

The list of dangerous occurrences in Schedule 2 of RIDDOR is designed to collect information about incidents with a high potential to cause death or serious injury, but which happen relatively infrequently.

Several types of dangerous occurrence require reporting in circumstances where the incident has the potential to cause injury or death. This assessment does not require any complex analysis, just a reasonable judgement as to whether the circumstances gave rise to a real, rather than notional, risk. Such judgement allows for prompt reporting and ensures that valuable information is not lost. Schedule 2 lists three kinds of reportable dangerous occurrence, as detailed below.

1. General (incidents occurring at any workplace)

These dangerous occurrences apply to all workplaces and include incidents involving lifting equipment, pressure systems, overhead electric lines, electrical incidents causing explosion or fire, explosions, biological agents, radiation generators and radiography, breathing apparatus, driving operations, the collapse of scaffolding, train collisions, wells and pipelines or pipeline works.

An electrical incident is defined as 'any explosion or fire caused by an electrical short circuit or overload (including those resulting from accidental damage to the electrical plant) which either: results in the stoppage of the plant involved for more than 24 hours; or causes a significant risk of death'.

2. General (incidents occurring at any place other than an offshore workplace)

These incidents do not require a report if they occur at an offshore workplace. They include structural collapses, explosions or fires, the release of flammable liquids and gases, and the hazardous escape of substances.

3. Incidents occurring at specific types of workplace

Industries with specific requirements are: offshore workplaces, mines, quarries and relevant transport systems.

How to make a RIDDOR report

Only 'responsible persons' including employers, the self-employed and people in control of work premises should submit reports under RIDDOR.

Reporting online

Responsible persons should complete the appropriate online report form. The form will be submitted directly to the RIDDOR database and they will receive a copy for their records.

Reporting by telephone

All incidents should be reported online, but a telephone service is also provided for reporting fatal/specified and major incidents only. To do so, call the Incident Contact Centre on 0345 300 9923.

What records need to be kept?

Employers must keep a record of any reportable injury, over three-day injury, disease or dangerous occurrence. They can print and/or save a copy of the online form; a copy of the form will also be automatically emailed to the address provided.

Figure 1.8: HSE Accident book

If you do not keep a copy of the online form, your records must include: the date and method of reporting; the date, time and place of the event; personal details of those involved; and a brief description of the nature of the event or disease.

In the case of accidents, employers who must keep an accident book (HSE BI 510) under Social Security Law, can use this for keeping the records of injuries. However, a separate method will be needed for cases of disease.

Information supplied to HSE in a RIDDOR report will not be passed on to insurance companies. If you think your insurer needs to know about a work-related accident, injury or case of ill health, you must remember to contact them separately.

The HSE Accident Book (BI 510)

As Social Security Law requires the injured worker or person acting for them to give the employer specific details of accidents as soon as practicable, both employers and employees normally use the HSE Accident Book to record details of work-related injuries for which state benefits could be payable. The accident book can be used to record accident information as part of the management of health and safety. It can also be used to record details of injuries resulting from accidents at work that employers must report under RIDDOR.

Note that the law changed on 6 April 2012. If a worker sustains an occupational injury resulting from an accident, their injury should be reported if they are incapacitated for more than seven days. There is no longer a requirement to report occupational injuries that result in less than three days of incapacitation, but employers must still keep a record of such injuries.

Summary

1. What does the abbreviation RIDDOR stand for? Give a brief summary of its purpose.

2. Name five specified injuries reportable under RIDDOR.

3. A site manager is inspecting a building site when he notices a scaffold erected near water. This alone would not be reportable under RIDDOR. What factor would make this reportable under RIDDOR?

Accident and emergency procedures

The Management of Health and Safety at Work Regulations 1999 require employers to have procedures in place for handling emergencies. Workplaces also need a plan for emergencies that have a wider impact. Special procedures are needed for emergencies such as serious injuries, explosion, flood, poisoning, electrocution, fire, the release of radioactivity and chemical or biological spills.

While quick and effective action may help to ease the situation and reduce the consequences, people are more likely to respond reliably in emergencies if they:

- are well trained and competent
- take part in regular and realistic practice
- have clearly agreed, recorded and rehearsed plans, actions and responsibilities.

An emergency plan should be prepared if a major incident at your workplace could involve risks to the public, rescuing employees or co-ordinating emergency services. Equally, where you share your workplace with another employer, you should perhaps consider whether your emergency plans and procedures need to be co-ordinated.

Points to include in emergency procedures

- When planning procedures, consider what might happen and how the alarm will be raised. Don't forget night and shift working, weekends and times when the premises are closed.
- Plan what to do, including how to summon the emergency services. Help them locate the site by clearly marking your premises from the road. Consider drawing up a simple plan showing the location of hazardous items on site. (If you have 25 tonnes or more of dangerous substances, you must notify the fire and rescue service and put up warning signs.)
- Decide where to go to reach a place of safety or to get rescue equipment. You must provide suitable forms of emergency lighting and make sure there are enough emergency exits for everyone to escape quickly. Emergency doors and escape routes should be kept unobstructed and clearly marked.
- Nominate competent people to take control (a competent person is someone with the necessary skills, knowledge and experience to manage health and safety). Decide which other key people you need, such as a nominated incident controller, someone who is able to provide technical and other site-specific information if necessary, or first-aiders.
- Plan essential actions such as emergency plant shutdown, isolation or making processes safe. Clearly identify important items like shut-off valves and electrical **isolators**, etc.
- Train everyone in emergency procedures. Don't forget the needs of people with disabilities and vulnerable workers. Work should not resume after an emergency if a serious danger remains. If you have any doubts, ask for assistance from the emergency services. Don't forget that emergency procedures should be tested, evaluated and modified if required, to ensure they are working.

Key term

Isolators – mechanical switching devices that separate an installation from every source of electrical energy

Summoning the emergency services

The official emergency telephone number in the UK is 999. This number can be used to summon assistance from the main emergency services (police, fire and rescue, ambulance) or more specialist services, such as HM Coastguard.

An emergency can be:

- a person in immediate danger of injury or their life is at risk
- suspicion that a crime is in progress
- another serious incident that needs immediate emergency service attendance.

When you make a 999 call, ask for the service you need and then you will be asked to provide the following information:

- your telephone number
- the location of the incident and your location
- the type of incident
- the number, gender and ages of any casualties
- details of any injuries that may have occurred
- any information you may have observed about hazards, such as power cables, fog, ice or gas leaks.

The application of first aid and Basic Life Support (BLS)

Planning for an emergency can help to minimise the time taken for emergency services to reach you. However, first aid can also save lives, reduce pain and help an injured person make a quicker recovery.

Employers and the self-employed need to assess their first-aid requirements and make sure there are enough trained first-aiders and facilities to help casualties of illness or injury immediately, and that an ambulance or other professional help can be summoned without delay.

First-aid kits

You should carry a personal first-aid kit while at work. It should contain at least a large wound dressing, a pair of plastic gloves and a Resusciade (see Figure 1.9) or similar device.

You should also identify items that need to be in the worksite first-aid kit. This kit should take account of:

- the nature of the work
- the history and consequences of injuries
- the nature and distribution of the workforce

Figure 1.9: A Resusciade mouth shield is placed over a patient to prevent contamination from bodily fluids

- the remoteness of the site from the emergency services, including location, terrain and weather conditions
- working on shared or multi-occupied sites
- holidays and other absences of first-aiders
- the presence of trainees and the public
- the possibility of medical conditions or allergies.

Safety

You should avoid working alone and ideally your employer should have a policy on the subject. However, if you must do so, make arrangements for someone to check on you at regular intervals: the greater the risk, the more frequent the checks should be. As a minimum requirement, always inform your contact when work starts and finishes.

Safety

If you are part of a team scattered across an area, everyone in the team should arrange to meet at agreed times throughout the day. A notice in the site cabin is a good way of giving information to workers about the appointed person or first-aider.

First-aid facilities

The Health and Safety (First Aid) Regulations 1981 require you to provide adequate and appropriate equipment, facilities and personnel to enable first aid to be given to your employees if they are injured or become ill at work. The minimum provision for all sites is:

- a first-aid kit, with enough equipment to cope with the number of workers on site (See Figure 1.10)
- an appointed person to take charge of first-aid arrangements
- information telling workers the name of the appointed person or first-aider and where to find them.

An appointed person will take charge in the event of an injury and may not always be a trained first-aider. A first-aider is someone who has undergone a training course in administering first aid at work and holds a current first aid at work certificate. The number of qualified first-aiders needed depends on the risk of injury and ill health on site – Table 1.9 gives you a guide.

Numbers employed at any location	Number of first-aid personnel
Fewer than five	At least one appointed person
5 to 50	At least one first-aider
More than 50	One additional first-aider for every 50 employed

Table 1.9: Number of first-aiders needed

JTL tips   JTL

Never misuse the contents of a first-aid kit and always replace used items immediately. You never know when they will be needed again… and it may be you that needs them!

Figure 1.10: Contents of a first-aid kit

The first-aid arrangements should cover any shift working, night and weekend working. This may mean appointing or training several people.

Providing first aid at work

This section provides basic advice on first aid for use in an emergency. However, there is no substitute for receiving effective training and holding a first-aid qualification.

Priorities

Your immediate priorities are to:

- stay calm – you will be more effective if you remain calm
- assess the situation – do not put yourself, the casualty or any bystanders in danger
- make the area safe
- assess all casualties and attend first to any unconscious casualties
- send for help – do not delay.

Basic Life Support (BLS)

Once you have completed the above checks, carry out the procedure below to offer basic life support.

Check for a response

Begin by gently shaking the casualty's shoulders and asking loudly, 'Are you all right?'

If they respond, leave them in the position that you found them in (provided that it's safe to do so). Then, try to find out what is wrong with them – getting help if required and re-assessing their condition regularly.

If they do not respond, your priorities are to:

- shout for help
- open the airway
- check for normal breathing
- take appropriate action.

Airway	**Open the airway.** Turn the casualty onto their back. Place your hand on the forehead and gently tilt their head back. With your fingertips under the point of the casualty's chin, lift the chin to open the airway as shown in Figure 1.11. 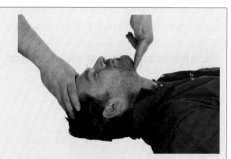 Figure 1.11: Open the airway

Breathing	**Check for normal breathing.** **Look** for chest movement. **Listen** at the mouth for sound of breath. **Feel** for normal breathing (for example on your cheek), for no more than 10 seconds. In the first few minutes after cardiac arrest, the casualty may be barely breathing or taking infrequent, slow and noisy gasps. Do not confuse this with normal breathing. If you have any doubt whether breathing is normal, act as if they are not breathing normally and prepare to start CPR.
Dial 999	**Take appropriate action and call an ambulance (999).** Ideally ask a helper to make the call, otherwise call 999 yourself. If possible stay with the casualty when making the call. Activate the speaker function on the phone to aid communication with the ambulance service.
Casualty is breathing normally	Place the casualty in the recovery position shown in Figure 1.12. Check for continued breathing. Figure 1.12: The recovery position
Victim is not breathing normally (or appears not to be breathing normally)	Call for someone to get an Automated External Defibrillator (AED). (Under PUWER, the AED must come with instructions for use.) If you are on your own, do not leave the victim. Start CPR.
CPR (cardio-pulmonary resuscitation)	**Start chest compressions.** Kneel by the side of the casualty. Place the heel of one hand in the centre of the casualty's chest (the lower half of the casualty's breastbone (sternum)). Place the heel of your other hand on top of the first hand. Interlock the fingers of your hands and ensure that pressure is not applied over the casualty's ribs otherwise you can break them (see Figure 1.13). Keep your arms straight. Do not apply any pressure over the upper abdomen or the bottom end of the bony sternum (breastbone). Position your shoulders vertically above the casualty's chest and press down on the sternum to a depth of 5–6 cm. After each compression, release all the pressure on the chest without losing contact between your hands and the sternum. Repeat compressions at a rate of 100–120 times per minute. Figure 1.13: Chest compressions

Rescue breaths	**After 30 compressions, open the airway again using the head tilt and chin lift (see Figure 1.11) and give two rescue breaths, as follows.** Pinch the soft part of the nose closed, using the index finger and thumb of your hand resting on the casualty's forehead. Allow the mouth to open, but maintain chin lift. Using a Resusciade if necessary, take a normal breath and place your lips around the casualty's mouth, making sure that you have a good seal. Blow steadily into the casualty's mouth while watching for the chest to rise, taking about 1 second as in normal breathing – this is an effective rescue breath. Maintaining head tilt and chin lift, take your mouth away from the casualty and watch for the chest to fall as air comes out. Take another normal breath and blow into the casualty's mouth once more to achieve a total of two effective rescue breaths. Do not interrupt compressions by more than 10 seconds to deliver two breaths. Then return your hands without delay to the correct position on the sternum and give a further 30 chest compressions. Continue with chest compressions and rescue breaths at a ratio of 30:2. If you are untrained, unwilling or unable to do rescue breaths, give chest compression only CPR (i.e. continuous compressions at a rate of at least 100–120 times per minute).
If an AED (Automatic External Defibrillator) arrives	AEDs are compact, portable and very effective. They are designed to be used by anyone, as the machine guides the operator through the process with both verbal instructions and visual prompts. They are safe and will not allow a shock to be given unless the heart's rhythm requires it. They are designed to be stored for long periods without use and require very little routine maintenance. **Switch on the AED.** Attach the electrode pads to the casualty's bare chest as shown on the AED. If more than one rescuer is present, continue CPR while attaching electrode pads to the casualty's chest. Follow the spoken/visual directions given by the machine. Ensure that nobody is touching the victim while the AED is analysing the rhythm. **If a shock is indicated, deliver the shock.** Ensure that nobody is touching the casualty while the AED is analysing the rhythm. Push the shock button as directed (fully automatic AEDs will deliver the shock automatically). Immediately restart CPR at a ratio of 30:2. Continue as directed by the machine's voice/visual prompts. **If no shock is indicated, continue CPR.** Immediately resume CPR at a ratio of 30:2. Continue as directed by the machine's voice/visual prompts. 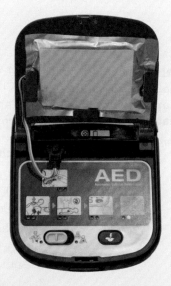 Figure 1.14: An automatic external defibrillator

Continue CPR	**Do not interrupt resuscitation until:**
	• a health professional tells you to stop
	• you become exhausted
	• the casualty is definitely waking up, moving, opening their eyes and breathing normally.
	It is rare for CPR alone to restart someone's heart. So, unless you are certain the person has recovered, continue CPR.
Recovery position	If you are certain the casualty is breathing normally but they are still unresponsive, place them in the recovery position, removing their glasses if they wear them. Check their breathing regularly.
	Be prepared to restart CPR immediately if the victim deteriorates or stops breathing normally.

Severe bleeding

If the casualty is suffering from severe bleeding:

• apply direct pressure to the wound

• raise and support the injured part (unless broken)

• apply a dressing and bandage firmly in place.

Broken bones and spinal injuries

If a broken bone or spinal injury is suspected, get expert help. Do not move the casualty unless they are in immediate danger.

Burns

Burns can be serious and you should seek medical help. However, you can aim to cool the affected part of the body with cold water until pain is relieved. This must be for ten minutes or more but must not delay the person being taken to hospital.

Eye injuries

If there is something in the casualty's eye, try to loosen it by rinsing out the eye with clean water or a sterile fluid. Do not attempt to remove anything that has become embedded in the eye.

Choking

How to recognise choking

Choking occurs when someone's airway is blocked by a foreign body. Recognising when someone is actually choking is the key here: it is important not to confuse this emergency with any other that may cause sudden respiratory distress, cyanosis (a bluish tinge to the skin or mucous membranes) or loss of consciousness. Table 1.10 shows you how to distinguish choking from other problems.

General signs of choking	
Attack occurs while eating Victim may clutch their neck	
Signs of mild airway obstruction	**Signs of severe airway obstruction**
Response to question 'Are you choking?' Victim speaks and answers 'yes'	*Response to question 'Are you choking?'* Victim unable to speak Victim may respond by nodding
Other signs Victim is able to speak, cough and breathe	*Other signs* Victim unable to breathe Breathing sounds wheezy Attempts at coughing are silent Victim may be unconscious

Table 1.10: Signs to see if someone is choking

Choking first-aid sequence

If the victim shows signs of mild airway obstruction

- Encourage them to continue coughing but do nothing else.

If the victim shows signs of severe airway obstruction and is conscious

- Give up to five back blows with a flat hand (a fist could cause damage).
  - Stand to the side and slightly behind the victim.
  - Support the chest with one hand and lean the victim well forwards so that when the obstructing object is dislodged it comes out of the mouth rather than goes further down the airway.

- Give up to five sharp blows between the shoulder blades with the heel of your other hand.

- Check to see if each back blow has relieved the airway obstruction. The aim is to relieve the obstruction with each blow rather than necessarily to give all five.

- If five back blows fail to relieve the airway obstruction, give up to five abdominal thrusts.
  - Stand behind the victim and put both arms round the upper part of his or her abdomen.
  - Lean the victim forwards.
  - Clench your fist and place it between the navel (tummy button) and the bottom end of the breastbone
  - Grasp this hand with your other hand and pull sharply inwards and upwards.
  - Repeat up to five times.

- If the obstruction is still not relieved, continue with five back blows.

Safety

Abdominal thrusts can save lives but can cause serious internal injuries at the same time. All victims who have received abdominal thrusts should be examined for injury by a doctor.

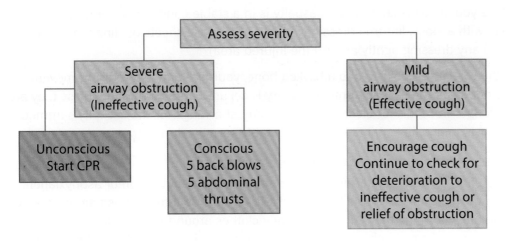

Figure 1.15: Treatment for adult choking

If the victim becomes unconscious

- support the victim carefully to the ground

- immediately call an ambulance

- begin CPR (see instructions on page 43). Healthcare providers, trained and experienced in feeling for a carotid pulse, should start chest compressions even if a pulse is present in the unconscious choking victim.

Treatment for electric shock

In the case of low voltage

- Ideally turn the power off at the mains.

- Remove any cables/power tools, etc. still in contact with the casualty.

- If the supply cannot be turned off, use a non-conducting item such as a piece of wood or a wooden broom, to knock the person away from the supply.

In the case of high voltage

Be aware that high voltage electricity has the ability to 'jump' or 'arc' up to distances of 18 metres or more. So if you are faced with a casualty resulting from high voltage electricity:

- do not approach

- stay at least 25 metres away from the casualty until the power has been switched off by an official agency such as the electricity board or network operator.

Shock is the medical condition where the circulatory system fails and insufficient oxygen reaches the tissues. If this shock is not treated quickly the vital organs can fail, leading ultimately to death. To treat shock you need to follow the process of Basic Life Support explained on pages 42–45.

An electric shock may result in other injuries as well as unconsciousness. There may be burns at both the entry point and exit point of the current. The treatment for these burns is to flood the site of the injury with cold water for at least ten minutes. This will halt the burning process, relieve the pain and minimise the risk of infection.

JTL tips   **JTL**

If you think someone is receiving or has received an electric shock, ensure the power source is isolated before you treat the casualty.

Once you are satisfied that the casualty is in a stable condition, cover any burned skin with a loose, lint-free dressing, or even with loose sheets of cling film (do not wind any dressing tightly around the injured area).

If the casualty had sustained a broken bone, your first aim is to prevent movement. Do not move the casualty until the injury is secured and supported, unless they are in danger from further electric shock. You must arrange for the casualty's immediate removal to hospital, maintaining comfortable support during transport.

Treatment for smoke and fume inhalation

If you find someone suffering from the effects of fume inhalation or asphyxiation, then provided that it is safe to do so, get them outside into the fresh air as soon as possible. Informing them first, loosen any clothes around their neck or chest that may impair their breathing. Call the emergency services and refer to the earlier guidance in this section regarding Basic Life Support (see pages 42–45).

Summary

1. What is the minimum first aid provision for any site?
2. A company employs 100 people who all work on the same site. How many first aiders should the company make sure they have on this site?
3. Someone has received an electric shock while working on site. You discover them lying on the floor possibly unconscious. What is the first thing you must do?

Fire safety

Key term

Oxidation – a chemical process in which a substance combines with oxygen. During this process, energy is given off, usually in the form of heat.

What is fire?

Essentially, fire is very rapid **oxidation.**

Rusting iron and rotting wood are common examples of slow oxidation. Fire, or combustion, is rapid oxidation because the burning substance combines with oxygen at a very high rate and energy is given off in the form of heat and light. Because this energy production is so rapid, we can feel the heat and see the light as flames.

How fire happens

All matter exists in one of three classic states: solid, liquid or gas (vapour). The atoms or molecules of a solid are packed closely together; those of a liquid are packed loosely and the molecules of a gas are not really packed together at all and are free to move about.

In order for a substance to oxidise, its molecules must be well surrounded by oxygen molecules. The molecules of solids and liquids are packed too tightly for this to happen, and therefore only gases can burn.

However, when a solid or liquid is heated, its molecules move about rapidly and if enough heat is applied, some molecules break away from the surface to form a gas just above the surface and this gas can now mix with oxygen. If there is enough heat to raise the gas to its ignition temperature, and if there is enough oxygen present, the gas will oxidise rapidly and it will start to burn.

So what we call burning is the rapid oxidation of millions of gas molecules. The molecules oxidise by breaking apart into individual atoms and recombining with oxygen into new molecules. It is during the breaking-recombining process that energy is released as heat and light. The heat that is released is radiant heat, which is pure energy and it radiates (travels) in all directions. Therefore, part of it moves back to the fuel of the fire.

Part of this heat releases more gas and part of it raises the gas to the ignition temperature, while at the same time air is being drawn into the area where the flames and gas meet. This results in an increase in flames as the newly formed gas begins to burn and this 'chain of events' will continue while there is still a fuel source reducing as the fuel is used up. Think of a log fire that will produce less and less heat and eventually die once the log has been used up.

The fire triangle

From the above description you may have noticed that there are three things needed for combustion to take place:

- fuel (to vaporise and burn)
- oxygen (to combine with fuel vapour)
- heat (to raise the temperature of the fuel vapour to its ignition temperature).

The fire triangle shows us that fire cannot exist without all three together and that if any side of the fire triangle is missing, a fire cannot start; or if any side of the fire triangle is removed, the fire will go out.

Figure 1.16: The fire triangle

Classes of fire

Combustible and flammable fuels have been broken down into the five categories shown in Table 1.11.

Class name	Class A	Class B	Class C	Class D	Electrical fires	Class F
Class icon	A	B	C	D METAL		F
Type of fire/fuel	Freely burning materials Wood, paper, straw, textiles, coal, etc.	Flammable liquids Petrol, diesel, oils, paint, paraffin, etc.	Flammable gases Methane, propane, natural gas, etc.	Flammable metals Magnesium, aluminium, lithium, etc.	Electrical appliances Computers, fuse boxes, etc.	Combustible cooking media Cooking oil, fats, grease, etc.

Table 1.11: The categories of combustible and flammable fuels

There is also an unofficial sixth category, sometimes referred to as Class E. It is used for electrical fires but is unofficial because electricity is seen as a source of ignition (rather than a fuel) that will feed a fire until switched off or isolated.

Fire prevention

Fires can spread rapidly. Once established, even a small fire can generate sufficient heat energy to spread and accelerate the fire to surrounding combustible materials. Fire prevention is therefore largely a matter of common sense and good housekeeping. Keep the workplace clean and tidy. If you smoke, don't throw lit cigarettes on to the ground, and don't leave flammable materials lying around or near sources of heat or sparks.

From an electrical perspective, make sure all leads are in good condition, fuses have the correct rating and circuits are not overloaded. Any alterations or repairs to electrical installations must be carried out only by qualified personnel and to the standards laid down in the IET Wiring Regulations (BS.7671).

Firefighting

A fire safety officer once said: 'People should only use a portable fire extinguisher to break the window so that they can escape from the building'. The point he was making is that it is dangerous to try to fight a fire, and the use of fire extinguishers should only be considered as a first-response measure: for example, where the fire is very small or where it is blocking your only means of exit. Firefighting is a job for the professional emergency service.

Safety
The new fire fighting regulations state that fire-fighting equipment in the workplace is there only to enable a small fire to be attacked, to prevent it from spreading.

Extinguishers

There are many types of fire extinguisher, each with a specific set of situations in which it may or may not be used as explained in the fire classes section. All fire extinguishers have a coloured stripe that indicates their type and their uses, so always be sure you have the right type before use. The six main types of extinguisher and their applications are shown in Table 1.12.

Type of fire extinguisher	Colour	Image	Fire classification	Description
ABC dry powder	Blue		A, B, C + Electrical	Used in mixed risk environments, offering excellent all-round fire protection. The Class C rating makes them effective for fire with flammable gases.
AFFF foam	Cream		A, B	Used with fires involving solid combustible materials and highly effective with flammable liquid fires as the layer of foam helps prevent reignition.
CO_2 carbon dioxide	Black		B + Electrical	Suitable for use on flammable liquid fires and extremely effective with electrical fires. Very clean and leaves no residue.
Water	Red		A	Suitable for environments with solid combustible materials (e.g. wood, paper, textiles). As water conducts electricity they should not be used with electrical fires.
Wet chemical	Yellow		A, F	Normally provided with a special application lance. Useful for oil fires, and well suited for kitchens.
Water mist	White		A, B, C, F, + Electrical	A new technology that cools fire, suffocates it and then cools the burning media to prevent reignition by using microscopic water particles. Ideal for covering areas with multiple fire risks.

Table 1.12: Types of fire extinguisher (images supplied courtesy of Safelincs)

Safety

When considering using a fire extinguisher:

- never use a fire extinguisher unless you have been trained to do so
- do not touch the horn on a CO_2 extinguisher as this can freeze burn the hands
- do not use the CO_2 extinguisher in a small room as this could cause suffocation
- read the operating instructions on the extinguisher before use.

Sprinkler systems

To reduce risk from fire, ideally fire sprinkler systems should be installed as they are by far the most efficient and effective safety devices available.

In support of that claim, the UK fire service has said that every day two people die and 50 are injured in fires in the UK, yet no one has ever died in a fire in a home fitted with residential sprinklers. Additionally, a typical sprinkler system will discharge less than 5 per cent of the water used by the fire service, therefore resulting in less property damage.

The hot gases from a fire are usually enough to activate the thermal element in a sprinkler head. This means that sprinklers can be individually heat-activated and the entire system won't go off at once. Sprinkler systems operate automatically, whether the building is occupied or not, and should also sound the alarm when they go off. This means that they can both alert you and tackle the fire.

Detection, alarm and evacuation procedures

Current UK fire alarm regulations (The Regulatory Reform (Fire Safety) Order 2005) state that all business premises must have:

- a responsible person carry out a fire risk assessment of the premises and review it regularly
- an 'appropriate fire detection system', which means that an outbreak of fire can be easily detected and occupants can be easily warned. However, this does not necessarily mean that all business premises will need a fire alarm system.

Safety

Smoke alarms will alert you to slow-burning, smoke-generating fires that may not create enough heat to trigger a sprinkler.

Regular fire drills must be held and all personnel must be familiar with normal and alternative escape routes. Fire routes should be clearly marked and emergency lighting signs fitted above each exit where applicable. You should make sure that you know where your assembly point is and also where the alarm system break glass contacts are, in case you're the one who discovers a fire.

Figure 1.17: A fire sprinkler system

As part of the fire risk assessment, employers should produce a fire emergency evacuation plan (FEEP). This is a written document (often in the form of a building layout poster) that includes the action to be taken by all staff in the event of fire (including following designated escape routes) and the arrangements for calling the fire brigade. In the event of a fire, the general guidance would be:

- raise the alarm immediately

- leave by the nearest exit

- call the fire service out

- if in doubt stay out

- close, but don't lock, windows to help starve the fire of oxygen

- go to your assembly point and report to your supervisor

- do not return to the building until you are authorised to do so.

Work activities and their effect on the environment

Climate change

The planet's climate and temperature has changed over time. However, the current period of warming is occurring more rapidly than in past times. Most scientists are concerned that the natural fluctuation of temperature is being overtaken by a rapid period of warming caused by human actions and that this has serious implications for the planet's climate.

Scientists believe we are adding to the natural greenhouse effect with gases released from industry and agriculture (known as emissions), trapping more energy in the atmosphere and increasing the temperature. This is commonly referred to as global warming or climate change, and is the term used to describe the long-term alteration of the world's weather patterns.

As a result of global warming, the melting of mountain glaciers and the retreat of polar ice sheets are also important contributors to climate change. Most glaciers in temperate regions of the world and along the Antarctic Peninsula are in retreat. The Greenland Ice Sheet has experienced record melting in recent years and if the entire sheet melted, it would raise world sea levels by 6 metres.

Therefore, in all parts of the construction industry, climate change is a live issue and one you need to consider. Tackling climate change needn't damage the economy, but industry will have to adapt, and jobs and working practices will change. It may even be that more jobs are created overall as we look at the way that we interact with our environment.

Figure 1.18: Emissions from industry and agriculture are contributing to the greenhouse effect

Understand how work methods and procedures can reduce material waste and impact on the environment

As just discussed, global warming is likely to worsen if we don't begin to think and act sensibly regarding our emissions. However, there are also other problems to consider, such as the contamination of the land, air or water by dangerous substances, processes, temperatures and wastes.

There are several areas you need to be aware of when choosing work methods and procedures to reduce material wastage. You will need to:

- report any hazards to the environment

- choose methods that can help to reduce material wastage

- use environmentally friendly materials, products and procedures that can be used in the installation and maintenance of electrotechnical systems.

The importance of reporting hazards to the environment

Additionally, if during your work you even think that something is having a negative effect on the environment (for example, fumes, noise or asbestos particles), inform your supervisor immediately and get it checked out. The consequences to everyone, both fellow workers and passers-by, could be disastrous if you don't.

Reducing material waste and using environmentally friendly materials, products and procedures

Using less energy can save companies and households money, and 'greener' living and working are going to be key factors. As an overview of practical measures for householders, the UK government currently suggests the following options. Bear in mind how these could be applied to the world of work.

Saving energy and water

Burning fossil fuels to heat our homes or produce electricity releases carbon emissions, which cause climate change. The energy you use at home is likely to be your biggest contribution to climate change. Approximately 80 per cent of it goes on heating and hot water, so this is a good place to look for savings.

Water is a precious resource and we should use it wisely at all times, because it's not as abundant as you might think. Using water, especially hot water, also uses energy and increases emissions of greenhouse gases contributing to climate change.

Here are some ways to save energy.

- Turn down the thermostat – turning your thermostat down by one degree could reduce carbon emissions and cut fuel bills by up to 10 per cent.

- Look for the labels – when buying products that use energy (this could be anything from light bulbs to fridge-freezers) help tackle climate change by looking for the Energy Saving Recommended label or European energy label rating of A or higher. The European energy label also tells you how much water appliances use, so you can choose a more efficient model.

- Improve insulation – more than half the heat lost in your home escapes through the walls and roof. Cavity wall insulation costs about £450, can take a couple of hours to install, and could save about £100 a year on fuel bills, as well as reducing your carbon footprint.

- Install water efficient products – low flush-volume toilets, water-efficient showerheads and aerating heads on washbasin taps help to reduce your water use significantly.

- Fix dripping taps – this and fitting a 'hippo' device in toilet cisterns are cheap ways of saving water. You can also collect rainwater in water butts and use it for watering your garden instead of a hose.

Figure 1.19: Exhaust fumes from traffic produce a large amount of pollution

- Fix leaking pipes – every day more than 3.3 billion litres of treated water – 20 per cent of the nation's supply and 234 million litres a day more than a decade ago – are lost through leaking pipes in England and Wales. The water lost would meet the daily needs of 21.5 million people.

Saving energy spent on transport

Travelling accounts for around a quarter of all the damage individuals do to the environment, including climate change effects. Individual car travel is responsible for most of these impacts, so if you're buying a car, look for the fuel efficiency label to choose the most efficient model.

Also try to reduce your car use, especially for short trips, which are the least energy efficient. With flying, consider alternatives to taking a plane. Walking, cycling, or taking the bus or train will help reduce local air pollution and climate change effects, and help your personal fitness too.

If you must fly, you can offset your CO_2 use. However, why not consider options for reducing your travel, such as taking fewer, longer breaks instead of several short ones? Maybe you can find what you want closer to home, by taking a holiday in the UK or travelling to nearby countries by rail or sea.

Saving energy when eating and drinking

Producing, transporting and consuming food is responsible for nearly a fifth of our climate change effects. Some foods have a much bigger impact on the environment than others, so:

- look for the labels – to help you choose food that has been produced with the aim of reducing the negative impact on wildlife and the environment

- buy fresh, local and in season – unprocessed or lightly processed food is likely to mean that less energy has been used in its production. Providing it has been produced and stored under similar conditions, choosing food that has travelled a shorter distance will help to reduce any congestion and transport emissions that contribute to climate change

- reduce your food waste – the average UK household spends £424 a year on food that goes in the bin. If this ends up in landfill, it produces methane, a greenhouse gas judged to be more than 20 times as powerful as carbon dioxide in causing climate change. Throwing less food away produces less methane and reduces other harmful environmental impacts from producing, packaging and transporting food.

Activity

▶ Use the internet to research 'reducing energy' and see how many websites you can find. Try some of their ideas or carry out an audit as a group on energy conservation.

As a trial, work in groups to monitor your own household's daily water usage. Does the amount surprise you? What could you do to reduce it?

Recycling and cutting waste

Reducing, reusing and recycling waste saves on raw materials and energy needed to make new paper, metal, glass and other items, so:

- reuse and repair and recycle more – nearly two thirds of all household rubbish can be recycled. Most councils run doorstep recycling collections for paper, glass and plastics, often more. Local sites often accept many other things, from wood and shoes, to textiles and TVs

- take a bag – keep your shopping bags and take some with you when you next go to the supermarket.

Reducing energy use in the workplace

Buildings produce nearly half of the UK's carbon emissions. The way a building is constructed, insulated, heated, and ventilated, and the type of fuel used, all contribute to its carbon emissions. Measures to improve the energy performance of our buildings have been introduced by the government, including:

- the introduction of Energy Performance Certificates (EPCs) for all buildings, whether they are built, sold or rented out

- requiring public buildings to display EPCs

- requiring inspections for air conditioning systems

- giving advice and guidance for boiler users.

An EPC shows the energy efficiency rating (running costs) of a non-dwelling. The rating is shown on an A–G rating scale like those used for fridges and other electrical appliances. The EPC includes recommendations on how to improve the energy efficiency, *but* there is no statutory requirement to carry out any of the recommended energy efficiency measures stated.

The selection of construction materials, air conditioning systems and boilers is the work of others, but it is clear that the selection of efficient materials and systems before installation and the maintenance of any existing systems will be key factors in reducing energy use.

Planning work methods

Planning can make a big difference. A carefully planned installation can reduce the environmental impact in terms of the number of visits to site, consequent travel and welfare arrangements, material and equipment delivery arrangements, selection of material and equipment, in terms of both installation and maintenance factors and the removal or disposal of waste.

One trend in construction that is gathering momentum is the move away from traditional 'on-site' construction to 'off-site' (modular) construction. Prefabricated construction has been around for some time but, with modern technology at our disposal, the modular approach is felt to offer many advantages. Although definitive statistics are difficult to find, some well-respected architects have said that some of the advantages are:

- up to 60 per cent less energy required to produce a modular building compared to an equivalent traditionally built project

---

JTL tips

If during your work you think something is having a negative effect upon the environment, inform your supervisor immediately.

- up to 90 per cent fewer vehicle movements to site, reducing carbon emissions, congestion and disruption
- a potential reduction in on-site waste by up to 80 per cent.

In the construction industry many things can impact upon the environment. Table 1.13 shows some ways to apply energy saving within an eco-friendly building.

Materials
Use natural, sustainably managed renewable sources (for example there are timber building companies in Norway that have planting policies which mean they are growing more trees than they cut down to make their products).
Source materials near to the point of use, reducing transportation effects.
Building should be made using minimal processing or with added content such as chemicals.
Make use of their natural insulation properties.
Use non-toxic and non-hazardous to users or building occupants (e.g. paint fumes)
Use durable materials with low maintenance.
Materials should have the capability to be recycled.
'Measure twice, cut once' is a good rule to avoid wastage.
Energy
Use natural light wherever possible.
Use low-energy appliances wherever possible (e.g. 'A' rated washing machines).
Use local expertise and labour wherever possible, thus reducing the effects of transportation.
Use renewable sources where possible.
Water
Use rainwater harvesting (using rainwater for irrigation, vehicle washing or toilet flushing).
Use grey-water recycling (using water from baths, showers, etc. for toilet flushing).
Use low-volume flush toilets.
Use aerated taps (these make the water spray).
Use instantaneous water heaters over sinks instead of heating large volumes of water.
Lag hot water pipes to avoid losing heat.
Only heat as much as you need in a kettle or boiler.

Table 1.13: Methods of saving energy in eco-friendly buildings

The Building Regulations

The current Building Regulations 2010 set standards for the design and construction of most buildings, primarily to ensure the safety and health for people in or around those buildings, but also for energy conservation and access to and about buildings.

There are currently 16 parts to the building regulations, as shown below. Each part is supported by an approved document that both states the legislation and provides the means deemed to satisfy the regulations.

- Part A – Structure
- Part B – Fire safety
- Part C – Site preparation and resistance to contaminates and moisture
- Part D – Toxic substances
- Part E – Resistance to the passage of sound
- Part F – Ventilation
- Part G – Sanitation, hot water safety and water efficiency
- Part H – Drainage and waste disposal
- Part J – Combustion appliances and fuel storage systems
- Part K – Protection from falling, collision and impact
- Part L – Conservation of fuel and power
- Part M – Access to and use of buildings
- Part N – Glazing safety (withdrawn)
- Part P – Electrical safety
- Part Q – Security
- Part R – Physical infrastructure for high-speed electronic communication networks

Part L (Conservation of fuel and power) is particularly relevant in the context of the environment. It states that 'responsible provision shall be made for the conservation of fuel and power in buildings by limiting heat gains and losses and by providing and commissioning energy-efficient fixed building services with effective controls'.

Part L is a direct outcome of the government's Energy White Paper commitment to:

- raising the energy performance of buildings by limiting heat losses and excessive solar gains
- ensuring that energy-efficient fixed building services are installed
- ensuring that the building owner is provided with the information required to maintain the building and its services, and to enable the building to be operated so that it uses no more fuel and power than is reasonable under the circumstances.

As the need for heat is the major energy demand in a building, it is vital to address the problem. To reduce overall energy consumption it is also necessary to reduce the heat lost by a building, by making it more air tight and improving levels of insulation.

Once this is done, low or zero carbon alternatives, such as heat pumps, can be used to deliver renewable heat, thereby removing the need for direct fossil fuel use on site (which typically results in higher direct emission levels).

Dealing with waste

Current government policy regarding this could be summarised as 'protection of human health and the environment by producing less waste and by using it as a resource wherever possible'. The government want to encourage more sustainable waste management, such as reduction, reuse, recycling, composting and using waste as a source of energy, to break the link between economic growth and the production of waste.

This introduces a hierarchy of waste management shown in Figure 1.20, where waste prevention is the preferred option and disposal the least favourite.

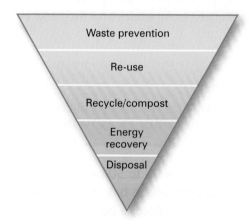

Figure 1.20: Hierarchy of waste management

Waste prevention

Preventing waste in the first place is the best option of all. Examples would be using less product packaging, restricting junk mail, using reusable shopping bags or sustainability in building design.

Reuse or recycle?

There are two aspects to the broader idea of recycling:

- reusing a product you no longer want, even if that product contained a hazardous material – called reuse

- taking something and turning it, or parts of it, into something new – usually what most people mean by recycling.

Reuse

One example could be a half-full tin of paint. It can't be turned into something new, but it could be taken to a recycling plant and carefully distributed for use by others, for example in community projects which may not have enough money to purchase new tins of paint.

Equally, a school or youth club may be grateful to receive that old PC monitor that you were going to throw on the scrap heap. You might give items you don't want to a charity shop or community project.

Recycle

Items made out of materials that can be turned into something new provide the basic concept for recycling.

Most paper-based products such as magazines, newspapers, flyers, and Christmas and birthday cards, can be processed via **pulping** and turned into new paper-based products. Juice cartons and the like can go through a similar process.

Industrial oil can be usefully recovered and used as a fuel. Larger quantities of used oil, such as hydraulic fluid or lubricants from lorries, buses or mechanical plants, should be stored securely before collection by a registered waste carrier. Specialist companies will collect used cutting oils, and then treat and recover the oil.

Cooking oils from commercial users, such as caterers and fish and chip shops, must not be disposed of with the general waste stream. The waste oils are not hazardous but are subject to a duty of care in terms of their disposal. Such disposal can see waste oils collected by specialist contractors and they can even be reused as fuel for diesel engine cars.

Key term

Pulping – where paper-based products are dropped into a huge tank and blitzed with water, which separates the paper from any impurities

Activity

▶ Find out what waste disposal facilities there are in your local area. Which of these might you use in your work as an electrician, and what for?

Food and drink cans are made up of up to 50 per cent steel. You may only be able to drink that cola or eat those beans once but, by recycling the can, you can use the same steel again and again. Steel in Europe contains 56 per cent recycled steel and is fully recyclable.

Energy recovery

Energy recovery (sometimes known as 'waste to energy') systems create energy in the form of electricity or heat from the incineration of waste materials.

Incineration has brought its own problems, namely the release of acid gases and the ash left by the burning process. However, modern plants now use lime filters in the chimney to control the problem.

Use of these plants can be linked to the development of what is termed 'district heating' in UK cities such as Newcastle upon Tyne, Nottingham and Sheffield. In such systems, the incinerator acts as a huge central boiler that then supplies heat to a large area, such as a housing estate.

Less common are Advanced Thermal Treatments (ATT) such as:

- gasification (which produces combustible gas, hydrogen and synthetic fuels)

- pyrolysis (which produces combustible tar/bio-oil and a liquid fuel similar to diesel).

Disposal

The most common disposal methods, particularly in the UK, are landfill and, to a lesser extent, incineration. There are over 4000 landfill sites in the UK, and each year millions of tonnes of controlled waste (household, commercial and industrial) are disposed of there. Some waste from sewage sludge is also placed in landfill sites, along with waste from mining and quarrying.

Safety

Emulsified cutting oils are highly polluting in water, so take great care when disposing of them. Contact a specialist contractor for advice.

Safety

Generally, the burning of waste in the open is an environmentally unsound practice, and you should use less damaging options for waste disposal.

As landfill waste decomposes, methane is released in considerable quantities. Methane is a strong greenhouse gas that contributes to global warming. Also, the leachate fluids formed from decomposing waste can permeate through the underlying and surrounding ground, polluting groundwater, which may be used for drinking water supplies.

Anaerobic digestion is another method of waste disposal. It is less common, but more sustainable than incineration or landfill. In this process, waste decomposes in an enclosed chamber, unlike in a landfill site. Digestion takes place in an oxygen-free environment where bacteria decompose waste by breaking down the molecules to form gaseous by-products (methane) and small quantities of solid residue. Anaerobic sewage plants produce significant quantities of methane, which can be burnt to generate electricity. Liquid and solid organic fertilisers are also formed with this method.

Waste transport

You can transport most business waste directly to an authorised waste management site or recycling facility. However, a business must register with their environmental regulator as a 'waste carrier' if they transport:

- construction and demolition waste produced by the business

- any waste produced by another business.

As waste carriers, the business must check that it holds the correct registration for the type of waste being transported. It must also complete a Waste Transfer Note (WTN) for every load of waste passed on or accepted. Copies of all WTNs must be held for at least two years. Figure 1.21 gives guidelines for good waste disposal practice.

❏ Do not burn waste on site; find another method of disposal.

❏ Before allowing any waste hauler or contractor to remove a waste material from your site, ask where the material will be taken and ask for a copy of the waste management licence or evidence of exemption for that facility.

❏ Segregate the different types of waste that arise from your works. This will make it easier to supply an accurate description of the waste for waste transfer purposes.

❏ Minimise the quantity of waste you produce to save you money on raw materials and disposal costs.

❏ Label all waste skips – make it clear to everyone which waste types should be disposed of in each skip.

❏ Check if waste is hazardous or special waste before you transport it.

Figure 1.21: Checklist for good waste disposal practice

You must complete a consignment note whenever you or anyone else moves or transfers hazardous waste. Copies of consignment notes must be kept for at least three years and if you transport hazardous/special waste you must:

- keep it separate from other wastes

- use sealed and clearly labelled containers

- check that it is transferred to a facility that is authorised to receive it.

Summary

1. In the hierarchy of waste management what is the first stage that must be considered and give an example of how this stage could be achieved?

2. In the WEEE Regulations how many categories of electrical and electronic equipment are there?

3. What could a business do to limit noise and statutory nuisance?

3. Procedures for establishing a safe working environment

How do you prevent accidents?

Many accidents have 'environmental causes' as they relate to the environment that you are working in. Such causes can be unguarded machinery, defective tools and equipment, poor ventilation, excessive noise or workplaces that are poorly lit, overcrowded, untidy or dirty.

The other main cause of accidents is people. It would be nice to think that we all possess common sense, but the 'human' causes of accidents include:

- carelessness
- bad and foolish behaviour
- improper dress
- lack of training
- lack of experience
- poor supervision
- fatigue
- use of alcohol or drugs.

Safety

If the hazard is something that is easy to fix, then you should fix it, as long as it is not dangerous to yourself to do so. Remember to make sure that you still report it to your supervisor.

Health and safety in the workplace is something you need to take personal responsibility for. By thinking about what you are doing, or are about to do, you can avoid many potentially dangerous situations. Always report potentially dangerous situations, hazards or activity to the right people. Even if the hazard is something you can easily fix yourself – for example, moving a brick to prevent a trip hazard – still report it to your supervisor. The fact that the brick was there at all might indicate that someone is not doing their job properly and it could happen again.

The secret is to be aware of all possible danger in the workplace and have a positive attitude towards health and safety. Follow safe and approved procedures where they exist, and always act in a responsible way to protect yourself and others.

Hazard or risk?

A hazard is any thing or situation that may cause harm, such as chemicals, dusts, asbestos, electricity, working from ladders or scaffolding or unguarded machinery.

A risk is the chance, high or low, that somebody will be harmed by the hazard and taking into consideration how serious that harm could be.

Producing risk assessments

Accidents and ill health can ruin lives. They can also affect business if output is lost, machinery is damaged, insurance costs increase or employers have to go to court. This is why employers are legally required to assess the risks in their workplace.

A risk assessment is nothing more than a careful examination of what, during working activities, could cause harm to people, so that employers can weigh up whether they have taken enough precautions or should do more to prevent harm. The aim is to make sure that no one gets hurt or becomes ill.

The important questions to answer through a risk assessment are:

- what are the hazards
- are they significant
- are hazards covered by satisfactory precautions so that the risk is small?

For example, we know that electricity is a hazard that can kill, but the risk of it doing so in a tidy, well-run office environment is remote, provided that the installation is sound, 'live' components are insulated and metal casings are properly earthed.

How to assess risks in the workplace

Some years ago the HSE produced guidance for employers to help with the process, called 'Five Steps to Risk Assessment'. This has become an invaluable tool for grasping the essentials of risk assessment. Here are the five steps.

- Step 1 Identify the hazard.
- Step 2 Decide who might be harmed and how.
- Step 3 Evaluate the risks and decide on precautions.
- Step 4 Record your findings and implement them.
- Step 5 Review your assessment and update it if necessary.

The HSE provide the following example of a risk assessment, as seen in Figure 1.22.

To help you understand the concepts, as you read on, try to put yourself in the position of an employer carrying out a risk assessment and using the form depicted in Figure 1.22 to do so.

Risk assessment

All employers must conduct a risk assessment. If you have fewer than five employees you don't have to write anything down.

We have started off the risk assessment for you by including a sample entry for a common hazard to illustrate what is expected (the sample entry is taken from an office-based business). Look at how this might apply to your business, continue by identifying the hazards that are the real priorities in your case and complete the table to suit.
You can print and save this template so you can easily review and update the information as and when required. You may find our example risk assessments a useful guide (http://www.hse.gov.uk/risk/casestudies). Simply choose the example closest to your business.

Company name: Date of risk assessment:

What are the hazards?	Who might be harmed and how?	What are you already doing?	Do you need to do anything else to control this risk?	Action by who?	Action by when?	Done
Slips and trips	Staff and visitors may be injured if they trip over objects or slip on spillages.	General good housekeeping is carried out. All areas well lit, including stairs. No trailing leads or cables. Staff keep work areas clear, eg no boxes left in walkways, deliveries stored immediately.	Better housekeeping in staff kitchen needed, eg on spills. Arrange for loose carpet tile on second floor to be repaired/replaced.	All staff, supervisor to monitor Manager	From now on xx/xx/xx	xx/xx/xx xx/xx/xx
						Hint, tab here for new row

You should review your risk assessment if you think it might no longer be valid (eg following an accident in the workplace or if there are any significant changes to hazards, such as new work equipment or work activities)

Figure 1.22: HSE risk assessment form

Step 1: Identify the hazards

Unless you actively look for hazards, by the time you discover them, you could already be in danger. Here are some ways in which you can find hazards before they find you.

- First you need to work out how people could be harmed. Remember that when you work in a place every day it is easy to overlook some small hazards.

- Walk around the workplace and look at what could reasonably be expected to cause harm. Employers should ask employees or their representatives what they think, as they may have noticed things that are not immediately obvious.

- Visit the HSE website as it can guide you towards HSE guidance on where hazards occur and how to control them.

- If you are a member of a trade association, contact them. Many produce very helpful guidance.

- Manufacturers' instructions or data sheets can also help you spot hazards and put risks in their true perspective.

- Have a look back at your accident and ill-health records – these often help to identify the less obvious hazards. Remember to think about long-term hazards, such as noise, as well as safety hazards.

Step 2: Decide who might be harmed and how

For each hazard you need to be clear about who might be harmed; it will help you identify the best way of managing the risk. That doesn't mean listing everyone by name, but rather identifying groups of people, such as 'people working in the storeroom' or 'passers-by'.

In each case, identify how they might be harmed – what type of injury or ill health might occur. For example, shelf stackers may suffer back injury from repeated lifting of boxes.

Some workers have particular requirements, for example:

- new cleaners, visitors, contractors or maintenance workers who may not be in the workplace all the time and young workers

- new or expectant mothers and people with disabilities who may be at particular risk

- members of the public, or people you share your workplace with, if there is a chance they could be hurt by your activities.

Ask other staff if they can think of anyone that you may have missed.

Step 3: Evaluate the risks and decide on precautions

Evaluate the risks and decide whether existing precautions are adequate or if more should be done. Consider how likely it is that each hazard could cause harm; this will determine whether more needs to be done to reduce the risk.

Even after all precautions, some risk usually remains. Decide for each hazard whether this remaining risk is high, medium or low.

- First, ask yourself whether you have done all the things that the law says you have to do. For example, there are legal requirements on prevention of access to dangerous parts of machinery.

- Then ask yourself whether generally accepted industry standards are in place.

Your real aim is to make all risks low by adding precautions as necessary. If something needs to be done, draw up an action plan and give priority to any remaining risks that are high or which could affect most people.

In taking action, ask yourself:

- can I get rid of the hazard altogether?

- if not, how can I control the risks so that harm is unlikely?

In controlling risks apply the following principles, ideally in this order:

- try a less risky option

- prevent access to the hazard, for example by guarding and using barriers and notices

- organise work to reduce exposure to the hazard

- issue personal protective equipment, such as clothing or goggles

- provide welfare facilities such as washing facilities for the removal of contamination.

Improving health and safety need not cost a lot. For instance, it costs little to place a mirror on a dangerous blind corner to help prevent vehicle accidents, or to put non-slip material on slippery steps. Failure to take simple precautions can cost you a lot more if an accident does happen.

If the work you do is very varied, or you or your employees move from one site to another, identify the hazards you can reasonably expect and assess the risks from them.

Step 4: Record your findings and implement them

If you have fewer than five employees, you do not need to write anything down, though it is useful and recommended to keep a written record of what you have done.

If you employ five or more people, you must record the significant findings of your assessment – the significant hazards and conclusions – and you must tell your employees about your findings. When writing down your results, keep it simple. For example, 'tripping over rubbish: bins provided, staff instructed, weekly housekeeping checks'.

The HSE does not expect risk assessments to be perfect, but they must be suitable and sufficient. You need to be able to show that:

- a proper check was made
- you asked who might be affected
- you dealt with all the obvious significant hazards, taking into account the number of people who could be involved
- the precautions are reasonable, and the remaining risk is low
- you involved your staff or their representative in the process.

Keep the written record for future reference or use; it can help you if an inspector asks what precautions you have taken, or if you become involved in any action for civil liability.

Safety

A written record can also remind you to keep an eye on particular hazards and precautions, and it helps to show that you have done what the law requires.

Step 5: Review your assessment and update it if necessary

Few workplaces ever remain the same. Sooner or later you will need to bring in new equipment, substances and procedures that could lead to new hazards. It makes sense to review what you are doing on an ongoing basis.

Every year or so, formally review where you are, to make sure that you are still improving, or at least not sliding back. If there is any significant change, add to the risk assessment to take account of the new hazard.

You do not necessarily need to amend your assessment for every trivial change or new job. However, you will want to consider any significant new hazards in their own right and do whatever you need to keep the risks down. In any case, it is good practice to review your assessment from time to time (no later than annually) to make sure that the precautions are still working effectively.

Safety

During the year, if there is a significant change, don't wait – check your risk assessment and, where necessary, amend it. If possible it is best to think about the risk assessment when you are planning your change – that way you leave yourself more flexibility. Set a review date for your risk assessment now so you check it as an annual event.

Key terms

Young people – according to the Management of Health and Safety at Work Regulations, people who have not reached the age of 18

Child(ren) – according to the Education Act 1996, persons who are below Minimum School Leaving Age (MSLA); this will be 15 or 16 years old depending on when their birthday falls

Risk assessments for young people

All risk assessments need to take into account certain features that apply to **young people**. It is important to remember that, when you are young, you will have little or no experience of hazardous substances and will work at a slower pace than others.

Before employing a young person, a health and safety risk assessment must take into account:

- the fitting-out and layout of the workplace

- the nature of any physical, biological and chemical agents, the length of time and the extent of the exposure

- the types of equipment to be used and how these will be handled

- the organisation of the work and processes involved

- the need to provide health and safety training and to assess this

- risks from particular agents, processes and work.

Safety

There is no need for a new risk assessment each time a young person is employed, as long as the current assessment takes into account the characteristics of young people and activities which present significant risks to their health and safety. Remember to take into account young people's experience and capacity.

As a young person, generic risk assessments can be useful if you are likely to be doing temporary or transient work. Many electricians carry out small works and visit more than one job a day. These risk assessments could be modified to deal with particular work situations and any unacceptable risks. In all cases, the risk assessment will need to be reviewed if the nature of the work changes or if there is reason to believe that it is no longer valid.

There are restrictions on when and where you can be employed and what work you can do. These do not apply in 'special circumstances'. An example of this could be if you are over the minimum school leaving age, doing work necessary for your training under proper supervision by a competent person and in conditions reduced, as far as is reasonably practicable, to their lowest level of risk.

Under no circumstances can **children** of compulsory school age do work involving these risks, whether they are employed or under training. This includes children on work experience.

Note that training includes government-funded training schemes for school leavers, modern apprenticeships, in-house training arrangements and work that qualifies for assessment for N/SVQs, such as craft skills.

Training and supervision

As a young person, you should:

- have training as soon as you start work

- be trained in the risks and hazards of the workplace, with the key messages checked and understood

- know basic health and safety procedures including first aid, which should be part of your training.

You are also likely to need more supervision. This also allows your employers to monitor how effective your training has been as well as your occupational competence.

Procedures for working in accordance with risk assessments, method statements and safe systems of working

After risk assessment, an employer should look to determine what can be done, as far as is reasonably practicable, to remove any hazards. If any hazards remain, then safe systems of work should be developed to work around them.

The process to follow in developing a modern, safe system of work is as follows.

- Make a risk assessment.

- Determine what can be done so far as is reasonably practicable to remove the identified hazards.

- Should hazards remain, develop a safe system of work.

- Where necessary, formalise these systems of work into procedures (method statements).

- Include in the procedures where necessary the use of Permits to Work coupled with physical lock-off systems for electrical supplies where necessary.

- Monitor the observance of all parts of the procedure.

- Feedback any information on weaknesses or failures in the system.

- Rectify these by modifying the system.

- Keep monitoring and modifying the systems as necessary.

A method statement takes information about significant risks from your risk assessment, and combines this with the job specification, to produce a practical, safe working method for the workers to follow on site. Method statements should be easy to read and specific to that job or site.

These should include the use of work permits and all parts of the procedure should be observed with feedback on any weaknesses so that the procedure can be improved if needed.

It is now common to hear the phrase 'RAMS' in relation to this topic. RAMS stands for Risk Assessment and Method Statement and is the bringing together of the two activities of assessing risk and a resultant method statement.

Safety

A generic method statement may be acceptable in some circumstances, such as for minor repetitive jobs in identical situations, but this is generally not the case. Generic information about frequently used company policies should form part of any general health and safety policy and be incorporated into induction training.

Permit to Work

A Permit to Work is a document that specifies the work to be done, the person(s) involved, when it is going to be done, the hazards involved and the precautions to be taken.

To understand how important a Permit to Work can be, read the Working life feature below, which is based on a real story and an area that continues to be of concern: the dangers of working in isolation.

Working life

Roger, a painter, has gone to paint some rooms one Saturday morning. Arriving on site, he says hello to a few people and goes off to start his work. Once there he realises that he also has a fairly large storage tank to paint.

Many hours later, his body is found inside the storage tank. He had been killed by the fumes from the specialist paint he was using.

· What precautions should Roger have taken before starting this work?
· Who would have been involved in the investigation of this accident?
· What recommendations do you think they would make?

The Working life feature is just one example of when it can be dangerous to work in isolation, but there are many more, such as:

· in confined spaces

· in trenches

· near, or on, live sources or equipment

· at height

· near to unguarded machinery

· where there is a risk of fire or in hazardous atmospheres

· with toxic or corrosive substances.

One contributing factor to the painter's death in the Working life feature was that no one knew exactly where he was or what he was doing. The Permit to Work specifies the work to be done, the persons involved, the hazards involved, when it is to be done (date/start/finish) and precautions taken.

As a Permit to Work is only 'active' for a set period, if the painter had not returned by the specified time, someone would have gone to investigate – and his life could have been saved.

As the Permit to Work has to be authorised, it is essential that the person doing the authorising is competent and fully able to understand the work to be done, the hazards and the proposed system of work and precautions needed. A sound knowledge of Regulations such as the Confined Spaces Regulations 1997 and COSHH is also essential.

The Permit to Work form aids communication between everyone involved and employers must train staff in its use. Ideally the company issuing the permit should design it, taking into account individual site conditions and requirements. On certain sites, separate permit forms may be required for different tasks, such as 'hot work' and entry into confined spaces, so that sufficient emphasis can be given to the particular hazards present and precautions required.

Provided documentation

You should bear in mind that documentation and systems prepared and provided for any situation are not foolproof.

Imagine you are driving to a location using a Sat-Nav system. The voice and the map tell you to turn left after 200 metres, but you can clearly see that doing so would take you the wrong way down a one-way street and into a river. Would you follow the instructions?

The point is that in life we all make mistakes, and situations change, so the information that is issued and received may not always be correct. Equally HASAWA makes it clear that both employers and employees have responsibilities for safety.

So be sensible. If any document you are issued with doesn't match the circumstances you are working in or sets alarm bells ringing in your mind, check with an appropriate person before you do anything.

Safety

There will always be circumstances where you will be involved in potentially dangerous tasks. For many situations, the answer is to use the Permit to Work system.

Safety

Remember – there are situations in construction and maintenance work where the nature of the task involves risks that are so high that you should not undertake those tasks alone.

Summary

1. The HSE has produced guidance for employees to help with the process of producing a risk assessment. How many stages are there and what is each stage called?

2. According to the Management of Health and Safety at Work Regulations a young person is classed as someone who has not reached the age of 18. Why might a risk assessment need to consider certain features for 'young people'?

3. If something on a Health and Safety document doesn't seem right what should you always do?

Personal Protective Equipment (PPE)

The use of PPE is governed by the Personal Protective Equipment at Work Regulations 1992, which were covered on pages 15–16. The point of the PPE Regulations is that PPE must be provided by the employer, free of charge, and used wherever there are risks to health and safety that cannot be adequately controlled by other means. In other words, PPE should always be thought of as the 'last resort' in terms of protective measures against risk. The 'hierarchy of controls' is shown in Figure 1.23.

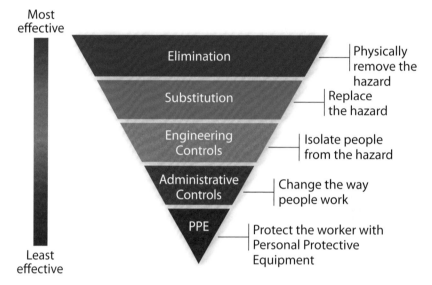

Figure 1.23: Hierarchy of controls for PPE

Eye protection

Every year thousands of workers suffer eye injuries, which result in pain, discomfort, lost income and even blindness. Following safety procedures correctly and wearing eye protection can prevent these injuries. There are many types of eye protection equipment available: for example, safety spectacles, box goggles, cup goggles, face shields and welding goggles. To be safe, you must have the right type of equipment for the specific hazard you face.

Figure 1.24: Safety goggles

Figure 1.25: Helmet with a visor face screen

Figure 1.26: Half-face mask

Foot and leg protection

Guarding your toes, ankles, feet and legs from injury also involves protecting your whole body from injury caused by improper footwear, for example an injury caused by electric shock.

Protective footwear can help prevent injury and reduce the severity of injuries that do occur. Different types of PPE which can be used to prevent injuries to legs and feet are outlined in Table 1.14.

PPE	Usage
Safety shoe, boot or trainer 	Basic universal form of foot protection. Safety clogs can also be worn, which give particularly good protection against hot asphalt
Spats, often made of leather and worn over the shoe	Protect the feet from stray sparks during welding
Gaiters, worn over the lower leg and top of the shoe	Used to give protection against foul weather/splashing
Leggings	Protect general clothing

Table 1.14: Types of leg and foot PPE

Hand protection

This involves the protection of two irreplaceable tools – your hands, which you use for almost everything, including working, playing, driving and eating. Unfortunately, hands are often injured and one of the most common problems other than cutting, crushing or puncture wounds is **dermatitis.**

Skin irritation may be indicated by sores, blisters, redness, or dry, cracked skin that is easily infected.

To protect your hands from irritating substances you need to:

- keep them clean by washing them regularly with approved cleaners
- wear appropriate personal protection when required
- make good use of barrier creams where provided.

 Figure 1.27: Rigger gloves

 Figure 1.28: Gauntlet gloves

Figure 1.29: Safety helmet

Head protection

Head protection is important because it guards your most vital organ – your brain! Head injuries pose a serious threat to your brain and your life.

Here is a list of good safety practice to help you protect your head.

- Know the potential hazards of your job and what protective headgear to use.
- Follow safe working procedures.
- Take care of your protective headgear.
- Notify your supervisor of unsafe conditions and equipment.
- Get medical help promptly in the case of head injury.

There are several types of protective headwear for use in different situations; use them correctly and wear them whenever they are required.

Safety helmets

Here are a few important rules.

- Adjust the fit of your safety helmet so it is comfortable: all straps should be snug but not too tight.
- Don't wear your helmet tilted or back to front.
- Never carry anything inside the clearance space of a hard hat, like cigarettes, cards or letters.
- Never wear an ordinary hat under a safety helmet.
- Do not paint your safety helmet as this could interfere with electrical protection or soften the shell.
- Only use approved types of identification stickers on your safety helmet, such as 'First-aider'.
- Do not use sticky tape or labelling tape as the adhesive could damage the helmet.
- Handle the helmet with care: do not throw it or drop it.
- Regularly inspect and check the helmet for cracks, dents or signs of wear, and if you find any, get your helmet replaced.
- Check the strap for looseness or worn stitching and also check your safety helmet is within its 'use-by' date, which is given in a dial on the underside of the peak of the helmet.

Safety

You should always wear PPE when required – an estimated 80 per cent of industrial head injuries happen to people who are not wearing any protective equipment.

Safety

If you have long hair and don't want it to be ripped off by something, tie it up or use a hair net.

Bump caps

For less dangerous situations, where there is a risk of bumping your head rather than things falling, or where space is restricted, bump caps, which are lighter than safety helmets, may be acceptable.

If you have to work outside in poor conditions, and a safety helmet is not a requirement, consider using a sou'wester and cape.

Working life

Fazal is a first-year apprentice who is starting his first day on a construction site. The electrician in charge gives Fazal a hard hat to wear. Fazal notices that the hat has a crack down one side and reports this to his supervisor. The supervisor tells Fazal that he must wear this hat because there are no more in the store and he needs to get on with his work.

• What should Fazal do in this situation?
• If an object hit Fazal on the head and he was injured because of the crack in the hat, who would be responsible for this injury?

Hearing protection

You may sometimes have to work in noisy environments. If you do, your employer must ensure compliance with Control of Noise at Work Regulations 2005. This would involve, if necessary, carrying out noise risk assessments and providing you with suitable hearing protection.

Like any other sort of PPE, hearing protection must be worn properly and you must check it regularly to make sure it is not damaged. This is because failure to use the proper ear protection can result in permanent damage to your hearing. Common types of hearing protection are:

• ear plugs that fit inside the ear

• ear defenders that sit externally, such as headphones.

Figure 1.30: Ear plugs   Figure 1.31: Ear defenders

Figure 1.32: Disposable dust respirator

Lung protection

We all need clean air to live and we need correctly functioning lungs to allow us to inhale that air. Fumes, dusts, airborne particles such as asbestos or just foul smells, such as in sewage treatment plants, can all be features of construction environments.

You can get a range of respiratory protection, from simple dust-protection masks to half-face respirators, full-face respirators and powered breathing apparatus. To be effective these must be carefully matched to the hazard involved and correctly fitted. You may also require training in how to use them properly.

Whole body protection

To complete your 'suit of armour' you need to protect the rest of your body. Usually this will involve overalls or similar, to protect against dirt and minor abrasions. However, you may also need:

* specialist waterproof or thermal clothing in adverse weather conditions

* high-visibility clothing on sites or near traffic

* chemical-resistant clothing, such as neoprene aprons, if you are working near or with chemical substances.

When working outdoors, sunscreen is now also a consideration.

Figure 1.33: High-visibility jacket

Figure 1.34: High-visibility waistcoat

Figure 1.35: Overalls

Safety

All items of PPE that are provided for your protection must be worn and kept in good condition.

When should I wear PPE?

Risk assessment and the hierarchy of controls are the key here. However, the following general principles shown in Table 1.15 will apply.

PPE	When worn
Hard hats	Where there is a risk of you either striking your head or being hit by falling objects
Eye protection	Drilling or chiselling masonry surfaces Grinding or using grinding equipment Driving nails into masonry Using cartridge-operated fixing tools Drilling or chiselling metal Drilling any material that is above your head
Ear protection	Close to noisy machinery or work operations
Gloves	If there is a risk to the hands from sharp objects or surfaces Handling bulky objects to prevent splinters, cuts or abrasions Working with corrosive or other chemical substances
Breathing protection	In dusty environments Working with asbestos Where noxious gases are present Where certain gases are present

Table 1.15: When to wear PPE

Other items

When working involves long periods of kneeling or having to take your weight on your elbows, you may be issued with specialist protectors for these areas. Other items you may use could include face masks, safety harnesses or breathing apparatus.

Personal hygiene

If necessary, use a barrier cream before starting work. This fills the pores of the skin with a water-soluble antiseptic cream so that, when you wash your hands, the dirt and germs are removed with the cream.

Always wash at the end of the work period, before and after using the toilet, and before handling food. Reapply barrier cream after washing.

Change your overalls regularly before they get too dirty and become a health hazard themselves.

Safety

Do not use solvents to clean your hands. They remove protective oils from the skin and can cause serious problems, such as dermatitis.

Summary

1. You turn up to work and when inspecting your safety helmet, you notice there is a dent and crack in the helmet, what should you do?
2. Give four examples of whole body protection.
3. Name four situations when breathing protection should be used.

Safe practices and procedures

Safety signs and guarding

The Health and Safety (Safety Signs and Signals) Regulations 1996 require employers to use a safety sign where there is a significant risk to health and safety that has not been avoided or controlled by the methods required under the relevant law, provided the use of a sign can help reduce the risk.

Safety signs are not a suitable substitute for those other methods of controlling risks, such as engineering controls and safe systems of work. However, understanding their meaning and taking notice of them is vital to site safety.

There are four types of safety sign – Prohibition; Mandatory; Warning; Information/ Safe Condition. Examples of these are shown in Figure 1.36.

	Prohibition signs	**Mandatory sign**
Shape	Circular	Circular
Colour	Red borders and cross bar. Black symbol on white background	White symbol on blue background
Meaning	Shows what must *not* be done	Shows what *must* be done
Example	No smoking	Wear eye protection

	Warning signs	**Information or safe condition signs**
Shape	Triangular	Square or rectangular
Colour	Yellow background with black border or symbol	White symbols on green background
Meaning	Warns of hazard or danger	Indicates or gives information on safety provision
Example	Danger: Electric shock risk	First aid post

Figure 1.36: Safety signs

Fire safety signs are covered as a separate item in the Regulations, but Figure 1.37 shows a typical example.

Figure 1.37: Fire sign

Summary

1. To maintain a safe working environment and avoid accidents, hazards and the risk of being harmed by that hazard need to be identified. Before work commences briefly outline what should be done.

2. You are requested to fix a series of hanging brackets onto a concrete wall. Identify what PPE you would expect to use to keep you safe. If one of the items of PPE were damaged and you were injured as a result, who would be responsible?

3. As a site operative you are required to know all the safety signs. What do the following safety signs look like: Prohibition, Mandatory, Warning and Information?

4. You hear a scream on site and upon investigation see a work colleague clearly suffering from electric shock. What are the implications and what would you do?

Identifying and dealing with hazards in the work environment

The construction industry presents many types of hazard, some general and some particular to the electrical trade. You will look at a range of these in this section.

Electricity (including temporary supplies and trailing leads and cables)

Electricity can kill. Even non-fatal shocks can cause severe and permanent injury as shocks from faulty equipment may lead to falls from ladders, scaffolds or other work platforms. Those using electricity may not be the only ones at risk, as poor electrical installations and faulty electrical appliances can lead to fires.

The good news is that most of these accidents can be avoided through careful planning and straightforward precautions. The main hazards are:

- contact with live parts causing shock and burns (mains voltage at 230 volts AC can kill)
- faults, which could cause fires
- fire or explosion where electricity could be the source of ignition in a potentially flammable or explosive atmosphere, for example, in a spray-paint booth.

Electrical equipment used on building sites (particularly power tools and other portable equipment and their leads) faces severe conditions and rough use and can become damaged and dangerous. Modern double-insulated tools are well protected, but their leads are still vulnerable to damage and should be regularly checked.

Where cables are needed for temporary lighting or mains-powered tools, run these at high level, particularly along corridors. Alternatively, use special abrasion-resistant or armoured flexible leads.

As with all aspects of health and safety, where possible, eliminate the risks.

Safety

The first person to alert about a health and safety issue should be your site supervisor or safety officer.

Safety

Many hazards can be reduced by precautions: safety guards and fences can be put on or around machines; safe systems of work introduced; safety goggles, helmets and shoes issued. Your employer should provide any additional PPE required, such as ear defenders, respirators, eye protection and overalls.

Using electrical power tools and lighting

One of the best ways of reducing the risk of injury when using electrical equipment is to limit the supply voltage to the lowest level needed to get the job done. This can be done by:

- running any temporary lighting at lower voltages
- using battery-operated tools in cases where electrically-powered tools are required
- using portable tools designed to be run from a 110 volt centre-tapped-to-earth transformer.

For other purposes, such as lighting, particularly in confined and wet locations, even lower voltages can be used and are even safer.

Working life

A joiner working on site asks if you can power up the socket outlets as he wishes to use his 230 V power tools.

- How should you respond to this request?
- What system should be adopted by the joiner?
- Whose responsibility would it be to supply power for the joiner?

If mains voltage has to be used, the risk of injury is high if equipment, tools, leads, and so on are damaged, or there is a fault. Residual current devices (RCDs) with a rated tripping current no greater than 30 mA with no time delay will be needed to ensure the current is promptly cut off if contact is made with any live part.

RCDs must therefore be kept free of moisture and dirt and protected against vibration and mechanical damage. They need to be properly installed and enclosed, including sealing of all cable entries. They should be checked daily by operating the test button. However, RCDs cannot give the assurance of safety that cordless equipment or a reduced low-voltage (such as 110 V) system provides.

Electrical systems should be regularly checked and maintained. Everyone using electrical equipment should know what to look out for. A visual inspection can detect about 95 per cent of faults or damage. Before any 230 V hand tool, lead or RCD is used, check it against the safety checklist shown in Figure 1.38 below.

Safety

Check any equipment to be used in a flammable atmosphere – it must not cause ignition!

❏ no bare wires visible

❏ cable covering not damaged and free from cuts and abrasions (apart from light scuffing)

❏ plug in good condition: casing not cracked, pins not bent, key way not blocked

❏ no taped or other non-standard joints (e.g. connector strips) in cable

❏ outer covering (sheath) of cable gripped at entry point

❏ coloured insulation of internal wires not visible

❏ equipment outer casing not damaged, all screws in place

❏ cables and equipment appropriate to the environment

❏ no overheating/burn marks on plug, cable or equipment

❏ RCDs working effectively – press 'test' button every day

Figure 1.38: Safety checklist for 230 V hand tools, leads and RCDs

Safety

Remember that overloading sockets by fitting adaptors can cause fires.

JTL tips

When you are working on an electrical installation, hazards can arise concerning the environment you are working in and the installation itself, whatever stage the installation is at.

Workers should be instructed to report any of these faults immediately and stop using the tool or cable as soon as any damage is seen. Managers should also arrange for a formal visual inspection of 230 V portable equipment on a weekly basis, and damaged equipment should be taken out of service as soon as the damage is noticed. Do not carry out makeshift repairs.

Safety

With lighting systems, provide protection for cabling in the same way as for tool supplies. Protect lamps against breakage. If breakage does occur, the exposed filaments may present a hazard.

Checking new installations

With a new installation, always ensure that it is installed to BS.7671 and that load characteristics and socket provision have been accurately calculated.

Once an installation has been put into service, make sure that it is adequately maintained. Simple preventative maintenance – a visual inspection supported by testing, if needed – can prevent most electrical risks.

The frequency of such inspection and testing depends upon the installation, the type of equipment, its frequency of use and the environment in which it is installed. BS.7671 contains appropriate instruction and recording the results of these activities also helps to assess the effectiveness of the system.

Table 1.16 uses the example of the construction of a new leisure centre to illustrate the typical stages of an installation and some typical hazards that you may come across.

Project activity	Hazards
Initial preparation and planning on site	Set-up may involve craning in large cabins – access arrangements Delivery arrangements – site access, safe handling and storage
Install	Working at height – use of scaffolding, ladders, etc. Presence of other trades – noise, fumes, traffic Electricity – temporary supplies Handling and storage of materials and equipment
Terminate and connect	As above, but live sources may not be present
Inspection and testing	As above, but live sources may not be present Other contractors may restrict access – inform them of your activities
Fault finding and maintenance	Work may be at height or in isolation Live sources are likely to be involved Presence of others may be dangerous – use barriers, communicate

Table 1.16: Hazards encountered in typical stages of an installation

Protecting site workers

Even qualified electricians are at risk if they don't follow recognised safe working procedures. The guidance in this section is based on information published by The Electricity Safety Council, taking into account the requirements of the Electricity at Work Regulations (EAWR). For more information on the EAWR, look back at pages 4–6.

The key regulations within the EAWR are:

- Regulation 12 – where necessary to prevent danger, suitable means must be available to cut off the supply of electrical energy to equipment and the equipment must be 'isolated', defined as the secure disconnection of the electrical equipment from every source of electrical energy

- Regulation 13 – the means of disconnection must be secured in the OFF position, with a warning notice or label at the point of disconnection, and proving 'dead' at the point of work with an approved voltage indicator

- Regulation 14 – 'dead' working should be seen as the normal method of carrying out work on electrical equipment or circuits. Live work should only be carried out in particular circumstances where it is unreasonable to work 'dead'

- Regulation 16 – no one shall engage in work with electricity unless they are competent to do so.

Most people are aware that certain activities require the circuit to be live (such as when fault finding). There can also be commercial pressure to carry out work on, or near, live conductors. However, you must take precautions to ensure safety, and the EAWR still applies.

Safe isolation

To ensure compliance with Regulations 12 and 13 of the EAWR, the following working principles must be followed:

- the correct point of isolation has been identified and the appropriate means used

- ideally the point of isolation is under the control of the person carrying out the work on the isolated conductors

- warning notices should be applied at the point(s) of isolation

- conductors must be proved dead **at the point of work** before they can be touched (see GS.38)

- the supply cannot be re-energised while the work is in progress.

Means of isolating a complete installation

Sometimes circumstances mean that you must isolate either a whole installation or large parts of an installation. When this is necessary, the normal method is to use the main switch or the DB switch disconnector (see Figure 1.39) mounted within the DB.

In either case, the locking device should be locked with a unique key or combination that remains in the possession of the person carrying out the work.

Safety

Live working should only be carried out when justified using the risk assessment criteria explained in HSE document HSG.85.

Activity

▶ What does HSG.85 cover? How could you use it in your work?

Figure 1.39: DB switch disconnector

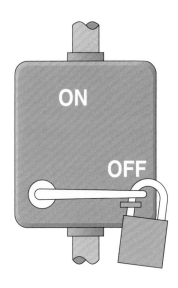

Figure 1.40: Device locked off with padlock

If locking off facilities don't exist on the relevant switch, you can also use a locked DB that prevents access to that switch, provided that it is locked with a device using a unique lock/combination as described on the previous page.

Means of isolating individual circuits or items of equipment

Obviously, there will also be circumstances where it is impractical to isolate a whole section of a building just to work on one item of equipment. For example, to repair a wall light in a hospital ward, you would not isolate the whole ward, just the relevant circuit. If you isolated the whole ward, you would endanger patients on various support systems.

The types of equipment used in circuits to provide switching and isolation of the circuits, and even complete installations, can be categorised as having one or more of the following functions:

- control
- isolation
- protection.

Safety

All live conductors must be isolated before work can be carried out, including the neutral conductor as this is a live conductor. This may mean removing the conductor from the neutral block in the distribution board. Not all distribution boards are fitted with double-pole isolators, so the connecting sequence for neutral conductors needs to be verified and maintained. Table 537.4 of BS.7671 gives comprehensive guidance on the selection of protective, isolation and switching devices.

Figure 1.41 gives a simple example of the control, isolation and protection functions, showing a one-way lighting circuit supplied from a distribution board with a main switch and circuit breakers.

Looking at Figure 1.41, you can see that:

- the distribution consumer unit combines all three functions of control, protection and isolation

- the main double-pole switch can provide the means for switching off the supply and, when locked off, complete isolation of the installation

- the circuit breakers provide protection against faults and over-currents in the final circuits

- when switched off and locked off, the circuit breakers can provide isolation of each individual circuit

- the one-way switch has only one function, which is to control the circuit enabling the luminaire to be switched 'on' or 'off'.

On- and off-load devices

Not all devices are designed to switch circuits 'on' or 'off'. It is important to know that, when a current is flowing in a circuit, the operation of a switch (or disconnector) to break the circuit will result in a discharge of energy across the switch terminals.

Single-pole one-way switch

Lamp

N

P

Distribution consumer unit incorporating double pole mains switch & circuit breakers

N   P

Figure 1.41: One-way lighting circuit with mains switch and circuit breakers

You may have seen this when you have entered a dark room, switched on the light and seen a blue flash from behind the switch plate. This is actually the **arcing** of the current as it dissipates and makes contact across the switch terminals. Similar arcing occurs when circuits are switched off or when protective devices operate, breaking fault current levels.

An isolator is designed as an off-load device and is usually only operated after the supply has been made dead and there is no load current to break. An on-load device can be operated when current is normally flowing and is designed to make or break load current.

A circuit breaker is an example of an on-load device. This is not only designed to make and break load current but must also withstand high levels of fault current.

Remembering the three previous functions, it is important to install a device that meets the needs of a particular part of a circuit or installation. Some devices can meet the needs of all three functions. However, some devices may only be designed to meet a single function.

All portable appliances should be fitted with the simplest form of isolator – a fused plug. When unplugged from the socket outlet, this provides complete isolation of the appliance from the supply. For equipment isolation, such a device should be mounted local to the equipment and be fitted with a means of being locked off.

Key term

Arcing – a plasma discharge as a result of current flowing between two terminals through a normally non-conductive media (such as air), producing high light and heat

---

Safety

A plug is not designed to make or break load current. The appliance should be switched off before removing the plug.

The means of isolation could also be an adjacent local isolation device, such as a plug and socket, fused connection unit, circuit breaker or fuse. However, for this to be allowed it must be under the direct control of the competent person carrying out the work and must be visible by them at all times to stop anyone interfering with it.

Sometimes more than one person can work on different circuits supplied from the same DB. Here you should ideally isolate and lock off each individual circuit using the appropriate devices. When this is not possible, you should use a multi-lock hasp on the main switch or DB switch disconnector.

A typical multi-lock hasp is shown in Figure 1.42.

As can be seen, this holds more than one padlock (one for each person working, each having a unique key or combination) and cannot be removed until all of the locks have been removed by those people.

If the facility does not exist to isolate the circuit like this, then it is permissible to disconnect the circuit from the DB, provided that the disconnected conductors are made safe against inadvertent re-energising of the circuit. Suitable labelling is essential. However, work carried out inside a live DB is classed as live working when there is access to exposed live conductors and in such cases, you should take the appropriate precautions (HSG85 with respect to Regulation 14 of the EAWR).

Figure 1.42: A multi-lock hasp

Figure 1.43: A switch fixed with a locking device and label that must be placed on padlock to prevent removal

Safety

When there is no local means of isolation, the preferred method of isolating circuits or equipment is to use the main switch or DB switch disconnector as if you were isolating a whole installation. It helps if each circuit has the facility to have a suitable locking device and padlock fitted.

Individual circuits protected by circuit breakers

Where circuit breakers are used as the means of isolation, they should be locked using an appropriate locking-off clip and padlock that can only be operated with a unique key or combination, both of which must be retained throughout by the individual working on the circuit.

A warning notice should also be fitted at the point of isolation.

Individual circuits protected by fuses

Where a fuse is the means of isolation, it must be removed and retained by the person carrying out the work. Also, a lockable fuse insert should be fitted in the gap remaining and should be locked using a padlock that can only be operated with a unique key or combination. A warning notice must also be fitted.

If lockable fuse inserts are not available then consider either:

- fitting a 'dummy' fuse (a holder with no fuse in)

- padlocking the DB door (retain unique key, fit notice)

- disconnection of the circuit (fit warning notice).

Remember that the practice of placing insulating tape over a circuit breaker to prevent inadvertent switching on is **never** a safe means of isolation.

Things to watch out for

Circuit identification

For a new installation, make sure all protective devices are correctly identified at the DB before the circuit is energised. Equally, on older installations, make sure all records of the installation are available and that circuits have been correctly identified.

Automatically controlled circuits

'I know it's dead,' he said, 'because I've just tested all the terminals on the equipment are dead.' And then five minutes later this person was just as dead.

Although the terminals were dead when he tested them, they were on a circuit that was controlled by a time switch that suddenly kicked in. You have been warned!

Neutral conductors

Even though BS.7671 forbids it, the practice of using the neutral of one circuit to supply another still remains, with lighting and control circuits being the favourite culprits.

Be aware that in BS.7671 a neutral is referred to as a 'live conductor' because, in the situation above, a neutral can be live if disconnected and the circuit borrowed from has its load energised.

Proving isolated equipment or circuits are dead

Just because you think you have isolated something, it doesn't mean that you have. You should never assume that just because you locked what you thought was the right circuit in the off position, that it's actually dead. Always assume and treat something as being live until you have proved otherwise.

Test instruments

All test equipment must be regularly checked to make sure it is in good and safe working order. If you have any doubt about an instrument or its accuracy, ask for assistance: test instruments are very expensive, so avoid causing any unnecessary damage.

Safety

You must ensure your test equipment has a current calibration certificate, which indicates that the instrument is working properly and providing accurate readings. If you do not do this, test results could be void.

Guidance Note GS.38

Published by the Health and Safety Executive, GS.38 is for electrical test equipment used by electricians. It gives guidance to electrically competent people involved in electrical testing, diagnosis and repair. Electrically competent people may include electricians, electrical contractors, test supervisors, technicians, managers or appliance repairers.

Voltage-indicating devices

Instruments used solely for detecting a voltage fall into two categories:

- detectors that rely on an illuminated lamp (test lamp) or a meter scale (test meter). Test lamps are fitted with a 15 watt lamp and should not give rise to danger if the lamp is broken. A guard should also protect them

- detectors that use two or more independent indicating systems (one of which may be audible) and limit energy input to the detector by the circuitry used. An example is a two-pole voltage detector: that is, a detector unit with an integral test probe, an interconnecting lead and a second test probe.

Both these types of detector are designed and constructed to limit the current and energy that can flow into the detector. This limitation is usually provided by a combination of the circuit design using the concept of protective impedance, and current-limiting resistors built into the test probes.

The detectors are also provided with in-built test features to check the functioning of the detector before and after use. The interconnecting lead and second test probes are not detachable components.

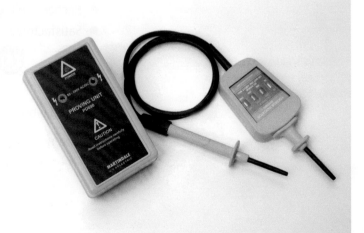

Figure 1.44: Voltage-indicating device

These types of detector do not need additional current-limiting resistors or fuses provided that they are made to an acceptable standard and the contact electrodes are shrouded.

It is recommended that test lamps and voltage indicators be clearly marked with the maximum voltage which may be tested by the device and any short-time rating if applicable. This rating is the recommended maximum current that should pass through the device for a few seconds, as these devices are generally not designed to be connected for more than a few seconds.

An industry accepted safe isolation process is shown in Figure 1.45.

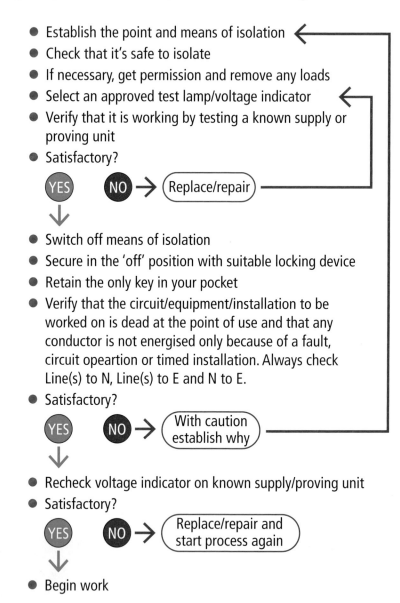

Figure 1.45: Safe isolation process for complete isolation

Restoration of the supply

After a fault has been rectified, which may have resulted in either parts being replaced or simple reconnection of conductors, it is important that the circuit is tested for functionality. These tests may be simple manual rotation of a machine or the sequence of tests as prescribed in BS.7671.

For example, a simple continuity test will check resistance values, open and closed switches and their operation.

Working life

A plumber protests to you that he has received an electric shock while connecting the boiler on site. On investigation it is clear that the supply is on.

- What requirements do the Electricity at Work Regulations 1989 place upon operatives working on circuits?
- What procedure should have been followed?
- What essential steps would be taken to ensure the circuit is made safe for work to be carried out?

JTL tips

On 1 April 2004 the insulation colours changed to the current colours. However, for many years to come, you will continue to find existing installations with the old colours. These were:

- single-phase and neutral – red, black
- three-phase – red, yellow and blue
- three-phase and neutral – red, yellow, blue and black.

Summary

1. What would be the most common way of isolating a complete installation?
2. When verifying that the complete installation is dead what combinations of Phase, Neutral and CPC should be tested?
3. What must be done if when you re-check the voltage indicator by testing on a known supply or proving unit, the result is not satisfactory?

Slippery or uneven surfaces

A simple slip or trip is the single largest cause of injury on construction sites, with more than a thousand major injuries being reported each year. The main causes of this type of accident are:

- having to walk over uneven ground, particularly when carrying unwieldy objects
- tripping over building materials or waste that has been left lying around
- tripping over trailing cables
- slipping caused by wet surfaces or poor ground conditions
- trips caused by small changes in level.

Each of these could easily be avoided, but in reality this can be difficult on a constantly changing construction site. Site managers must exercise good control, and everybody on site must take responsibility for ensuring they do not create a risk for others.

The checklist shown in Figure 1.46 gives you some simple rules to help prevent accidents from slips and trips.

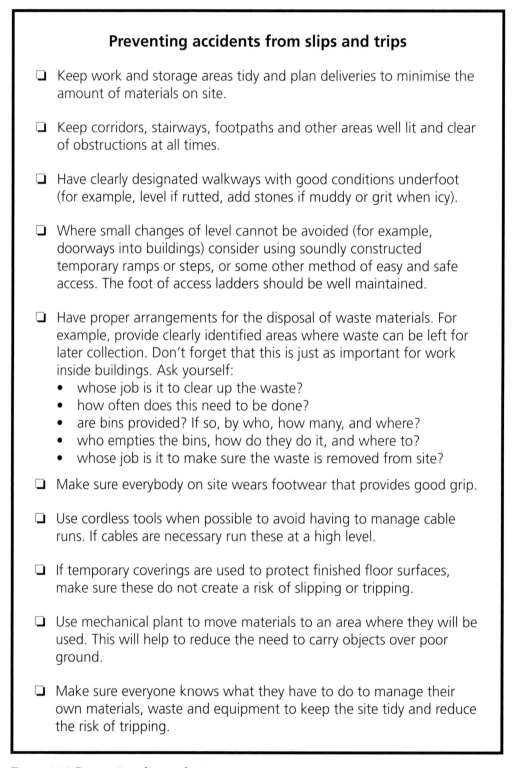

Preventing accidents from slips and trips

❏ Keep work and storage areas tidy and plan deliveries to minimise the amount of materials on site.

❏ Keep corridors, stairways, footpaths and other areas well lit and clear of obstructions at all times.

❏ Have clearly designated walkways with good conditions underfoot (for example, level if rutted, add stones if muddy or grit when icy).

❏ Where small changes of level cannot be avoided (for example, doorways into buildings) consider using soundly constructed temporary ramps or steps, or some other method of easy and safe access. The foot of access ladders should be well maintained.

❏ Have proper arrangements for the disposal of waste materials. For example, provide clearly identified areas where waste can be left for later collection. Don't forget that this is just as important for work inside buildings. Ask yourself:
  • whose job is it to clear up the waste?
  • how often does this need to be done?
  • are bins provided? If so, by who, how many, and where?
  • who empties the bins, how do they do it, and where to?
  • whose job is it to make sure the waste is removed from site?

❏ Make sure everybody on site wears footwear that provides good grip.

❏ Use cordless tools when possible to avoid having to manage cable runs. If cables are necessary run these at a high level.

❏ If temporary coverings are used to protect finished floor surfaces, make sure these do not create a risk of slipping or tripping.

❏ Use mechanical plant to move materials to an area where they will be used. This will help to reduce the need to carry objects over poor ground.

❏ Make sure everyone knows what they have to do to manage their own materials, waste and equipment to keep the site tidy and reduce the risk of tripping.

Figure 1.46: Preventing slips and trips

Safety

Common reasons for slips, trips and falls include leaving trailing cables across corridors and leaving waste materials in stairwells; so make sure you don't!

Presence of dust and fumes

On construction projects, dust and fumes can come from a wide range of sources, including:

- unmade roads
- drilling operations
- working in trenches
- welding

- woodworking
- cleaning activities
- plumbing work
- using chemicals as part of the activity.

Safety

COSHH requires you to substitute harmful products with less harmful ones or use adequate control measures if this is not possible. All control measures must be in good working order, including mechanical, administrative and operator controls.

Employers must decide whether breathing in fumes, vapours or dust is likely to harm anyone's health. Here are some questions that need to be asked.

- Does the manufacturer's information say there is a risk from inhaling the substance?
- Are large amounts of the substance being used?
- Is the work being done in a way that results in heavy air contamination, such as spray application?
- Is the work to be done in an area that is poorly ventilated, such as a basement or container?
- Does the work itself generate a hazard? For example, hot cutting metal covered with lead causes lead fumes.

Safety

It is important to remember to assess both immediate risks (such as being overcome by fumes in a confined space) and longer-term health risks (such as developing asthma).

Breathing in certain dusts, gases, fumes and vapours within the workplace can cause asthma. Asthma is a serious health problem that can ruin lives. Shortness of breath, wheezing and painful coughing are just some of its symptoms. One of the main causes is rosin-based solder flux fume, caused when soldering; another cause is hardwood, softwood and wood composite dust that arise from sanding when wood machining.

Chronic Obstructive Pulmonary Disease (COPD) is a long-term illness that makes breathing difficult, because the lungs and breathing tubes are damaged, making it difficult to get air in and out. COPD is slow to develop – the symptoms tend only to start becoming a problem from your late forties onwards – and so many people do not realise they have the disease. Research findings suggest that for Great Britain:

- 15 per cent of COPD may be caused or made worse by work

- 4000 COPD deaths every year may be related to work exposures.

Safety

The risk of developing COPD is greatly increased if you breathe in dust or fumes in the workplace and you smoke. There is increasing research evidence that COPD can be caused or made worse by dusts, fumes and irritating gases at work.

Once COPD develops, the damage to the lungs cannot be reversed. It can be prevented from getting worse by reducing exposure to the dust, fume and irritating gases at work that are causing the problem and avoiding smoking.

Prevention

If harm from the substance is possible, first try to avoid it completely by not using it at all. This will mean either:

- doing the job in a different way (for example, instead of using acids or caustic soda to unblock a drain, use drain rods; damp down dusty areas)

- using a substitute substance (for example, instead of using spirit-based paints, use water-based ones, which are generally less hazardous).

However, always check that one hazard is not simply being replaced by another.

Control

If a substance has to be used because there is no alternative, or because use of the least hazardous alternative still leads to significant risk, try to control exposure.

Some of the ways this could be done include:

- transferring liquids with a pump or siphon (not one primed by mouth) rather than by hand, keeping containers closed except when transferring

- rather than spraying solvent-based materials, use a roller with a splash guard or apply by brush

- using as little of the hazardous substances as possible – don't take more to the workplace than is needed

- using cutting and grinding tools and blasting equipment fitted with exhaust ventilation or water suppression to control dust

- ensuring good ventilation in the working area by opening doors, windows and skylights – mechanical ventilation equipment might be needed in some cases

- using a Permit to Work system.

If, and only if, exposure cannot be adequately controlled by any combination of the measures above, then you need to use personal protective equipment (PPE).

If you are using a respirator with replaceable cartridges, make sure the correct type is fitted, that they have not become exhausted or clogged and that they are still in date (many filters have a limited shelf life). Always have replacement filters available.

Safety

Any PPE must be selected with care. Respirators can protect against dusts, vapours and gases but make sure the respirator is the correct type for the job. For example, dust masks may not protect against vapours. Never use unserviceable tools or equipment. Either repair or replace them and always remove unsafe equipment from the site.

Safety

Cartridge-operated tools can be very dangerous, especially if you have an accidental discharge, which can cause serious injuries from ricochets. Make sure you have been given instruction on the safe and correct methods of use. Some tools may require a licence before use. You may need a licence to store cartridges – check with your local authority to see if this is the case.

Handling, transport and storage of tools, equipment and materials

You will use a variety of materials, tools and pieces of equipment in your work as an electrician. All of them are potentially dangerous if misused or neglected. Instruction in the proper use of materials, tools and equipment will form part of your training and you should always follow safe working methods.

You have already looked at COSHH, which relates to substances, but hand tools and manually operated equipment are often misused too.

You should always use the right tool for the job and never just make do with whatever tool you may have to hand. For example, never use a hammer on a tool with a wooden handle as you may damage the wooden handle and create flying splinters.

Here are some general guidelines.

- Keep cutting tools, saws, chisels and drills sharp and in good condition.

- Make sure handles are properly fitted and secure, and free from splinters.

- Check that the plugs and cables of hand-held electrically powered tools are in good condition. Replace frayed cables and broken plugs.

- Electrically powered tools of 110 volts or 230 volts must be portable appliance tested (PAT) in accordance with your employer's procedures.

Key terms

Embolism – an obstruction in a blood vessel due to a blood clot in the bloodstream

You may also come into contact with high-pressure airlines. Used carelessly, compressed air can be dangerous, causing explosions or blowing aside tools, equipment and debris. Never use an airline to blow dust away; never aim it at any part of your body and never point it at somebody else. If high-pressure air enters the body through a cut or abrasion or through one of the body's orifices it can cause an air **embolism**, which at best is very painful and at worst can be fatal.

Equally, any piece of equipment – for example, a toolbox, portable floodlight or conduit bender – can deteriorate with use. Equipment should always be visually inspected before use, used correctly and stored appropriately when not in use. If it is damaged or broken, it should not be used, as it could cause an accident or injury.

When using equipment such as grinders or drills, make sure that:

- any required guards are in place

- the equipment is appropriate, undamaged and fit for purpose (for example, correct grinding wheel or drill fitted)

- you do not exceed vibration exposure limits

- you wear suitable PPE (for example, gloves, eye protection, respirators, ear defenders) where required

- you have been trained to operate the equipment (especially when using cartridge operated tools)

- suitable ventilation is available

- signs and barriers to prevent unauthorised access are provided where required.

Figure 1.47: A portable circular saw – one of the portable tools you may encounter on site

Untidy working and storage

Trailing cables and air hoses, spilt oil and so on can cause people to slip, trip or fall. Clutter and debris should be cleared away to prevent fire hazards. Tools and equipment left lying around are also targets for thieves, making it difficult for an employer to maintain effective levels of insurance cover.

Safety

It is especially important to keep emergency routes clear. Make sure that all flammable waste materials (such as packaging and timber offcuts) are cleared away regularly to reduce fire risks.

You should therefore plan how the site will be kept tidy and how housekeeping will be managed.

- After any work, all tools should be cleared away and the workplace left in a safe condition.

- Keep walkways and stairways free of tripping hazards such as trailing cables, building materials and waste.

- Keep inside floor areas clean and dry.

- Outdoor footpaths should be level and firm and should not be used for storing materials.

- Keep all storage areas tidy, whether in an agreed storage area or on the site itself.
- Try to plan deliveries to keep the amount of materials on site to a minimum.

Figure 1.48: An untidy work area can present many trip hazards

Designate storage areas for plant, materials, waste, flammable substances (for example, foam plastics, flammable liquids and gases such as propane) and hazardous substances (for example, adhesives or cutting compounds). Flammable materials will usually need to be stored away from other materials and protected from accidental ignition.

Do not store materials where they obstruct access routes or where they could interfere with emergency escape. For example, do not store flammable materials under staircases or near to doors or fire exits.

If materials or equipment are stored at height and people could fall when stacking or collecting them, make sure that necessary guard rails are in place and that suitable access equipment is used.

Lifting and moving

Many people suffer long-term injury from regularly lifting or carrying items that are heavy or awkward to handle, such as paving slabs, bagged products like cement or large distribution boards. Within the context of the electrical industry, manual handling can involve items such as scaffolding, tools, equipment, switchgear and motors.

To avoid problems, it is essential that you plan all material handling properly. Where possible, avoid having to lift materials at all. Where lifting is unavoidable, provide mechanical handling aids wherever possible, such as a conveyor, a pallet truck, an electric or hand-powered hoist or fork-lift truck. Make sure all equipment used for lifting is in good condition and used by trained and competent workers.

The Manual Handling Operations Regulations 1992, as amended in 2002, apply to a wide range of manual handling activities, including lifting, lowering, pushing, pulling or carrying.

Activity

▶ Where possible, avoid manual handling. Think about a manual handling task you may need to carry out. Does a large workpiece really need to be moved, or can the activity be done safely where the item already is?

Safety

Automated plant still needs cleaning and maintaining, and fork-lift trucks must be suited to the work and have properly trained and certified operators. The movement of loads by machine requires careful planning to identify potential hazards.

The requirements and responsibilities for manual handling are shown in Table 1.17.

Employer requirements	Employee responsibilities
Reduce the need for hazardous manual handling, so far as is reasonably practicable.	Follow appropriate systems of work laid down for employee safety.
Assess the risk of injury from any hazardous manual handling that cannot be avoided.	Make proper use of equipment provided for employee safety.
Reduce the risk of injury from hazardous manual handling, so far as is reasonably practicable.	Co-operate with the employer on health and safety matters.
	Inform the employer if you identify hazardous handling activities.
	Ensure that your activities do not put others at risk.

Table 1.17: Requirements and responsibilities for manual handling

The planning of material handling involves carrying out a risk assessment. Table 1.18 shows the areas such a risk assessment should look at.

Problems to look for when making an assessment	Ways of reducing the risk of injury
Do the tasks involve: • holding loads away from the body? • twisting, stopping or reaching upwards? • large vertical movement? • strenuous pushing and pulling? • repetitive handling? • insufficient rest or recovery time? • a work rate imposed by a process?	**Can you:** • use a lifting aid? • improve workplace layout to improve efficiency? • reduce the amount of twisting and stooping? • avoid lifting from floor level or above shoulder height, especially heavy loads? • avoid repetitive handling? • vary the work, allowing one set of muscles to rest while another is used? • push rather than pull?
Are the loads: • heavy, bulky or unwieldy? • difficult to grasp? • unstable or likely to move unpredictably? • harmful (for example, sharp or hot)? • awkwardly stacked? • too large for the handler to see over?	**Can the load be made:** • lighter or less bulky? • easier to grasp? • more stable? • less damaging to hold? If the loads come in from elsewhere, have you asked the supplier to help, for example, to provide handles or smaller packages.

Table 1.18: Making a manual handling risk assessment

Problems to look for when making an assessment	Ways of reducing the risk of injury
Does the working environment have: • constraints on posture? • bumpy, obstructed or slippery floors? • variations in levels? • hot/cold/humid conditions? • gusts of wind or other strong air movements? • poor lighting conditions? • restrictions on movements or posture from clothes or personal protective equipment (PPE)?	**Can you:** • remove obstructions to free movement? • provide better flooring? • avoid steps and steep ramps? • prevent extremes of hot and cold? • improve lighting? • provide protective clothing or PPE that is less restrictive? • ensure your employers have the right clothing or PPE that is less restrictive?
Does the job: • require unusual capability (for example, above average strength or agility)? • endanger those with a health problem? • endanger those with a learning/physical disability? • endanger pregnant women? • call for special information or training?	**Can you:** • pay particular attention to those who have a physical weakness? • take extra care of pregnant workers? • give your employees more information (for example, about the range of tasks they are likely to face)? • provide more training? • get advice from an occupational health advisor if you need to?
With handling aids: • is the device the correct type for the job? • is it well maintained? • are the wheels on the device suited to the floor surface? • do the wheels run freely? • is the handle height between the waist and the shoulders? • are the handle grips in good order and comfortable? • are there any brakes and do they work?	**Can you:** • provide equipment that is more suitable for the task? • carry out planned preventative maintenance to prevent problems? • change the wheels, tyres, and/or flooring so that equipment moves easily? • provide better handles and handle grips? • make the brakes easier to use, reliable and effective?
Some other questions • Is the work repetitive or boring? • Is the work machine or system-based? • Do workers feel the demands of the work are excessive? • Have workers little control of the work and working methods? • Is there poor communication between managers and employers?	**Can you:** • change tasks to reduce the monotony? • make more use of workers skills? • make workloads and deadlines more achievable? • encourage good communication and teamwork? • involve workers in decisions? • provide better training and information?

Table 1.18: Making a manual handling risk assessment (cont.)

Some practical tips for safe manual handling

Step 1
Think before lifting/handling, plan the lift

- Can handling aids be used?
- Where is the load going to be placed?
- Will help be needed with the load?
- Remove obstructions such as discarded wrapping materials.
- For a long lift, consider resting the load midway on a table or bench to change grip.

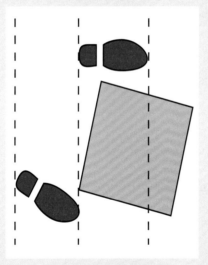

Step 2
Keep the load close to the waist

- Keep the load close to the body for as long as possible while lifting.
- Keep the heaviest side of the load next to the body.
- If a close approach to the load is not possible, try to slide it towards the body before attempting to lift it.
- Be prepared to move feet during the lift to maintain stability.
- Avoid tight clothing or unsuitable footwear, which may make this difficult.

Adopt a stable position

- Your feet should be apart, with one leg slightly forward to maintain balance (alongside the load, if it is on the ground).
- Test the weight of the load by pushing it with your foot.

Step 3
Get a good hold

- Hug the load as close as possible to the body. This may be better than gripping it tightly with hands only.
- Start in a good posture.
- At the start of the lift, slight bending of the back, hips and knees is preferable to fully flexing the back (stooping) or fully flexing the hips and knees (squatting).

Step 4

Don't flex the back any further while lifting

- This can happen if you start to straighten your legs before starting to raise the load.
- Avoid twisting your back or leaning sideways, especially while your back is bent.
- Keep your shoulders level and facing in the same direction as your hips.
- Turning by moving your feet is better than twisting and lifting at the same time.
- Keep your head up when handling.
- Look ahead, not down at the load, once you are holding it securely.

Step 5

Move smoothly

- Don't jerk or snatch the load as this can make it harder to keep control and can increase the risk of injury.
- Don't lift or handle more than you can manage easily.
- There is a difference between what people can lift and what they can safely lift. If in doubt, seek advice or get help.

Step 6

Put down, then adjust

- If you need to position the load precisely, put it down first, then slide it into the desired position.

Pushing and pulling

Here are some practical points to remember when pushing and pulling loads.

Handling devices

Aids such as trolleys should have handle heights between the shoulder and waist and be of high quality and well maintained, with large-diameter, smooth-running wheels.

Force

The amount of force needed to move a load over a flat, level surface using a well-maintained handling aid is at least 2 per cent of the load weight. Try to push rather than pull when moving a load, provided you can see over it, steer it and stop it.

Slopes

Get help whenever necessary as pushing and pulling forces can be very high. For example, if you want to move a load of 400 kg up a slope of 1 in 12 (about 5 degrees), it will take over 30 kg of force, even in ideal conditions. This is just above the guideline weight for men, and well above the guideline weight for women.

Uneven surfaces

On uneven surfaces, the force needed to start the load moving could increase to 10 per cent of the load weight, and to even more on soft ground. Larger wheels may help here.

Stance and pace

To make it easier to push or pull, keep your feet well away from the load and go no faster than walking speed. This will stop you becoming too tired too quickly.

General risk assessment guidelines

There is no such thing as a completely 'safe' manual handling operation. However, working within the lifting guidelines shown in Figure 1.49 on the next page will help to reduce the risk.

Use the diagram to make a quick and easy assessment. Each box contains a guideline weight for lifting and lowering in that zone. As you can see, the guideline weights are reduced if handling is done with arms extended, or at high or low levels, as that is when injuries are most likely to occur.

Observe the work activity you are assessing and compare it to the diagram. First, decide which box or boxes the lifter's hands pass through when moving the load. Then, assess the maximum weight being handled.

- If it is less than the figure given in the box, the operation is within the guidelines.

- If the lifter's hands enter more than one box during the operation, use the smallest weight.

- Use an in-between weight if the hands are close to a boundary between boxes.

The guideline weights assume that the load is readily grasped with both hands and that the operation takes place in reasonable working conditions, with the lifter in a stable body position.

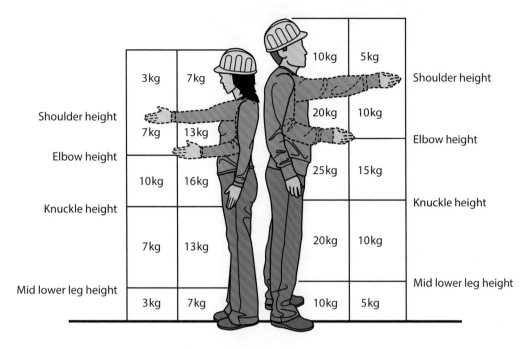

Figure 1.49: Lifting chart for men and women

Working life

A number of items of electrical equipment are to be delivered on site. Before the electrical operatives are involved in moving these to their locations there are a number of duties that need to be performed.

- What should the employer consider before the work is undertaken?
- How should employees act once tasks have been delegated?
- If you are unsure about how capable you are to lift a particular load, how should you proceed?

Summary

1. Name three possible causes of injury if a site has wet surfaces or poor ground conditions.
2. What method would form part of your training to prevent injuries when handling, transporting and storing tools, equipment and materials?
3. What are the employer's requirements in relation to lifting and moving objects?
4. Where lifting is unavoidable what could be used to avoid injury?

Working at height

Ladders and stepladders

Ladders, stepladders and trestles are NOT banned on construction sites, but they are perhaps the most commonly used access equipment on sites and also perhaps the most misused. Where work at height is necessary, you need to use risk assessments and a hierarchy of controls to decide the best method. Here are some factors you need to consider.

According to the HSE, falls from height are the most common cause of fatal injury and the second most common cause of major injury to employees, accounting for 15 per cent of all such injuries.

Is it a suitable activity?

'Suitable' here is to do with the type of work and how long it goes on for. As an approximate guide, the HSE advises only using a ladder or stepladder:

- in one position for a maximum of 30 minutes

- for 'light work'.

They are not suitable for strenuous or heavy work. If a task involves a worker carrying more than 10 kg while working at height it will need to be justified by a detailed manual handling assessment:

- where a handhold is available on the ladder or stepladder

- where you can maintain three points of contact (between hands and feet) at the working position.

On a ladder where you cannot maintain a handhold for long, other measures will be needed to prevent, or reduce the consequences of, a fall. On stepladders where a handhold is not practicable, a risk assessment will have to justify whether it is safe or not. On a ladder or stepladder do not:

Figure 1.50: User maintaining three points of contact with ladder

- overload – do not exceed the highest load stated on the ladder

- overreach – keep your belt buckle (navel) inside the stiles (the long side parts of the ladder that hold the rungs) and both feet on the same rung throughout the task (see Figure 1.50).

When working on stepladders, avoid work that imposes a side loading, such as side-on drilling through solid materials (such as bricks or concrete). Instead, have the steps facing the work activity.

Where side-on loadings cannot be avoided, take steps to prevent the steps from tipping over – such as tying the steps to a suitable point – or use a more suitable type of access equipment.

You should also avoid holding items when climbing. If you must carry something when you are using a ladder, leave one hand free to grip the ladder, or use a tool belt.

On a stepladder where you cannot maintain a handhold you will need to take into account:

- the height of the task

- a safe handhold still being available on the stepladder

- whether it is light work

- whether it avoids side-loading

- whether it avoids overreaching

- whether your feet are fully supported

- whether you can tie the stepladder.

Is it a safe place to use a ladder or stepladder?

As a guide, only use a ladder or stepladder:

- **on firm ground** or where you can spread the load (e.g. use a board)

- **on level ground**. For stepladders refer to the manufacturer's instructions; for ladders the maximum safe ground slopes on a suitable surface (unless the manufacturer states otherwise) are:

  - side slope 16°, but the rungs still need to be levelled (see Figure 1.51)
  - back slope 6° (see Figure 1.51)

- **on clean, solid surfaces**, such as paving slabs. These need to be free of loose material so the feet can grip. Shiny floor surfaces can be slippery even without contamination

- **where it has been secured**.

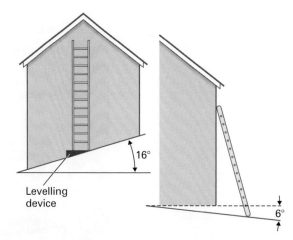

Figure 1.51: Ladder showing maximum angles at 16˚ on a side slope and 6˚ on a back slope

Here are some options for securing a ladder, which you should try in the order shown.

- Tie the ladder to a suitable point, making sure both stiles are tied as shown in Figures 1.52–1.55 on the following page.

- Use a safe, unsecured ladder or a ladder supplemented with an effective ladder stability device.

- Securely wedge the ladder, for example against a wall.

- As a last resort, get another worker to foot the ladder. That said, footing should be avoided, wherever possible, by using more appropriate access equipment.

Ladders used for access to another level should be securely tied and must extend at least 1 metre above the landing point to provide a secure handhold, as shown in Figure 1.56.

Figure 1.56: Ladder being used to provide a secure handhold to another level

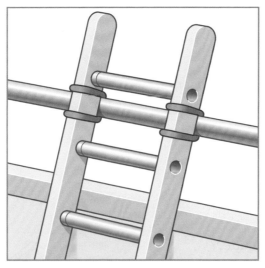

Figure 1.52: Ladder tied at top stiles

Figure 1.53: Tying part way down

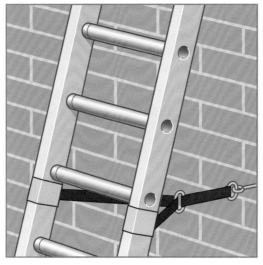

Figure 1.54: Tying near the base

Figure 1.55: Securing at the base

Stepladders should not be used like this unless they have been designed for the purpose. Only use ladders or stepladders where:

- they will not be struck by vehicles – protect them with barriers or cones

- pedestrians cannot walk under or near them – stop them with cones or barriers or a person standing guard

- they will not be pushed over by doors or windows – secure doors and windows if possible, have a person standing guard, or tell people not to open them

- ladders can be put up at the correct angle of 75° – use the angle indicator marked on the stiles or the 1 in 4 rule as shown in Figure 1.57 (4 units up for each unit out)

- the restraint devices on stepladders can be fully opened – engage any locking devices.

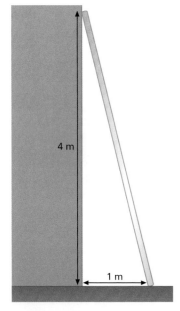

Figure 1.57: Ladder showing correct 1 in 4 angle

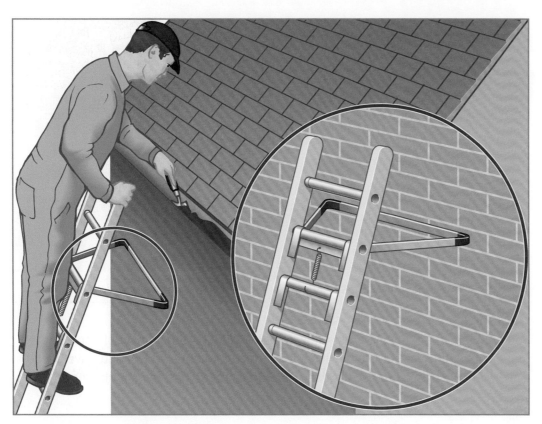

Figure 1.58: Stand-off device and working maximum height on a ladder

On a ladder or stepladder:

- don't work within 6 metres horizontally of any overhead power lines – unless they are dead or protected with temporary insulation

- always use a non-conductive ladder or steps for live electrical work

- don't rest it against weak upper surfaces, such as glazing or guttering – use spreader bars or stand-off devices (see Figure 1.58).

Is the ladder or stepladder safe to be used?

Only use ladders or stepladders that:

- have no visible defects – **pre-check** them before use each working day – wooden ladders should not be painted as this hides defects

- have a current **detailed visual inspection**

- are suitable for work use

- have been maintained and stored in accordance with the manufacturer's instructions.

Ladders that are part of a scaffold system still have to be inspected every seven days.

Key terms

Pre-check – a basic visual check done to spot obvious defects

Detailed visual inspection – a more detailed inspection for visible defects according to the manufacturer's instructions, the results of which should be recorded

Safety

Ladder and stepladder feet must be part of the pre-use check: they are vital to stop slipping and wobbling. The feet should be in good repair, clean and in contact with the ground. Check ladder feet when moving from soft or dirty ground to a smooth, solid surface to make sure the foot, not the dirt, is touching the ground.

Figure 1.59: Two clear rungs from the top   Figure 1.60: Three clear steps

Does the user know how to use it safely?

You may think that anyone knows how to use a ladder – but you should only use a ladder, stepladder or stability device if you are competent – you should have been trained and instructed to use it safely. Here are some things you should know.

Don't:

- use the top three rungs of a ladder, or the top two of a stepladder without a suitable handrail (see Figure 1.59)

- use the top three steps of swing- back or double-sided stepladders where a step forms the very top of the stepladder (see Figure 1.60)

- use them during inclement weather, e.g. strong or gusting winds – follow safe working practices

- move it while standing on the rungs/steps

- support it by the rungs or steps at the base

- slide down the stiles

- stand it on moveable objects, such as pallets, trucks or bricks

- extend a ladder while standing on the rungs.

Do:

- wear robust, sensible, clean footwear in good repair and without dangling laces

- know how to prevent other workers and the public from using them

- make sure you are fit – certain medical conditions or medication, alcohol or drug abuse could mean you should not use a ladder, so check with a health professional

- know how to tie a ladder or stepladder properly.

Ladders used for access should project at least 1 metre above the landing point and be tied or have a safe and secure handhold available. The rungs or steps must be level – use a levelling device if you can't tell by eye.

Trestles

A 'trestle scaffold' consists of a pair of 'A' frames or adjustable steel trestles, spanned by scaffolding boards, to provide a simple working platform. Trestles are used less these days due to the development of lightweight steel platforms and podiums.

Trestles must:

- be erected on a firm, level base with the trestles fully opened

- use a scaffold board at least 600 mm wide and no higher than two-thirds of the way up the A frame

- use scaffolding boards of equal length and thickness, not overhanging the trestle by more than four times their own thickness

- be spaced 1 metre apart for 32 mm-thick boards, 1.5 metres for 38 mm-thick boards and 2.5 metres for 50 mm-thick boards

- use toe boards, guard rails and a separate access ladder for heights over 2 metres.

Trestles must not be used where anyone can fall more than 4.5 metres and also tie any trestles above 3.5 metres tall to the building structure.

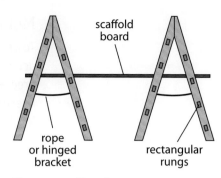

Figure 1.61: Trestles

Podium steps and mobile platforms

Podium steps and mobile platforms have become increasingly popular with tradespeople on site as they are portable and lightweight and can often fold away.

Mobile platforms are simple step-ups, generally 300 mm or 520 mm high and 300 mm, 450 mm or 700 mm wide. Accessories such as guard rails are available.

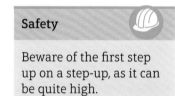

Safety

Beware of the first step up on a step-up, as it can be quite high.

Podium steps offer a number of advantages over more traditional access equipment because they:

- offer easy compliance with the Work at Heights Regulations 2005

- are compact, lightweight and foldaway, so are easy to store and transport

- are easy to erect, with guard rails that deploy automatically

- come in a range of sizes and platform heights (2.5 metre models are available)

- offer 360 degree working access without any need to move the podium

- have a wide range of accessories, such as tool trays

- can be easily combined with other variations, such as stair decks, to provide quick, safe and easy access to traditionally difficult working areas, such as staircases.

Figure 1.62: A mobile platform in use

Mobile scaffold towers

Tower scaffolds – or scaffold towers – are widely used and are involved in many accidents each year. These usually happen because the tower has not been properly erected or used. Made from light aluminium tube, towers are light and can easily overturn. They are built by slotting sections together and rely on all the parts being in place to ensure adequate strength; they can easily collapse if sections are left out.

Scaffold towers can be mobile (with wheels) or static with plates. Mobile ones are useful for installing long runs, such as factory lighting trunking installations.

Towers should be erected following a safe method of work. There are two approved methods recommended by the Prefabricated Access Suppliers' and Manufacturers' Association (PASMA), which have been developed in conjunction with the HSE.

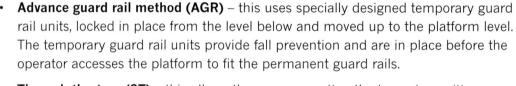

JTL tips

The manufacturer of any scaffold tower has a duty to provide an instruction manual explaining the erection sequence, including bracing requirements. If the tower has been hired, the supplier has a duty to provide this information, which must be passed on to the person erecting the tower.

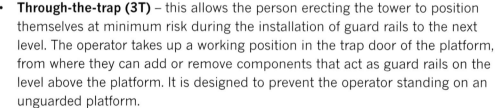

JTL tips

The progressive erection of guard rails from a protected area at a lower level ensures the operator is never exposed to the risk of falling from an unguarded platform.

Figure 1.63: Mobile scaffold tower

- **Advance guard rail method (AGR)** – this uses specially designed temporary guard rail units, locked in place from the level below and moved up to the platform level. The temporary guard rail units provide fall prevention and are in place before the operator accesses the platform to fit the permanent guard rails.

- **Through-the-trap (3T)** – this allows the person erecting the tower to position themselves at minimum risk during the installation of guard rails to the next level. The operator takes up a working position in the trap door of the platform, from where they can add or remove components that act as guard rails on the level above the platform. It is designed to prevent the operator standing on an unguarded platform.

Whichever method you choose, when you are working with a tower scaffold, you must:

- make sure the person erecting the tower is competent

- make sure the tower is resting on firm, level ground, with the wheels or feet properly supported – do not use bricks or blocks to take the weight of any part of it

- remember that the taller the tower, the more likely it is to become unstable. As a guide, if towers are used in exposed conditions or outside, the height of the working platform should be no more than three times the minimum base dimension; if the tower is to be used inside, on firm, level ground, the ratio may be extended to 3.5. So, for example, if the base of the tower is 2 metres by 3 metres the maximum height would be 6 metres for use outside and 7 metres for use inside.

Here are some more important points on how to use a tower scaffold safely.

- Before use, check the scaffold is vertical and any wheel brakes are on.

- There must be a safe way to get to and from the work platform. Do not climb up the end frames of the tower except where the frame has an appropriately designed built-in ladder, or a purpose-made ladder can be attached safely on the inside.

- Suitable edge protection should be provided where a person could fall more than 2 metres. Guard rails should be at least 910 mm high and toe boards at least 150 mm high. An intermediate guard rail or suitable alternative should be provided so that the unprotected gap does not exceed 470 mm.

- When moving a tower, check there are no overhead obstructions. Check the ground is firm and level. Push or pull only from the base; never move it while there are people or materials on the upper platforms or in windy conditions.

- Outriggers can increase stability by effectively increasing the area of the base, but must be fitted diagonally across all four corners of the tower and not on one side. When outriggers are used they should be clearly marked (for example, with hazard marking tape) to indicate a trip hazard is present.

- In public places, extra precautions may be needed such as reducing material and equipment storage on the platform, erecting barriers to prevent people from entering, and removing or boarding access ladders to prevent unauthorised access.

- Before use on a pavement, check if you need a local authority licence.

- Tower scaffolds must be inspected by a 'competent person' before first use and following any alteration or event that may affect their stability. If it remains in place longer than seven days, it should be inspected at regular intervals and a written report made, with all faults corrected.

Electricians may also use independent static scaffolding installed by a main contractor. These normally require bespoke design by qualified persons (see Figure 1.64).

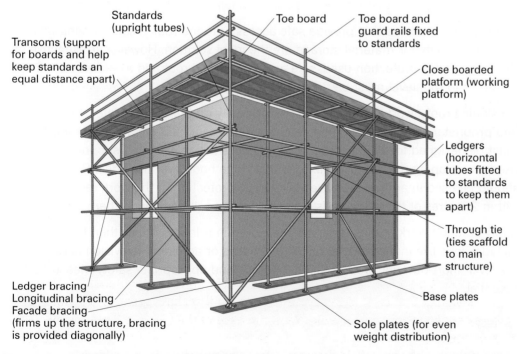

Figure 1.64: An independent static scaffold

Figure 1.65: Scissor lift

Figure 1.66: Boom lift

Scissor and boom lifts

This access equipment is often referred to as mobile elevating platforms (MEWPs) or 'powered platforms'. Those mounted on trucks are often referred to as 'cherry pickers'.

There is a wide range of machines available (including rough-terrain applications) so they can be used for various installations from large factories to external lighting. However, scissor lifts can only extend upwards. Sometimes it is necessary to 'reach' over objects to carry out work: for example, repairing a street-lighting column. Here a telescopic boom platform – a cherry picker – is likely to work better.

In both types of lift, it is essential that workers wear a safety harness. This must be attached to the lift and never to the structure being worked on. All operatives must be suitably trained.

Roof work and fragile surfaces

Almost one in five workers killed in construction accidents is doing roof work. The main causes of accidents are falling off the edges of roofs and falling through holes, roof lights and other fragile surfaces. All roof work requires a risk assessment and, if the work is extensive, a method statement setting out a safe system of work.

If work is going to be done on any roof, make sure there is:

- safe access onto the roof, such as a general access scaffold, tower scaffold (preferably of the stairway design) or mobile access equipment
- a safe means of moving across the roof, such as using proprietary staging or purpose-made roof ladders
- a means of preventing falls when working on the roof, such as edge protection consisting of guard rails and toe boards, a proprietary access system or a MEWP
- measures to prevent falls through fragile materials (such as barriers or covers) and to mitigate the consequences should a fall occur (for example, nets).

Independent scaffolds that provide safe access onto the roof, a safe working platform and the capacity for material storage are the ideal solution. However, irrespective of the type of edge protection used, safe access onto the roof and a safe way of lifting materials to roof level must be provided and maintained.

On sloping roofs, workers should not work directly on the tiles or slates. Roof ladders and proprietary staging should be used to enable safe passage across a roof. They must be designed for the purpose, of good construction, properly supported and, if used on a sloping roof, securely fixed with a ridge hook over the ridge. Roof ladders should be used in addition to eaves-level edge protection; if the work requires access within 2 metres of the gable ends, edge protection will be needed there too.

Short-duration work means tasks are measured in minutes rather than hours. It includes jobs like inspection, replacing a few tiles or adjusting television aerials. However short-duration work is still dangerous and appropriate safety measures are essential.

For short-duration work it may not be reasonably practicable to provide full edge protection, but you will need to provide something in its place. The minimum requirements for short-duration work on a roof are:

- a safe means of access to roof level

- a safe means of working on the roof:

- on a sloping roof, a properly constructed roof ladder

- on a flat roof, a harness attached to a secure anchorage and fitted with as short a lanyard as possible.

Safety

A suitably qualified person must supervise the installation of equipment to which harnesses will be fixed.

Safety harnesses

If work at height cannot be avoided, measures should be put in place to prevent falls. Harnesses and lanyards can be used to secure workers to the platforms. For this, the lanyard is kept as short as possible while allowing operators to reach their place of work. This prevents them from getting into a fall position, as they are physically unable to get close enough to the open edge (see Figure 1.67). This is acceptable for light, short-duration work and inspection and maintenance.

Figure 1.67: A harness and lanyard can prevent a worker from falling to the ground

Everyone who uses a harness must know how to check, wear and adjust it before use and how to connect themselves to the structure or anchor point.

Safety nets and soft-landing systems

The purpose of a soft-landing system is to mitigate the effect of falls from height during construction or maintenance activity by providing an energy-absorbing landing area.

Most are designed for use within a building where the bags will be enclosed and retained by walls or partitions. They won't prevent a fall, but they may reduce the personal harm from one.

Nets are a complex energy-absorbing system, and before gaining access to height you must decide whether nets can be installed at ground level. It is often feasible to incorporate this into the steelwork.

Figure 1.68 Excavations

Working in excavations

Many of the same rules for working at height also apply to working in excavations. Every year people are killed or seriously injured when working in excavations.

They are at risk from:

- excavations collapsing and burying or injuring people

- material falling from the sides into any excavation

- people or plant falling into excavations.

Excavation work has to be properly planned, managed, supervised and carried out to prevent accidents. Before digging any excavations, it is important to consider and plan for a whole range of potential dangers, as shown in Figure 1.69.

Before work starts:

- make sure the necessary equipment is available

- use locators to trace any services, and mark the ground accordingly – also look for valve covers or patching of a road surface

- provide good ladder access or other safe ways of getting into and out of the excavation

- put on a hard hat!

Make sure that:

- a competent person supervises the installation at all times

- the supervisor has service plans and knows how to use them

- any plant operators are competent

- everyone knows about safe digging practices and emergency procedures

- the edges of the excavation are protected against falling materials, using toe boards if necessary

- the sides and ends are battered to a safe angle or supported with timber, sheeting or proprietary support systems

- excavations do not undermine the footings of scaffolds or the foundations of nearby structures.

Wherever possible:

- keep vehicles away from excavations

- take steps to prevent people falling into excavations: if excavation is 2 metres or more then provide substantial barriers (e.g. guard rails and toe boards)

- keep workers separate from moving plant.

Safety

No ground can be relied upon to stand unsupported in all circumstances. Trenchless techniques should always be considered at the design stage as they replace the need for major excavations.

If necessary:

- put in extra support for the sides (if the excavation is 2 metres or more deep)
- use stop blocks to prevent tipping vehicles from overrunning
- use safe systems of work to prevent people being struck by moving plant or traffic
- fence off all excavations in public places
- take extra precautions where children might get onto a site out of hours.

Never:

- go into an unsupported excavation
- work ahead of the supports
- store spoil close to the sides of excavations as it can fall in or destabilise the sides.

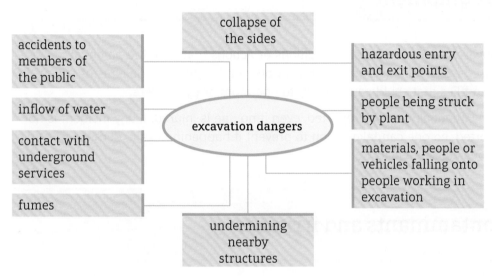

Figure 1.69: Dangers of excavation

Summary

1. What are the two approved methods of safely erecting a mobile scaffold tower?
2. What is classed as working at height with regards to health and safety regulations?
3. State four methods of securing a ladder and place them in the order in which they should be attempted.
4. When working in excavations what are the main health and safety risks?

4. Identifying and dealing with hazards in the work environment

Previously, we explained that:

- a hazard is any thing or situation that has the potential to cause harm

- a risk is the chance, high or low, that someone will be harmed (and how seriously) by that hazard.

Dangerous occurrences and hazardous malfunctions of equipment

Dangerous occurrences are conditions or actions that have the potential to cause hazardous malfunctions. Hazardous malfunctions are failures of objects or assemblies that could cause injury to operators or bystanders.

Both situations must be reported, even if no one is injured. If any incident is not reported, no one can take action to prevent it happening again, perhaps with more serious consequences.

Contaminants and irritants

Every year, thousands of workers are made ill by hazardous substances, contracting lung diseases such as asthma, cancer, and skin disease such as dermatitis. You should identify any hazardous substances, or processes that may produce hazardous materials, and assess the risk to workers or members of the public.

Ideally, project designers should eliminate hazardous materials from their designs. However, where this is not possible, they should specify the least hazardous product that will perform satisfactorily.

Generally, there are two categories of hazard: contaminant and irritant.

- A contaminant is a biological, chemical, physical, or radiological substance which, in a sufficiently concentrated form, can adversely affect living organisms, entering them through air, water, soil and/or food.

- An irritant is a chemical substance which, although not itself corrosive, may cause inflammation of living tissue (such as eyes, skin, or respiratory organs) by a chemical reaction at the point of contact. The effects vary depending on the degree of exposure. Typical irritants include cement, solvents, petrol, diesel and detergents.

Labelling and packaging

Most of the chemicals you might use at work are not dangerous, provided you use them properly and know what to do if something goes wrong, such as a spillage. However, some chemicals need more careful handling than others. Labels can help you identify the more hazardous chemicals, tell you what the hazards are and how to avoid them.

Where the supplier concludes that no hazardous properties have been identified, a chemical is not classified as hazardous and there is often nothing more to do. Where the supplier does conclude that a chemical could cause harm, they are expected to provide information about this on the label.

Fully effective from June 2017, all such labelling must conform to the Classification, Labelling and Packaging Regulations (CLP Regulations) of substances and mixtures.

Substance identification

People may be exposed to hazardous substances through handling, direct use (e.g. cement and solvents) or because their work creates the substance (e.g. scabbling concrete generates silica dust). You will need to identify and assess both kinds of hazard.

Manufacturers and suppliers have a legal duty to provide information on the hazardous substances they produce. Read the label on the container and/or the safety data sheet and approach the manufacturer or supplier directly for more information if you need it.

Under the CLP Regulations, a hazard label is made up of specific symbols (known as 'pictograms') and warnings. These are set out in law and chemical suppliers must use them, either singularly or in combination, where hazardous properties have been identified. The nine pictograms and their associated wording are shown in Table 1.19.

Pictogram	Associated wording
	Acute toxicity, very toxic (fatal), toxic, etc.
	Flammable gases, flammable liquids, flammable solids, flammable aerosols, organic peroxides, self-reactive, pyrophoric, self-heating, contact with water emits flammable gas
	Explosive, self-reactive, organic peroxide
	Gases under pressure

Table 1.19: Identifying hazardous substances

Pictogram	Associated wording
	Harmful skin irritation, serious eye irritation
	Respiratory sensitiser, mutagen, carcinogen, reproductive toxicity, systemic target organ toxicity, aspiration hazard
	Corrosive (causes severe skin burns and eye damage), serious eye damage
	Oxidising gases, oxidising liquids, oxidising solids
	Harmful to the environment

Table 1.19: Identifying hazardous substances (cont.)

Safety

Some hazardous substances may be on site before any work starts: for example, sewer gases or ground contaminants. You should assess these risks in the same way as for other hazardous substances. Information to help identify these risks may be available from the client, the design team or the principal contractor and should be contained in the pre-construction health and safety plan.

Assessment

To make an assessment, you will need to look at the way people are exposed to the hazardous substance in the particular job that they are about to do and decide whether it is likely to harm anyone's health.

You should assess both immediate risks (for example, being overcome by fumes) and long-term health risks. Materials like cement can cause dermatitis. Sensitising agents like isocyanates can make people have sudden reactions, even if they have used the substance many times before.

Inhalation

Here are some questions you should ask.

- Does the manufacturer's information say that there is a risk from inhaling the substance?
- Is the work being done in a way that results in heavy air contamination, such as spraying?
- Is the work to be done in a poorly ventilated space, such as a basement or enclosed space?

Direct contact with skin

Here are some questions you should ask.

- Does the manufacturer's information say there is a risk from direct contact?
- How severe is this risk – for example, are strong acids or alkalis being used?
- Does the method of work make skin contact likely, such as from splashes when pouring from one container to another, or from the method of application?

Ingestion

Some materials can contaminate the skin and hands. This contamination can then be passed to the mouth when the person eats or smokes. This is a particular problem when handling lead or sanding lead-based paints.

Prevention

If the substance is harmful, try to avoid it completely by not using it. This will mean either doing the job in a different way or using a substitute substance, for example, water-based paints instead of solvent-based. Always check one hazard is not being replaced by another.

Control

Ultimately, if the substance has to be used because there is no alternative, or because use of the least hazardous alternative still leads to a significant risk, the next step is to try to control the situation.

As an example, rather than spraying a substance, can it be applied with a brush? Can you use exhaust ventilation or water suppression to control dusts?

Safety

When using chemicals of any sort you must understand the dangers involved, follow all safety procedures recommended and know what to do in an emergency.

Liquid petroleum gas (LPG)

LPG is widely used in construction and building work as a fuel for burners, heaters and gas torches. Even small quantities of LPG mixed with air create an explosive mixture (LPG is a gas above −42°C).

Figure 1.70 LPG containers

LPG comes in cylinders and containers and is highly flammable. It needs careful handling and storage. Here are some guidelines.

- Everyone using LPG should understand the procedures to be adopted in case of an emergency.

- Appropriate firefighting extinguishers (dry powder) should always be available.

- Cylinders must be kept upright whether in use or in storage.

- When not in use the valve should be closed and the protective dust cap should be in place.

- When handling cylinders do not drop them or allow them to come into violent contact with other cylinders.

- When using a cylinder with an appliance, make sure it is connected properly, in accordance with the instructions you have been given, and that it is at a safe distance from the appliance or equipment that it is feeding.

LPG is heavier than air: if it leaks, it will not disperse in the air but instead sink to the lowest point and form an explosive concentration that could be ignited by a spark. LPG should therefore not be used in excavations as the gas cannot flow out of these areas.

Procedures for dealing with presence of asbestos

Asbestos is a mineral found naturally in certain rock types. When separated from rock it becomes a fluffy, fibrous material that has had many uses in the construction industry. In the past it has commonly been used in cement wall and roof panels, ceiling tiles, textured coatings such as Artex™ and insulation lagging around boilers and flash guards inside electrical distribution boards.

The use of asbestos is now banned but there are still a number of buildings containing asbestos and any building built or refurbished before the year 2000 is likely to have asbestos materials somewhere in the building.

Asbestos becomes a health hazard if you inhale the dust; some of the fine rod-like fibres may work their way into your lung tissue and remain embedded for life. This will become a constant source of irritation and can lead to lung diseases (mainly cancers), particularly if you are repeatedly exposed over a number of years. The inhaling of asbestos can lead to serious lifelong health problems, even though symptoms can take years to develop, and the health problems caused by asbestos can be fatal.

Asbestos is perfectly safe in its solid form, but it begins to pose a risk when it breaks down or is disturbed. It is estimated that around 20 tradespeople die every week from asbestos-related diseases.

As an apprentice electrician working in the construction trade, it is likely that you will come across this hidden killer at some point in your career. Remember: in its solid form (and only if it is left undisturbed) it poses little risk, and therefore wherever possible it should be left undisturbed or removed by a licensed contractor.

To protect yourself you should:

- avoid working with asbestos if possible – if you are unsure whether asbestos is present don't start work until your supervisor has confirmed it is safe to do so

- don't work if the asbestos materials are in sprayed coatings, boards or lagging on pipes and boilers – only licensed contractors should work on these

- know the hazards, avoid exposure and always follow recommended controls

- wear and maintain any personal protective equipment provided

- practise good housekeeping – use special vacuums and dust-collecting equipment

- report any hazardous conditions, such as unusually high dust levels, to your supervisor.

As an apprentice, you are not required to work with asbestos and you should inform your supervisor if you accidentally or otherwise come across it. To minimise any risk from exposure you should:

- wipe down your overalls after work with a damp rag and remove them before removing your mask

- dispose of overalls and so on properly – as with asbestos waste, don't take overalls home to wash

- not smoke, eat or drink in the work area.

Safety

The removal of asbestos must only be carried out by specialist contractors. Consider your health at all times. Don't work with asbestos under any circumstances. After all, it's your health, and nothing is more important.

Getting ready for assessment

EAL	City & Guilds

For this unit you will need to complete the following assessments:
• 25 question multiple choice online exam
• Practical task 01A – Extension Ladder
• Practical task 01B – Tower Scaffold
• Practical task 01C – Safe Isolation
• Practical task 01D – Equipment Safety
	For this unit you will need to complete the following assessments:
	• 25 question multiple choice online exam
	• Assignment 101
	  • Task 1 Workplace Hazards
	  • Task 2 Manual Handling
	  • Task 3 Ladders
	  • Task 4 Scaffold
	  • Task 5 Safe Isolation
	  • Task 6 Equipment Safety

▶ Preparing for this assessment

- Write down the sequence for safe isolation and try to remember the order for when the assessment starts. Making a small card may be helpful.

- Make sure the condition of all equipment is safe, especially when using access equipment.

- Practise the sequence of manual handling while you working on site, this way you will perform the assessment naturally.

- Remember these assessments are looking to see if you can follow safe working practices. Make sure you do these assessments following correct, best practice procedures, not how you may have seen someone do them on site. You should always follow best practice!

- Always ensure you wear the correct PPE for any tasks you are carrying out. If you are not sure what is required, just ask your assessor.

▶ Worked examples

This section will help you to understand some of the key concepts in this chapter. The answers show some of the best practice, and supply guidance to help you understand the reasons behind each of these concepts.

A. Who does the HASAWA places duties on? Give three examples for each of such duties.

The HASAWA places duties on both employers and employees.

Employers have duties to:

1. Care for the welfare, health and safety of their employees where it is practicable for them to do so.

2. Provide and maintain safe equipment, tools and plant within the workplace.

3. Provide any necessary information, instruction, training and supervision to ensure the health and safety of employees.

Remember when completing any assessment involving working at height, ensure the base of the equipment is on stable and level ground. If you are assembling the scaffold, then ensure you use a level so there is no chance of the tower tipping.

Employees have duties to:

1. Look after their own safety and that of colleagues and people around them.

2. Use any provided PPE correctly.

3. Help their employer to meet statutory obligations.

B.   What do the Working at Height Regulations require a duty holder to ensure?

The duty holder must ensure all work at height is properly planned and organised. The work must take into account weather conditions that could endanger health and safety. The duty holder must ensure those involved in work at height are trained and competent, and that the site where work at height is being carried out is safe. They must ensure all equipment used for working at height is appropriately inspected, that any risks from fragile surfaces or from falling objects are properly controlled.

C.   To ensure compliance with Regulations 12 and 13 of the EAWR, what working principles must be followed during the safe isolation procedure?

You must make sure that the correct point of isolation has been identified and the appropriate means used. Ideally the point of isolation should be under the control of the person carrying out the work on the isolated conductors. Warning notices should be applied at all points of the isolation and the conductors must be proved dead at the point of work before they can be touched. The supply must not be re-energised while any work is in progress.

D.   What are the six main steps that should be followed when completing a manual handling task?

1. Think before you lift, have you planned correctly?

2. Keep the load close to the waist and adopt a stable position.

3. Get a good hold whilst starting with a good posture.

4. Don't flex your back any further while lifting.

5. Move smoothly.

6. Put down and then adjust.

Remember when you complete the safe isolation assessment try to practice the order in your head as much as possible: writing the order on a card may help you to remember. Also don't forget to keep the padlock key with you (ideally in your pocket). If it's left in your toolbox or left out for people to access then they could switch the supply on while you are still working on the installation!

Remember if you cannot lift the load, do not attempt it. Either ask someone else for help or use a mechanical aid. When you complete any manual handling task assessment, make sure you have all the correct PPE and the area or route is safe before you start. This will help to prevent difficulties during the process and ensure that you are following best practice.

Check your knowledge

1. The Health and Safety at Work Act:
   a) Affects employers only
   b) Highlights the duties of employers and employees
   c) Highlights the duties of employers
   d) Affects employees only

2. Within reason, who should ensure a workplace is risk free?
   a) Employer
   b) Employee
   c) Client
   d) Supervisor

3. A near miss is:
   a) An accident that could have had serious consequences
   b) An accident that could have had minor consequences
   c) An incident that could have had minor consequences
   d) An incident that could have had serious consequences

4. The first thing you should do when discovering a fire should be to:
   a) Open the windows and make your escape
   b) Close the windows and make your escape
   c) Raise the alarm
   d) Operate the nearest fire extinguisher

5. Which of the following voltage systems would be best to use for powered hand tools?
   a) Cordless
   b) 230 V
   c) 55 V
   d) 110 V

6. Someone would receive an electric shock when they:
   a) Touch a cable
   b) Touch a conductor
   c) Touch some insulation
   d) Become part of a circuit

7. When working on an electrical installation, ensuring electrical safety is best achieved by:
   a) Switching off the supply
   b) Working during a night shift
   c) Fitting all live supplies with enclosures
   d) Isolating and securing the supply

8. When working at height for long periods of time the most appropriate piece of equipment to use would be:
   a) A ladder
   b) Scaffolding
   c) A mobile scaffold tower
   d) A stepladder

9. If the base of a ladder is placed at a distance of 2.5 m from a wall, the top of the ladder should be positioned at a height of:
   a) 10 m
   b) 7.5 m
   c) 8 m
   d) 6 m

10. PPE can:
    a) Limit the effects of accidents
    b) Stop 100% of all injuries
    c) Stop all accidents
    d) Limit accidents

11. Three components are necessary for a fire, they are:
    a) Fuel, wood and cardboard
    b) Petrol, oxygen and bottled gas
    c) Flames, fuel and heat
    d) Fuel, oxygen and heat

12. To show that people should not enter a secure area, you should use:
    a) An information sign
    b) A danger sign
    c) A prohibition sign
    d) A mandatory sign

CHAPTER 2
Understand how to plan and oversee electrical work activities

A key skill in all workplaces is the ability to share knowledge and communicate effectively with the people you work with. We need to be aware that everyone is different and may therefore see things differently from us. We can use this knowledge to help avoid misunderstandings or frustration, and to improve relationships in order to aid site progress and develop business.

This chapter looks at the methods and systems used to communicate within the construction industry.

This chapter will cover the following learning outcomes.

1. Requirements for liaising with others when organising and overseeing work activities.

2. Requirements for organising and overseeing work programmes.

3. Requirements for organising the provision and storage of required resources.

1. Requirements for liaising with others when organising and overseeing work activities

Qualification mapping

This chapter supports:

- Units 105/005 Understand How to Plan and Oversee Electrical Work Activities, from the City & Guilds Level 3 Electrotechnical qualification (5357-03)
- Unit NETK3/03 Understand How to Plan and Oversee Electrical Work Activities, from the EAL Level 3 Electrotechnical qualification.

Teamwork

Successful projects require good teamwork. But who is in the team, what is teamwork and why do we need it?

Who is in the team?

In one sense, everyone working on the project is in the team. However, it is more likely that each individua l contractor will see their own group of people as being the team, while recognising that their team will be working with teams in the other trades to complete the project.

What is teamwork?

Teamwork is the process of working collaboratively with a group of people to achieve a goal or target.

Why do we need teamwork?

- Teamwork can create a more efficient work model.
- A team can support each other.
- A team is better placed to solve problems.
- A team is better placed than an individual to suggest new ideas.
- Teamwork can increase staff morale and promote a sense of achievement.
- Teamwork allows knowledge to be spread throughout the team.

The construction industry 'team'

The construction industry is one of the biggest industries in the UK and the electrical contracting industry is just one sector within it. Organisations in the construction industry range from sole traders (for example, a jobbing builder) to large multinational companies employing thousands of workers.

The work done by these companies is very varied. However, we can broadly think of it as falling under three headings:

- building and structural engineering – which covers the construction and installation of services for buildings such as factories, offices, shops, hospitals, schools, leisure centres and, of course, houses
- civil engineering – which involves the construction and installation of services for large structures such as bridges, roads, motorways, docks, harbours and mines
- maintenance – which covers the repair, refurbishment and restoration of existing buildings and structures.

Larger construction companies will be able to undertake work in all of these areas, but smaller companies may specialise in one area. However, nearly every project, large or small, will involve a variety of different trades, such as bricklaying, plastering, plumbing and joining, as well as electrical work.

The ability to work and communicate well with others, and to establish good, professional relationships with colleagues and people in other trades, is crucial to the successful completion of a project.

The electrotechnical industry

Most people are unaware of the vast range of activities and occupations that make up the electrical industry. They usually think of an electrician as someone who installs lights and sockets in their house.

In reality, during their career, an electrician could be involved with the installation, maintenance and repair of electrical services (both inside and outside) associated with buildings and structures such as houses, hospitals, schools, factories, car parks, leisure centres and shops. There are also specialist areas that call for additional knowledge and training, such as motor repair, street lighting, alarm systems or panel building.

Electricians may be employed within the electrical contracting industry, but they may also be employed directly by organisations needing their skills, such as refineries or factories.

The electrical contracting industry structure

There are a number of organisations you should be aware of within the industry. You have already looked at the main health and safety organisation, the Health and Safety Executive (HSE) (see Chapter 1, page 28), but the following bodies play important roles too.

The Electrical Contractors' Association (ECA)

The ECA is the industry trade association and represents the interests of electrical installation companies in England, Wales and Northern Ireland. It is the major association in the electrical installation industry. Founded in 1901, it has around 3000 members companies, from small traders with only a few employees to large multinational organisations.

The ECA aims to ensure all electrical installation work is carried out to the highest standards by properly qualified staff. Firms that wish to become members of the ECA must demonstrate that they have procedures, staff and systems of the highest calibre.

National Inspection Council for Electrical Installation Contracting (NICEIC)

The NICEIC is a voluntary accredited certification body that protects users of electricity against the hazards of unsafe and unsound electrical installations. It is the industry's independent electrical safety regulatory body and is not a trade association.

The NICEIC maintains a roll of approved contractors who meet the council's rules relating to enrolment and national technical safety standards, including BS.7671 (IET Wiring Regulations). The roll is published annually and is regularly updated on the NICEIC website so that consumers and specifiers can select contractors who are technically competent.

The Council also employs inspecting engineers, who make annual visits to approved contractors to assess their technical capability and to inspect samples of their work for technical competence.

Unite the union

For many years workers within the electrical installation industry have enjoyed good labour relationships and co-operation with their employers, largely due to the Electrical, Electronic, Telecommunications and Plumbing Union (EETPU – the main trade union at the time) and the ECA. Since 2007, Unite, the UK's biggest trade union, has continued these excellent relationships. Unite has over 2 million members and represents a large number of other trades and industries.

If you are a Unite member, they promise to protect your rights, health, safety and well-being at work, negotiating on your behalf with employers and the UK and European governments to get a fair deal for you at work.

The Joint Industry Board (JIB)

The JIB for the Electrical Contracting Industry came into existence in 1968 through an agreement between the ECA and the EETPU. Effectively the industrial relations arm of the industry, the JIB has as its main responsibility the agreement of national working conditions and wage rates.

The Institution of Lighting Professionals (ILP)

The ILP is the UK's most influential professional lighting association, dedicated solely to excellence in lighting. Since its foundation, it has evolved to include lighting designers, architects, consultants and engineers among its 2500-strong membership. The ILE's key purpose is to promote excellence in all forms of lighting. This includes interior, exterior, sports, road, flood, emergency, tunnel, security and festive lighting as well as design and consultancy services.

The ILP is a registered charity, a limited company and a licensed body of the Engineering Council.

The Institution of Engineering and Technology (IET)

Formerly the IEE, the IET was founded in 2006 and is now the largest professional engineering society in Europe, with a worldwide membership of just over 375,000. As well as setting standards of qualifications for professional electrical, electronics, software, systems and manufacturing engineers, the IET prepares regulations for the safety of electrical installations for buildings. The IET Electrical Wiring Regulations (Requirements For Electrical Installations: BS.7671) has become the standard for the UK and many other countries.

Employer structure

There are over 20,000 electrical contracting companies registered in the UK, dealing with many tasks such as:

- handling initial enquiries

- estimating costs

- issuing quotations

- dealing with suppliers and sub-contractors

- supervising contracts

- carrying out the installation

- financial control of a project

- final settlement of accounts.

These companies range from one-person organisations to large multinational contractors, but the majority employ fewer than 10 people. The structure of electrical companies also varies considerably between firms, depending on the number of employees and the type and size of the business. You can think of them broadly in terms of two groups: small firms and large firms.

Small firms

In a small company, the main tasks are often the responsibility of one person, and there is only a narrow range of people at each management level. This type of company structure is known as a vertical structure.

The principal advantage is that lines of communication are short: everyone knows who is responsible for different aspects of a project. When someone from outside – another tradesperson, contractor or customer – needs any information, they know who to talk to, and are not passed from one department to another.

However, if the person dealing with the project is ill, on holiday, or has left the company, vital information may be missing and it can be difficult for someone else to continue handling the project smoothly.

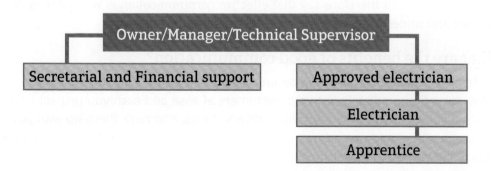

Figure 2.1: An example of a small firm organisational flow chart

Large firms

In larger companies, the tasks are allocated to a range of people: for example, estimators who handle the initial enquiry and produce an estimate, and contracts engineers who see that the work is done. This type of structure is known as a horizontal structure as there are more people at each management level.
The advantage is that individuals become specialists in a particular task and can work more efficiently.

Companies of this size often belong to a trade organisation such as the Electrical Contractors' Association (ECA) and, because of their structure, can offer good career development prospects.

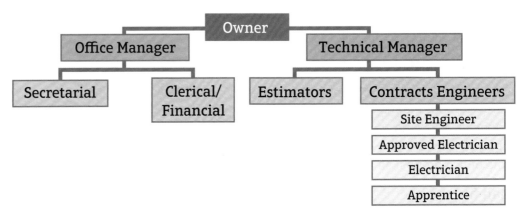

Figure 2.2: An example of a large firm organisational flow chart

Communication

All communication affects a business one way or another.

When communication is effective, it tends to encourage improved performance and job satisfaction, as people better understand their jobs and feel more involved in them. If communication is poor, then people may be forced to rely on rumours for information. We can therefore say that effective communication is when a message is received and understood as the sender intended.

What are the benefits of good communication?

The benefits of good communication are huge. Good attitude, appearance and behaviour will immediately put your customers at ease and earn you respect from others. If you clearly convey your thoughts and ideas, and back them up with good working practices and procedures, you will invariably improve productivity, increase profitability and produce satisfied customers.

Remember too that communication is about much more than just speaking or writing. You communicate an enormous amount by how you look, the gestures and facial expressions you use, and the way you behave. Even something as simple as a smile can make a big difference to your communication.

Speaking, writing, appearance, attitude and behaviour all combine to make up your personal 'communication package'. It affects your relationships with everyone you deal with – clients, architects, main contractors, other site trades, your supervisor and your work colleagues.

The following sections will look at some of the methods for communicating with others and some of the varied situations in which you may need to communicate with others.

Letter and report writing

Good written communication skills are vital for avoiding confusion, especially in an industry that relies heavily on documentation.

Writing good letters and reports is a part of the communication process. Letters can be used to request information (such as delivery dates from a wholesaler, or progress updates from a builder) or to inform people of situations.

Reports can be used to:

- summarise investigations into the causes and effects of problems or trends, and to recommend solutions (for example, why there has been an increase in absenteeism, or why a piece of work is below standard)

- provide statistical or financial summaries (such as end-of-week materials costs)

- record decisions made at meetings

- supply information for legal purposes (such as accident reports)

- monitor progress (for example, of negotiations, construction work or the implementation of a new system)

- look into the feasibility of introducing new procedures, processes or products, or changing company policy.

Step by Step

The writing process

Writing isn't too difficult if you break it down into steps and then focus on one step at a time. You can tackle almost any writing project if you follow this method.

Step 1

Have a clear idea about the overall purpose of your letter or report. Think about exactly what you want to say, and why. Most people get stuck because they have not thought carefully about what they are trying to achieve.

Step 2

Gather all the information you will need.

Step 3

Plan the logical order for presenting your ideas. Write a list of headings, and check that each one follows on from the previous one. If you are writing a report, the first paragraph should be a summary of the rest of the document; if you want your reader to take some action, say so in your last paragraph. Don't start writing in detail until you have completed this step.

Step 4

Now that you know what each section or paragraph will contain, go ahead and write each one. Then read your document through again and, if necessary, edit what you have written. Finally, present it as a properly formatted and typed document.

Hints and tips for good writing

Try to use simple language when writing and don't try to impress the reader with your huge vocabulary – it will only frustrate or annoy them. Don't use jargon or abbreviations unless you are sure your reader is familiar with them.

Avoid 'wordy' and complicated sentences wherever possible. As an example, read this sentence:

> 'I found out that I should take an investigative look at the new plant room in order to establish a prospective plan to help us re-evaluate the installation methods and techniques that we intend to use for the duration of the task.'

You could write this as:

> 'I will be checking our proposed installation in the new plant room to see if there is a better way of doing things.'

Much easier to understand, isn't it?

Communication always involves at least two people: the writer/speaker and the reader/listener. Remember to think about your reader and write for them, clearly conveying your ideas so that they can easily understand them. For example, you wouldn't expect to write the same way for a five-year-old as you would for a college lecturer.

Make your writing interesting

Don't let your document become boring and repetitive. Use a **thesaurus** to find alternative words to use.

Activity

▶ You will find a thesaurus function on your computer. For example, instead of using the word 'wherewithal' in the sentence 'I have the wherewithal to pay the bill', the thesaurus suggests you could use words like 'means', 'resources', or 'ability'.

Use your thesaurus to find alternatives for the following words: 'interpret', 'divide', 'meaning' and 'develop'.

Note that the alternatives provided by the thesaurus may not make sense to you or may require putting into context. If that's the case, look up their meaning in a dictionary or check for an alternative using the thesaurus. You'll be so much better when watching 'Countdown' if you do!

Check your work before sending it

Everyone makes mistakes. Therefore, checking your written work (also known as proofreading) is an important aspect of writing. Pay attention to grammar, spelling and punctuation.

If you are using word-processing software to write your letter or report, it will often indicate when something might be wrong. Get into the habit of finding out what the problem is and correcting it. However, always remember that the software cannot detect every mistake. For example, the following sentence has several errors, but they won't all show up on the computer screen (try typing it in to see what happens!).

Two many electricians were note iced too bee erecting the too extract fans in 2 the to staff toilets.

A dictionary can help: if you aren't sure how to spell a word, look it up. If possible, don't proofread something immediately after you have written it. You are more likely to spot any mistakes or find a better way of saying something if you go back to it later.

Report writing

Reports usually describe a problem or an investigation. Their purpose is to help someone, or a team, to make a decision, by setting out all the relevant facts and perhaps making some recommendations for action. Some reports will present a solution to a problem; others may simply list historical and factual data.

Many companies will have a standard structure or format for reports and you should use this whenever you can. However, a lot depends on the subject and type of the report: there is no point rigidly following a format if it makes it difficult to understand what the report is about.

As with any writing, it is important to be clear about what you are trying to say, and then to put that into a style and format that will be acceptable to the reader.

Style, although hard to define, can make a big difference to the success of a report. A good style can help to convince the reader of the merits of the report and its recommendations. A bad style may put the reader off, even if the content is perfectly good.

Activity

▶ Find some examples of reports and look through them. What features do they have in common? What sort of information do they contain? How are they presented? Who are they aimed at? Use them to help you to complete your own report about an issue you may have encountered in a work environment.

Report structure

Companies may have a required format for reports, but they will probably include most, or all of the elements described below. For a business report or memo, this will include:

- basic identification data – who the report is for, who is writing it, the date, subject, reference number
- summary – the project or problem and the purpose of the report
- background – the history of the issue being reported
- relevant data – the evidence you have gathered
- conclusions and recommendations.

When writing a more technical report, consider organising it under the following headings, in the order shown:

- Title page
- Acknowledgements
- History of any changes
- Contents list
- Report summary
- Introduction
- Technical chapters
- Conclusions and recommendations
- References
- Appendices (these contain specific, additional information).

Whatever style and format you use in your report, the principles of good writing, as shown in Table 2.1, will always apply.

Be clear	• The reader must be able to easily understand the report. • Explain any symbols, tables or diagrams. • Never assume that your reader has prior knowledge of issues. • Don't use jargon or abbreviations unless you know that the reader will be familiar with them.
Be concise	• Don't waffle. • Be succinct without making the report hard to understand. • Think about what the reader wants to know, i.e. your evidence and conclusions – do not give a vivid description of the valiant effort you made to compile them.
Be logical	• Ensure that you have a beginning, a middle and an end. • There should be a sensible flow between sections, chapters, paragraphs and sentences. • Avoid jumping randomly from idea to idea. • Take out unnecessary distractions, such as pretty graphics that don't add any extra information.
Be accurate and objective	• Base your report on honest facts – an inaccurate report is at best pointless and at worst harmful. • Remember that someone may make an important decision based on your recommendations. • If you have to make assumptions, make it clear that you have done so. • Be tactful. What you say may contradict others or what the reader thinks. • If you feel very strongly about something, don't send the report until you have had some time to think about it and make sure it contains only facts. • Don't use reports as a sounding-off platform. It is very easy to destroy a relationship by sending an angry, ill-conceived letter or report.

Table 2.1: Basic rules for good report writing

Organisational procedures for completing documentation

Now that you know a bit more about writing, you can look at the various types of documentation in use on a site and how you can apply your communication skills to them.

Job sheets

Job sheets give detailed and accurate information about a job to be done. Electrical contracting companies issue them to their electricians. They will include:

- the customer's name and address

- a clear description of the work to be carried out

- any special instructions or special conditions (e.g. whether you need to pick up special tools or materials).

Sometimes extra work is done which was not included on the job sheet. In this case it is recorded on a day-work sheet so that the customer can be charged for it.

Job Sheet   **Evan Dimmer**
Electrical contractors

Customer   **Dave Wilkins**

Address   **2 The Avenue**
Townsville
Droopshire

Work to be carried out
       Install 1 x additional 1200 mm
       fitting to rear of garage

Special conditions/instructions
       Exact location to be specified
       by client

Figure 2.3: An example of a typical job sheet

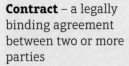

Key term

Contract – a legally binding agreement between two or more parties

Variation Orders

A Variation Order (VO) is issued or 'raised' when the work done varies from the original work agreed in the **contract** or listed in the job sheet. If this situation arises, it is important for the site electrician to tell their supervisor immediately. A VO can then be made out to enable the new work to be done without breaking any of the terms of the contract.

The purpose of the VO is to record the agreement of the client (or the consulting engineer representing the client) for the extra work to be done, as well as any alteration that this will make to the cost and completion date of the project.

Day-work sheets

Work done outside the original scope of the contract – perhaps as a result of a VO initiated by the architect, engineer or main contractor – is known as day work. When the work is completed, the electrician or supervisor fills out a day-work sheet and gets a signature of approval from the appropriate client representative.

Day work is normally charged at higher rates than the work covered by the main contract, and these charges are usually quoted on the initial tender. Typical day-work charges are:

- labour – normal rates plus 40 percent
- materials – normal costs plus 25 percent
- plant – normal rate plus 10 percent.

Disputes over day work can easily arise, so it is important that the installation team on site records any extra time, plant and materials used when doing day work.

Activity

▶ Can you think of two situations on a project that might warrant the issue of a Variation Order?

Figure 2.4: An example of a typical day-work sheet

Time sheets

Time sheets are very important to you and your company, because they are a permanent record of the labour used on a site. Time sheets include details of:

- each job

- travelling time

- overtime

- expenses.

This information allows the company to track its costs on a project and also to make up your wages. If you work on several sites during the week, you may need to fill in a separate time sheet for each job.

Accurate time sheets are essential to make sure you get paid correctly and that your customer is charged the right amount for the job.

Time Sheet

Evan Dimmer
Electrical contractors

Employee   Project/site

Date	Job No.	Start time	Finish time	Total time	Travel time	Expenses
Mon						
Tue						
Wed						
Thu						
Fri						
Sat						
Sun						
Totals						

Employee's
signature

Supervisor's
signature

Date

Figure 2.5: An example of a typical time sheet

Purchase orders

Before a supplier dispatches any materials or equipment, they will require a written purchase order. This will include details of the material, the quantity required and sometimes the manufacturer; it may also specify a delivery date and place. In many cases the initial order is made on the telephone, or via email or the internet, and a written confirmation is sent immediately afterwards.

The company keeps a copy of the original order in case there are any problems.

Usually the purchasing department sends out these orders, but sometimes an order is raised directly from the site if there is a need for immediate action.

Delivery notes

Delivery notes are usually forms with several copies that record the delivery of materials and equipment to the site. All materials delivered directly to the site by a third party will arrive with a delivery note. As the company representative on site, this is the form you are most likely to deal with.

The delivery note should give the following information:

- the name of the supplier

- details of whom the materials are being sent to

- a list of the type and quantity of materials that are being delivered to the site in this particular load, including descriptions

- the time period allowed for claims for damage.

When materials arrive on site you should make sure that they are unloaded and stored correctly, and check each item against the delivery note and for obvious signs of damage.

If everything is OK, sign the note. If not, note any missing or rejected items on the delivery note, then you and the delivery driver should both sign it. Make sure you store your copy of the note safely.

Check the materials thoroughly for damage within the given time stated in the delivery note (usually 3 days) and inform the supplier immediately if there are any problems.

A delivery won't always contain all the materials listed in the purchase order. Sometimes the materials are not all needed on site at the same time and they will be delivered in several loads. This helps to reduce the need for on-site storage and minimises the risk of damage or loss.

Incomplete deliveries may also occur if the supplier is out of stock, or if some of the order is coming direct from the manufacturer. Linked to the delivery note, a completion order records the fact that all the material on an original purchase order has been delivered.

Delivery note		**A. POWERS** *Electrical wholesalers*	
Order No.		Date	
Delivery address		Invoice address	
2 The Avenue Townsville Droopshire		Evan Dimmer Electrical Contractors	
Description	Quantity		Catalogue No.
Thorn PP 1200 mm fit fitting	1		
1.5 mm T/E cable	50 m		
Comments			
Date and time of receiving goods			
Name of recipient		Signed	

Figure 2.6: An example of a typical delivery note

INTERNAL MEMO

To: D Boss, Contracts Engineer

From: A Foreman, Site Supervisor

Project: The New Hospital

Following the arrival of the new essential services generator on site, we have found that it is too big for the entrance to the existing generator house. I have spoken to the Main Contractor, and we believe that a section of roof could be removed easily and the generator craned into position.

Please advise.

A Foreman

Figure 2.7: An example of a memo

Site reports, memos and minutes of meetings

The site foreman, supervisor or engineer in charge usually compiles reports for companies. Site reports contain details of work progress, defects, problems and delays. Sometimes other reports will be made about specific problems or incidents.

A memo is usually a short document sent to a relevant person about a single issue: for example, a problem installing a piece of equipment, or materials not being delivered on time.

Although this may be more to do with the site engineer or supervisor, no installation project will be complete without a site meeting. Normally chaired by the main contractor, with representatives from the consultants and all related contractors present, these meetings seek to establish whether a project is progressing as hoped, and attempt to solve any identified problems.

A record of each meeting is then sent to all relevant parties. These 'minutes' should be checked for accuracy and retained, as often there will be actions for you to comply with.

Should any difficulty arise as a project progresses, these minutes can prove a useful tool to establish the situation at a given moment in time.

Access for personnel

During normal on-site work, it is inevitable that sites will receive visitors, from delivery drivers to architects and clients. This may be less of a problem in places such as factories, office blocks or hospitals, where a construction site may be located within the boundary of the organisation, as they probably already have a visitor facility. The same can also be said for larger construction sites.

At sites without designated facilities, the communication, motivation and co-operation of all site personnel is key. Regardless of the quality of the facilities available for receiving visitors, the reasons for putting into practice a 'visitor procedure' remain the same:

- to meet with health and safety requirements
- to maintain site security
- to project a professional approach for the company
- to establish and maintain good client relationships.

Generally speaking, the following are some simple points of good practice when receiving visitors.

- Be polite and courteous, responding only to requests that are within your authority.

- Check the identity of the visitor and the reason for their visit.

- Brief them on site safety and issue them with PPE if necessary.

- Ask them to complete the site visitors' book, an example of which is shown in Figure 2.8.

Date	Visitor's name	Company	To see	Time in	Time out	I.D. checked	Badge number	H&S briefed	Visitor's signature
Enter date	PRINT visitor's name	Enter name of company or organisation visitor is representing	Name of person to be visited	Time visitor is booked into the site	Time visitor is booked out of the site	Type of I.D. used – e.g. student card, letterhead	Number of visitor pass or badge issued	Enter 'Yes' when briefed and PPE issued, if required	Ask visitor to sign here

Figure 2.8: An example of a site visitors' book

When you communicate with someone, you usually have a clear purpose in mind. Here you will look at four of the main reasons you will have to communicate as an electrician.

Communicating with a purpose

Motivation

Motivation happens when individuals or teams share their common aims, purposes and values. However, motivation will often take a different form for different people.

The following case study gives an example of this.

Case study

A BBC radio journalist once interviewed a worker in a biscuit factory. Here is a transcript of their conversation:

Interviewer: How long have you worked here?

Worker: Since I left school, oh, about 15 years ago.

Interviewer: What do you do?

Worker: I take packets of biscuits off the conveyor belt and put them into cardboard boxes.

Interviewer: Have you always done the same job?

Worker: Yes.

Interviewer: Do you enjoy it?

Worker: Oh yes, it's great; everyone is so nice and friendly and we have a good laugh.

Interviewer: Really? Don't you find it a bit boring?

Worker: Oh gosh no, sometimes they change the biscuits …

The point here is that you should never assume things that motivate one person will motivate someone else. This means that motivational methods need to be varied, from inspirational speeches, quotes and poems through to team-building games and activities. Team workshops and meetings can also prove motivational.

Playing 'games' can enable people to experience achievement in a new way, and that experience of success tends to lead to higher motivation. This is one reason why Outward Bound courses and paintballing are successful – they create an environment that allows people to achieve outside of their normal work environment, as individuals and as teams. When people play games, socialise or compete in teams they learn about each other, communicate, and see each other from a different perspective. Mutual respect can grow out of these activities.

Role-play exercises do not have the best reputation but, used correctly, they can be another highly effective motivational tool. Role play can aid instruction by getting people to be practically involved, and can encourage co-operation, as those taking part get to see situations and issues from perspectives other than their own.

Activity

▶ People often enjoy non-work-related activities, especially if managers are seen to take part alongside everyone else. What activities would you like to see take place at your employer to help improve respect, morale and motivation?

Instruction

There are various methods available for instructing. To choose the right one, you will need to consider what the instruction is for and the learning style of the person being instructed.

There are many different learning styles, but for this industry most learners could be said to be:

- **visual** – learn through seeing (thinking in pictures, visual aids such as slides, diagrams, handouts, etc.)

- **auditory** – learn through listening (lectures, discussions, tapes, etc.)

- **reading** – learn through reading and writing

- **kinaesthetic or tactile** – learn through experience, moving, touching and doing (active exploration of the workplace, projects, experiments, etc.).

Some of the most common instruction methods you will come across are:

- **tutor-led** – tutor presents information and interacts by frequently questioning and providing periodic summaries or logical points of development

- **demonstration** – observation of a procedure, technique, or operation, which shows you how to do something or how something works

- **practice** – repeated performance of previously learned actions, sequences, operations or procedures

- **independent** – independent learning and practice, perhaps at home, with advice on offer if required.

To cater for the mixture of learning styles, instructors should try to use a range of learning methods.

Monitoring

All learning needs to be monitored, in order to:

- provide an effective means of measuring the progress of an individual or project
- establish levels of skill and understanding
- regularly assess the achievement of technical, financial and economic goals
- determine whether any corrective actions or training are required
- assist in defining new or modified performance techniques or measures.

Here are some key monitoring (assessment) techniques:

- **Direct observation** – where an observer watches the real-time performance of an individual as they undertake work or visually inspects overall project progress. This can establish if an individual has a training need or whether a process needs changing within the project. It can be very effective: the personal approach is often appreciated by the individual.

- **Written examination** – an individual's knowledge is checked via an independent examination. Many courses, such as the IET Wiring Regulations, are assessed like this.

- **Interview** – where one or more people are interviewed to establish an outcome. This could be to check individual knowledge or to receive verbal updates to establish progress.

- **Reports or other written documents** – these are used to collect information from a variety of sources about specific circumstances or project progress.

To achieve the overall aim of a successfully completed installation, it is an advantage if staff understand, without suspicion, why monitoring is taking place. When this understanding exists, employers can introduce self-monitoring by staff themselves: this can be very useful in achieving targets.

Co-operation

The aim of motivating, instructing and monitoring is to help bring about co-operation between individuals and, as a result, aid the development of the team.

Team development

The Form-Storm-Norm-Perform model gives useful insights into how any team develops, whether the team is just the squad of electricians, or everyone working on the site.

As a team develops, relationships between team members shift, and the team leader must change their leadership style.

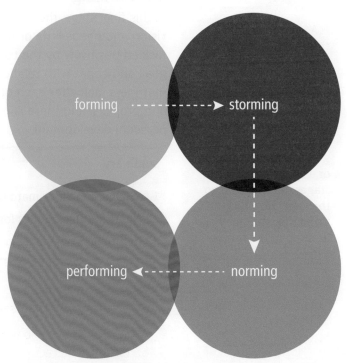

Figure 2.9: The Form-Storm-Norm-Perform model

1. Forming

This is the first stage, when the team has just come together. Team members probably don't yet know one another very well, and individual roles and responsibilities may be unclear. There is little agreement between members about what the team is trying to do. Some will feel confused and won't know what they should be doing. At this stage, the team relies heavily on the team leader for guidance and direction. The leader must provide lots of answers about the team's purpose and objectives, and relationships with groups outside of the team.

2. Storming

During this stage, team members jockey for position as they try to find themselves a role within the team. The leader might receive challenges to their authority from other team members. The team's purpose becomes clearer, but plenty of uncertainty remains, and decisions are hard to achieve because members may argue a lot. Small groups or factions may form, and there may be power struggles. The team needs to be focused on its goals to avoid being broken up by relationship and emotional issues. Some compromises will be needed to make any progress. The leader has to become less bossy and more of a coach.

3. Norming

This is a more peaceful stage, when team members generally reach agreements easily. Roles and responsibilities are clear and accepted by all, and the team works together. Members develop ways and styles of working by discussion and agreement together. Big decisions are made by the whole team or the team leader, but smaller decisions are left to individuals or small groups within the team. The team may also enjoy fun and social activities together. The leader now acts to guide the team gently, enabling it to do its job. They have no need to enforce decisions. The team may share some leadership roles.

4. Performing

In this final stage, the team knows clearly what it is doing and why. It has a shared vision and needs little or no input from the leader. If disagreements occur, they are tackled positively by the team itself. The team works together towards achieving the goal, and copes with relationship, style and process issues along the way. Team members look after each other. The leader's role is to delegate and oversee tasks and projects, and there is no need for instruction or assistance, except for individual personal development.

Summary

1. What are the four main reasons for communicating as an electrician?
2. Name four techniques for monitoring on site.
3. In the four stages of team development, at what stage will decisions be hardest to make?

Activity

▶ As you read through this team development model, try to apply it to teams you have been involved with. It could be your team at work but could also be in your social life – a gang of mates, perhaps, or a sports team. What stages did the team go through? How do you think the team may develop in the future?

Determining the competence of operatives

It is important that anyone supervising site work is adequately trained and experienced, and can manage the project. To do so, they must be aware of the competence levels of their project team before setting them to work, including any training they have received and their experience and working practices.

There are several ways to check the competence of an individual.

Checking competency cards

Competency cards are a practical tool. They generally have an individual's identification and competency level on one side of a card with the behaviours and levels printed on the opposite side. There are two cards that are widely used in your industry: CSCS and ECS cards.

Construction Skills Certification Scheme (CSCS)

The CSCS was set up to help the construction industry improve quality and reduce accidents. CSCS cards provide proof that individuals working on construction sites have the required training and qualifications for the type of work they are to carry out. The cards are increasingly demanded as proof of occupational competence by contractors, public and private clients and others, and they cover hundreds of occupations.

With a variety of grades available, the objective is to hold no less than a Skilled Worker card. People qualify for this card if they achieve an NVQ Level 2 and have passed the appropriate Construction Skills Health, Safety and Environment test.

Electrotechnical Certification Scheme (ECS)

It is now almost impossible to gain access to a construction site without proof of identification, competence and qualification levels. For this reason, the electrotechnical industry combines the requirements of the CSCS card with a sector-specific card known as the ECS card.

Safety

If the installation team is to succeed, everyone must be of the correct ability level to handle the tasks that they are asked to do.

ECS is currently the sole ID and competence card scheme for electrotechnical operatives in the UK. Holding an ECS card means an individual can prove their identity, qualified status and occupation when working on site. It also proves that you have passed a health and safety assessment.

The ECS is affiliated to the CSCS, and endorsed and supported by UK Part P Competent Person Schemes.

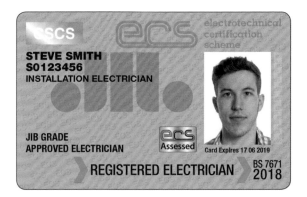

Figure 2.10: An example of an ECS Installation Electrician card

Checking technical qualifications

It is important to understand what type of qualification certificate you are looking at and what you hope to gain from checking it. In essence, there are two types: those that certificate knowledge and those that certificate both knowledge and practical performance.

Working life

In response to an advert for someone to carry out electrical inspection and testing, an electrician approaches a contracting company to seek employment. The electrician presents the following documents for consideration:

- C&G Unit 301 Certificate of Unit Credit
- EAL BS.7671 certificate.

What would you do if you were the manager? You will need to think about what level of practical experience these certificates prove.

In the Working life feature, the problem is that the documents the electrician has presented are all knowledge-only certificates – you have no proof of the person's practical ability. You need to be aware that a Certificate of Unit Credit is not a full certificate – it records success in one part of a certificate. The individual has not fully met the industry knowledge requirements.

There may be a number of valid reasons for this scenario, and the individual may actually have all of the knowledge and practical experience needed for the job. However, as a manager, you would be expected to dig deeper before you could safely make an offer of employment. Here are some other things you might want to check.

Written references

Although the source of the reference needs to be established as trustworthy, a reference from a previous employer can help to establish whether someone has relevant experience, as well as indicating their attitude and skill when dealing with work.

Monitoring of performance

If an employer remains uncertain of someone's ability, they can employ them for a period of time to assess their suitability. Known as a 'probation period', this usually lasts between one and three months. It allows an employer to see whether an applicant fits in with the company ethos, whether they have the abilities needed for the job and whether they are able to form satisfactory relationships with colleagues. Normally, during this period, trusted members of staff will mentor the applicant, monitoring their progress and reporting back to management.

As an employee, a probation period requires you to work under modified terms of employment. For example, should you choose to leave the company (or for that matter, if the firm decides to fire you), your notice period will be reduced. Other employers may not allow you your full holiday entitlement until this initial term has elapsed.

Appropriateness of different customer relations, methods and procedures

Who is your customer?

At first, you'll probably think of the person who wants the work done and is paying for it – but does this mean you can ignore everyone else you meet in your job? A wider definition of a customer is: anyone who has a need or expectation of you.

Using this definition, almost everyone you work with becomes your customer, and you will, in turn, be theirs. They may be architects, consultants, clients, other tradespeople or members of the public. They may ask you to do some complex task, or simply ask you a question. Whatever the case, they will certainly expect a good, polite response.

Customer relations

There may be certain procedures to follow when responding to customers: for example, all architect enquiries may have to be directed via the site engineer. However, treating everyone as a valuable customer and always trying to give them your best service will bring you many benefits. Dealing with people is an important part of your job. It is never wise to upset people, if only because it may cause problems later for you or your firm. Table 2.2 contains general guidance for improving customer relations.

DO	DON'T
• be honest • be neat and tidy in your personal appearance, and look after your personal hygiene • learn how to put people at ease, and be pleasant and cheerful • show enthusiasm for the job • try to maintain friendly relationships with customers, but don't get over familiar • know your job and do it well – good knowledge of the installation and keeping to relevant standards gives the customer confidence in you and your company • explain what you are going to do, and how long it will take • ask, if you are not sure about something.	• 'bad-mouth' your employer • use company property and materials to do favours for others • speak for your employer when you have no authority to do so • use bad language • smoke on customer premises • gossip about the customer or anyone else • tell lies – the customer will find out eventually if they are being misled or ripped off • assume that you know what your employer wants without bothering to ask.
When working in someone's home or office	
• ensure you protect their property – use dust covers, and ask them to remove objects that might get damaged • make sure that you understand exactly what the client expects • if you have recommendations for improvements or alterations, take time to discuss these with the client and explain any technical information.	• work with pets or small children around – ask them to be kept well away from the working area • use hazardous substances without informing the customer – take the correct precautions and respect any instructions from the customer.

Table 2.2: Some dos and don'ts to improve customer relations

Always try to provide customers with answers to any questions they have about your work. You might be asked the following questions.

- Is this the right product for the job?
- Will I be able to use it?
- Will it cost a lot to buy and install?
- How easy is it to repair?
- Will it do what I need?
- How long does the guarantee last?
- How reliable is it?
- Will you be finished on time?

Before answering a question, try to understand why the customer is asking it: what do they really want to know? Are they worried that they cannot afford the installation? Have they booked a holiday that starts just after you are scheduled to finish?

If you don't know the answer, don't just guess, promise to find out. The client fully understands how to use the installation, and leave behind any manufacturers' user guides or installation manuals. Invite the customer to contact you if there are any problems in the future.

✔ co-operate with other trades – it's always better than conflict	✔ take good care of your and others' property
✔ be patient and tolerant with others	✔ keep noise down, especially from your radio
✔ attend site meetings regularly – this helps liaison with other trades	✔ show respect for everyone on site – make an effort to learn their names
✔ keep to the agreed work programme	✔ make sure everyone, including visitors to the site, has the right PPE
✔ do your work in a professional manner	✔ report any breakdown in discipline or disputes between co-contractors promptly to the site supervisor
✔ finish your work on time; don't hold others up if you can help it	
✔ respond cheerfully to reasonable requests from colleagues	✔ keep a current edition of the Wiring Regulations or the Amicus guide book with you on site
✔ don't leave the site for long periods of time	✔ always do your best to answer questions from visitors or other tradespeople
✔ don't borrow tools and materials unless it is necessary, and return them promptly and in good condition if you do	✔ never play practical jokes on colleagues (for example hiding tools, lunch boxes, car keys). This can cause bad feeling and may result in injury or accident.
✔ tell your employer if you have personal or work difficulties – don't be too proud	

Figure 2.11: A checklist for good relationships with fellow workers

Remember that when you talk with customers you are representing not just yourself, but your company. People will judge the company by the way you behave. If you do well, your company could get more work from the client; if you don't, contracts may be lost and you may find yourself out of a job.

If you follow this advice, you will have excellent relationships with your customers. In the unlikely event that a dispute arises, you will both need to seek the help of an independent mediator to settle your differences.

Lastly, don't forget about your fellow workers. They are customers too.
Figure 2.11: gives examples of best practice in that area.

Summary

1. Name four ways to check the competence of an individual.
2. How would a written reference help establish competence?
3. What two competency cards are widely used and recognised within the electrotechnical industry?

2. Requirements for organising and overseeing work programmes

To understand work programmes, you first need to understand the people and sequence of events involved in their preparation.

Project roles and responsibilities

Many different people are involved in a construction project, from its initial design through to construction and completion. As an electrician, you will be dealing with many of these people, and it is important that you understand their job function and how they fit into the overall project.

The following sections cover the people involved in the three main stages of a typical construction project: design, tendering and construction.

The design stage

Client	Person or organisation that wants the work done and is paying for it • Specifies the purpose of the building • Usually gives an idea of number of rooms, size, design, etc. and any specific wants • May also give an idea of the price they are willing to pay for the work
Architect	Designs the appearance and construction of the building so that it fulfils its function • Advises the client on the practicality of their wishes • Ideally provides a design solution that satisfies the client and also complies with the appropriate rules and regulations for the type of building • For small projects, may draw up a complete plan • For larger, more complex buildings, consults specialist design engineers about technical details
Consulting engineer (Design engineer)	Acts on behalf of the architect, advising on and designing specific services such as electrical installation, heating and ventilation • Creates a design that satisfies the client and architect, the supply company and regulations • Ensures that cable sizes have been calculated properly, that the capacities of any cable trunking and conduit are adequate, and that protective devices are rated correctly • Produces drawings, schedules and specifications for the project that will be sent out to the companies tendering for the contract • Answers any questions that may arise from this • Once the contract has been placed, produces additional drawings to show any amendments • Acts as a link between the client, the main contractor and the electrical contractor

Quantity surveyor (QS)	Manages and controls costs for a building project • Responsible for taking the plans and preparing an initial **bill of quantities** • During construction, monitors the actual quantities used, and also checks on claims for additional work and materials
Clerk of works	Checks that the quality of the materials, equipment and workmanship used on the project meet the standards laid down in the specification and drawings (on big contracts there may be several clerks of work, each responsible for one aspect, such as electrical, heating or ventilation) • Effectively employed by the client • Inspects the job at different stages • Checks any tests carried out • May also be given the authority by the architect to sign day-work sheets and to issue Architect's Instructions for alterations or additional work

Table 2.3: People involved at the design stage

Key term

Bill of quantities – a list of all the materials required, their specification and the quantities needed; contractors who are tendering for the project use this information to prepare their estimates

The architect, consulting engineer, quantity surveyor and clerks of works are traditionally part of the architect's design team. However, installations may not always be tackled like this.

For example, on a small job, the client may approach an electrical contractor directly and ask it to carry out the work. The client will provide a few basic details and requirements and expects the electrician to ensure that the installation is properly designed and carried out.

JTL tips

Larger electrical contractors, and in particular those that are multi-disciplinary, often offer a design service for customers. This eliminates the need to use an external architect and makes things simpler (and possibly cheaper) for the client. However, if a dispute arises over design aspects of the job, the client no longer has anyone to arbitrate.

The tendering stage

Tendering is the process by which a contractor bids for contracts. The contractor works through the drawings and specifications issued by the consulting engineer and submits, in writing, a total cost for carrying out the work, including materials, tools, equipment and labour.

This is done in competition with other firms who also want to carry out the work. Most invitations to tender (also known as enquiries to submit a tender) have strict guidelines about the information to be supplied and a fixed deadline by which the tender must be received.

The estimator

The estimator's task is to calculate the total cost that will be given in the tender. At the start of the tendering process, a consulting engineer or building contractor usually issues an invitation to tender. This contains various documents, such as:

- a covering letter, giving a broad description of the work, including start and finish dates

- the form of contract that will be applicable to the project (for example, whether it is to be a fixed or a fluctuating price)

- drawings and specifications for the project

- a tender submission document that must be used

- a day-work schedule.

A fixed price contract is exactly what it says. The contractor agrees to complete the job for the price quoted in the tender, even if material or labour costs go up before the project is completed.

A fluctuating price contract always has a time limit, so that the contractor is not held to a fixed price if the project is delayed. This allows the contractor to claim back the difference between costs included at the time of estimate and actual costs incurred at the time of installation.

When the invitation to tender is received, the estimator will check with their management (sometimes the contracts manager) to see whether the company wishes to tender on the basis of the submitted documents. If it does, the estimator reads the specifications carefully to understand the requirements.

Most specifications have two sections and these need to be read together. Using this information and the scaled drawings, the estimator calculates the amount of materials and labour required to complete the job within the time specified by the client. This information is then recorded on a 'take-off' sheet (see Figure 2.12).

Item	Qty	Description	Init cost	Discount	Material cost £	Hours to install	Hourly rate £	Total labour £
1	200 m	20 mm galvanised conduit	1.2/m	0	240.00	70	9.50	665.00
2	30	Earthing couplings	.24	0	7.20	0	0	0
3	30	20 mm std. brass bushes	.10	0	3.00	0	0	0
4	150	20 mm distance saddles	.48	0	72.00	0	0	0
5	150	1.5 x 8 brass screw and plugs	.03	0	4.50	0	0	0

Figure 2.12: An example of a take-off sheet

Nowadays this work is normally done using dedicated computer software. The final tender is based on the results of these calculations.

The construction stage

The contract

Before any work starts, contracts must be agreed and entered into by all the firms involved. Any failure to comply with the details of the contract by either party could result in a court action and heavy financial damages. This might happen if the contractor does not complete the work or uses sub-standard materials, or if the client does not pay.

Contracts do not have to be made in writing. A verbal agreement, even one made on the telephone, can constitute a legal contract. However, most companies use written contracts covering all aspects of the terms and conditions of the work to be carried out.

Several conditions must be met in order for a contract to be binding:

- An offer must be made that is clear, concise and understandable to the customer.

- The customer must accept the offer, and the contractor must receive this acceptance. The acceptance must be unqualified (i.e. with no additional conditions). Up to this point, there is no agreement or obligation binding either side. The contractor is free to withdraw the offer, and the customer can reject it.

- There must be a 'consideration' on both sides. This shows what each party is agreeing to do for the other.

There are several reasons why a contract may not be made. Here are just some of them.

- **Withdrawal** – the contractor can withdraw the offer at any time until the offer is accepted. The contractor must notify the customer of the withdrawal.

- **Lapse due to time** – most offers put a time limit on acceptance. After this time, the offer expires and the contractor is under no obligation, even if the customer later accepts the offer.

- **Rejection** – the customer can simply reject the contractor's offer; no reason has to be given. If the customer asks the contractor to submit a second offer (for additional work, or simply to lower the price), the contractor is under no legal obligation to quote again. Each quote is self-contained: the terms or conditions for a previous quote do not automatically apply.

- **Death of contractor** – if the contractor dies before the offer is accepted, the customer must be notified; otherwise the customer could agree (within the offer time limit) and the contract would become valid.

A breach of contract occurs when one of the parties does not fulfil the terms of the contract: for example, if the contractor does not perform the work to the specification in the offer or if the customer refuses to pay for the work. Note that it is the contractor's responsibility to ensure that the installation is in complete compliance with the specification.

Contract law is very complex, and it cannot be covered fully in this book. To minimise the risks, you can use a standard form of contract. The Joint Contracts Tribunal (JCT) Standard Form of Contract (normally for projects of a complex nature or in excess of 12 months' duration) or the Intermediate Form of Contract are typical of contracts used in the industry.

In line with understanding your responsibilities, if you are involved in any kind of contract, it is always advisable to seek professional legal assistance before making or accepting an offer.

Once contracts are agreed, you will move into the construction stage, in which construction and installation work begin and many more people become involved, each with their own particular roles and responsibilities. Table 2.4 shows the roles and responsibilities of those people most commonly involved.

Main contractor	• Usually the builders, because they have the bulk of the work to carry out • Has the contract for the whole project • Employs sub-contractors to carry out different parts of the work • In refurbishment projects, where the amount of building work is small, the electrical contractor could be the main contractor • Responsible for paying and co-ordinating sub-contractors
Nominated sub-contractors	• Named (nominated) specifically in the contract by the client or architect to carry out certain work • Must be used by the main contractor • Normally have to prepare a competitive tender • Sub-contractors will include electrical installation companies
Non-nominated sub-contractors	• Companies chosen by the main contractor, rather than being specified by the client • Their contract is with the main contractor
Nominated suppliers	• Supplier chosen by the architect or consulting engineer to supply specific equipment required for the project • Main contractor must use these suppliers
Non-nominated supplier	• Selected by main contractor or sub-contractors • For electrical supplies, this will be a wholesaler selected by the sub-contractor who can provide the materials needed for the project
Contracts manager	• Oversees the work of the contracts engineers • May also be responsible during tendering for deciding whether a tender is to be submitted, and the costs and rates to be used in it
Contracts engineer	• Employed by the electrical contractor to manage all aspects of the contract and installation through to completion • Responsible for planning labour levels, and ordering and organising materials required • Ensures the contract is completed within the contract timescales and on budget • Liaises with suppliers to ensure planned delivery dates and builders' work programme are acceptable • May negotiate preferential discounts with suppliers • Attends site meetings

Table 2.4: People involved in the construction stage

Project engineer	Role definitions vary within the industry but generally the role is similar to that of a contracts engineer • Responsible for day-to-day management of on-site operations relative to a specific project • Often based on site
Site supervisor	• Contractor's representative on site • Oversees normal day-to-day operations on site • Experienced in electrical installation work – normally an Approved Electrician • Uses the drawings and specification to direct the day-to-day aspects of the installation • Liaises with contracts engineer to ensure that the installation is as the estimator originally planned it • Ensures materials are available on site when required • Liaises with the contracts engineer where plans are changed or amended to ensure additional costs and labour/materials are acceptable and quoted for
Electricians, apprentices and labourers	• The people who actually carry out the installation work • They work to the supervisor's instructions
Electrical fitter	• Usually someone with mechanical experience • Involved in varied work including panel building and panel wiring, and the maintenance and servicing of equipment
Electrical technician	*Job definition varies from company to company* • Can involve carrying out surveys of electrical systems, updating electrical drawings and maintaining records, obtaining costs and assisting in the inspection, commissioning, testing and maintenance of electrical systems and services • May also be involved in recommending corrective action to solve electrical problems
Service manager	*Similar role to contracts manager (and in some cases the roles are combined) but focuses on customer satisfaction rather than contractual obligations* • Monitors the quality of the service delivered under contract • Checks that contract targets (e.g. performance, cost and quality) are met • Ensures customer remains fully satisfied with the service received
Maintenance manager	*Once the building has been completed* • Keeps installed electrotechnical plant working efficiently • May issue specifications and organise contracts for a programme of routine and preventive maintenance • Responsible for fixing faults and breakdowns • Ensures legal requirements are met • Carries out maintenance audits

Table 2.4: People involved in the construction stage (cont.)

Limits of responsibility for supplying technical and functional information

As you can see from Table 2.4, there can be many people involved with an electrical installation. Their needs in terms of information may change daily, depending on the circumstances.

As an apprentice, you may be required to give information to, or receive information from, any of them. However, when doing so, you must be aware of your level of responsibility. This will involve recognising when you have reached a limit to that responsibility.

As an example, if the main contractor approaches you and asks where the main switchboard panel will be located and when it will be delivered to site, you may well be in possession of the correct information. However, it is more likely that you know the 'where' part, but not the 'when'.

If you do not know the answer, either fully or partially, then do not guess. Just say that you don't know, but that you'll ask your supervisor to get back to them with the information.

And if you say you are going to do something, do it!

As a contractor on site, your presence will be the result of your employer having

Summary

1. What is the difference between a quantity surveyor and an estimator?
2. What is the main responsibility of a contracts manager?
3. How would an electrical apprentice's roles and responsibilities compare to those of an electrical technician?

How a work programme is developed

successfully tendered for the work. This will have involved your company estimator working with various documentation, drawings and specifications.

In our industry, estimators use the layout drawings and specification provided by the consulting engineer during the tendering stage. The electrician will also need the same layout drawings during the installation stage – and there might be hundreds of them, especially if it is a large project like a school or hospital.

The next section looks at specifications and layout drawings, and how to interpret them. There are two types of specification; general and particular. A general specification represents the standard requirements and conditions for the installation. A particular specification clarifies or modifies certain sections of a standard specification and will therefore take precedence over it.

Working life

Here is an extract from an electrical particular specification for the refurbishment of the main warehouse within a university. It shows what the consultant has written about the proposed fire alarm installation.

Fire alarms

SYSTEM OF WIRING

The wiring of the fire alarm system shall be carried out using MICC cable (600 volt grade) Pyrotenax as manufactured by Pentair. The electrical contractor shall allow additional protection for cables to be provided at any point where it could be subject to mechanical damage.

Figure 2.13: Specification for a proposed fire alarm installation

You may think this extract is quite clear and easy to follow. However, within the general specification the consultant goes on to say this about MICC cables:

- Cables shall be made with ring-type glands with screw-on pot-type seals utilising cold plastic compound and neoprene sleeving and applied in the manner recommended by the manufacturer of the cable.
- Where ambient temperature is likely to exceed 150°C, medium temperature seals shall be used and completed with LSF (Low Smoke and Fume) shrouds and all fixing saddles shall be LSF (Low Smoke and Fume) coated or nylon throughout.
- Where cables pass through wall and floors, they shall be protected by galvanised conduit bushed at both ends. Cables rising on external or exposed wall surfaces shall be protected by galvanised conduit to a height of 2 metres above ground level. The conduit shall be suitably bushed and sealed with MICC sealing compound.
- Where MICC cables terminate into electric motors or similar equipment liable to vibration or movement, a vibration loop of a single coil of the cable shall be made before final connection.
- Where cables do not terminate in a conduit box with spouts, they shall be fitted with a coupling and brass bush.
- The cores of the cables shall be identified by means of coloured sleeves in accordance with BS.7671: 2008, Requirements for Electrical Installations Wiring Regulations Seventeenth Edition and BS 3858:1992.
- The whole of the system of cable and fittings shall provide both electrical and mechanical continuity and shall be efficiently earthed. Where the cable is cut, kinked or badly bent, shows signs of inferior workmanship, or an insulation reading less than 'infinity' is obtained, the Electrical Services Installer shall replace the defective cable or seals. All unmade ends of MICC cables on site shall be sealed to prevent the ingress of moisture.
- Wherever possible, the cable shall be covered with LSF (Low Smoke and Fume) oversheath.

As you can see, you must read the two sections of the specification together to fully comply with the installation requirements.

Layout drawings, which are scaled drawings based on the architect's drawings of the building, show the required position of all equipment, metering and control gear to be installed in 'plan' view, using standard IEC.60617 location symbols. The layout drawing will show where things go but will not specify the height of equipment such as switches or sockets, or the type and manufacturer of such equipment. This information will normally be contained in the specification.

Specifications

The electrical specification works alongside information given in the layout drawings, telling you the height of electrical work, how things are to be wired and what systems you need to use. These specifications are also generally prepared by the consulting engineer.

In its most basic generic format, an electrical specification comprises two sections.

- The general specification – this tends to give general information about installation circumstances, such as wiring systems, enclosures and equipment. The section gives generic requirements applicable to any project issued by the particular consulting engineer. It gives a general description of all the consultant's expectations and requirements for any installation circumstances.

- The particular specification – this gives the specific details of the project. For example, it may say that the installation will be carried out in galvanised steel conduit. However, although it may state specific conditions applicable to the project, you will also need to read the general specification to check the general requirements for installing galvanised steel conduit.

In reality, the electrical contractor will have to read both sections to understand the full requirements of the installation. The previous case study gave an example of this.

Be aware that there are no hard and fast rules when it comes to drawings and specifications. Some consulting engineers include details of equipment on the layout drawing, while others issue a specification with a clear and detailed 'specific' section that illustrates their total requirements for the project. Consulting engineers generally use IEC.60617 location symbols to show the location of systems and equipment. See Figure 2.15.

Layout drawings and their interpretation

Layout and assembly drawings give information about physical objects, such as the floor layout in a building, or a mechanical object.

If you were to make the drawing the same size as the object, most drawings would obviously be too big to handle. To make the drawing a sensible size, we use **scaled drawings**.

Key term

Scaled drawing – a drawing on which everything is drawn at a fixed ratio to the size of the actual object; this ratio is called the scale of the drawing, and should be indicated on the drawing itself

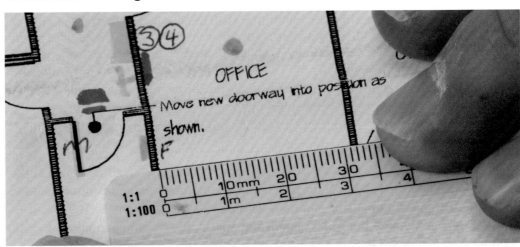

Figure 2.14: Using a scaled drawing

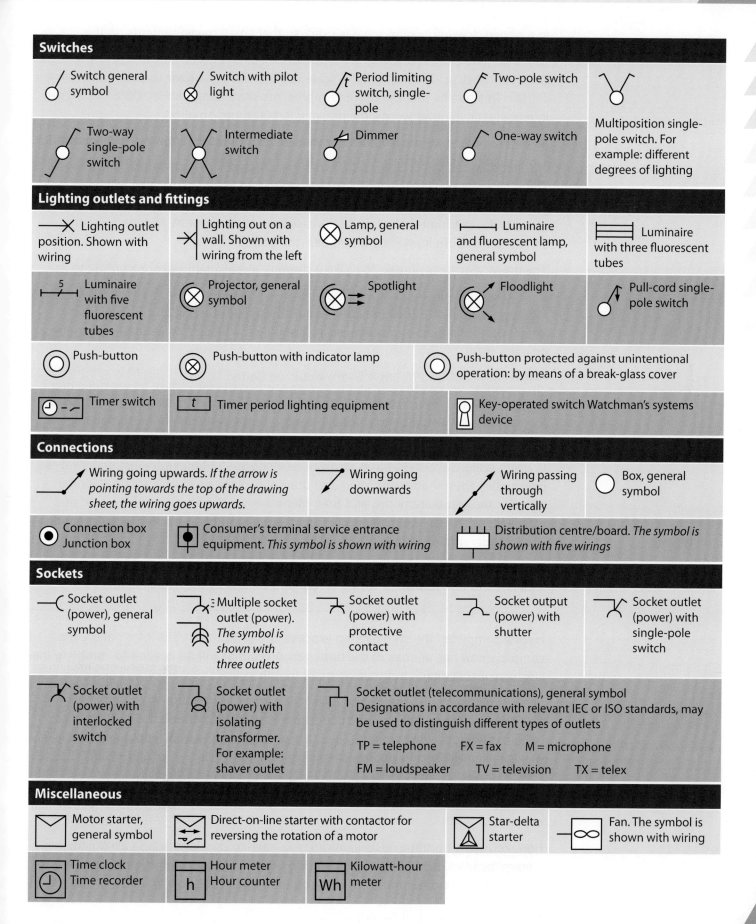

Figure 2.15: IEC.60617 lists the standard symbols for use in installation drawings

In a scaled drawing, a ratio scale is used, so that small measurements on the drawing represent much larger dimensions in real life.

On most construction projects, the scale used to show the floor layout of a building is 1:100. This means that the drawing represents something that is 100 times bigger in real life (or, in other words, the drawing is 100 times smaller).

As an example, if we measured a distance of 10 mm on the drawing, this equates to 1 metre in real life (10 mm × 100 = 1 m).

The ratio scale makes drawings easy to use. To find where something will be in real life, you simply measure the distance on the drawing and multiply it by the scale given. It doesn't matter what unit of measurement you choose, because you are simply going to multiply it by a number (the scale).

The drawing scale is chosen to make a drawing a reasonable size, according to its purpose.

Although a scale of 1:100 may be fine for the layout of a building, it would be impractical for a road map, because you would only be able to get a few kilometres on each sheet.

A scale of 1:500000 (1 cm = 5 km) would be better.

Occasionally, the reverse is true. If we used a scale of 1:100, the assembly drawing for a wristwatch would be too small to read. A better scale might be something like 20:1; where 20 mm on the drawing represents 1 mm on the actual watch.

In using scaled layout drawings to produce a successful tender, the estimator takes information from the specification and drawings, plans an electrical installation in line with those requirements, and then measures what materials are involved and establishes the likely time taken to install them. All of this is needed when preparing a work programme.

Let's work through the example opposite and compile a materials list, noting that we'll need to work out what wiring is required to control the installation.

Having completed the step by step process and armed with this information, the company now has an idea of the basic resources that will be needed to complete the electrical installation – but there is more to it than that.

The estimator will also have to consider the regulatory requirements that affect the planned installation. Legislation such as the HASAWA, CDM and the EAWR all need to be considered, along with BS.7671, if the installation is to be completed safely as well as being electrically and mechanically sound.

Looking at the warehouse example, you know you will be installing fluorescent lighting fittings at high level and therefore a mobile scaffold tower looks like the best option.

However, apart from the costs involved, you need to consider access arrangements, storage facilities, the ability of your staff to use the scaffold and whether you can use it when there are other trades working on the project, possibly in the same area at the same time.

Step by Step

Let's look at the example of a university warehouse, focusing this time on the lighting installation fed from the new DB. The layout drawing shows the layout of the building, the location of specific services and how some items are to be installed and connected. As it is to scale (1:50), you can measure it to find the actual dimensions of the building and prepare a materials list for the job.

You can also scale up positions shown on the drawing and mark them for real inside the building itself. However, what the drawing doesn't tell you is anything about the fitments or how they should be installed. This information will be in the specification, so you'll need a copy of that too. Below is an extract from the specification, which tells us what we need to know.

> The warehouse lighting and sub-main installation will be completed in PVC single-core cable contained within galvanised steel conduit and galvanised steel trunking where required. All fluorescent lighting fittings will be 1700 mm type LEDLITE RTWPLED5 and suspended on chain from back boxes. All light switches will be of MK type Metalclad Plus with an aluminium front plate. The installation will be fed from the new lighting distribution board (Eaton-MEM), which will be fed from the existing MCB DB located in the warehouse.

Step 1: Count up all the major pieces of equipment needed

Looking at the plan and referring to the specification, we can see that we need:

- 12 LEDLITE RTWPLED5 sealed LED lighting fittings
- 1 MK Metalclad Plus 4-Gang one-way surface switch with aluminium front plate
- 1 Eaton-MEM three-way SPN Type A Memshield surface-mounted DB (distribution board).

Step 2: Decide the best runs of conduit and trunking

A logical way would be to install the 50 × 50 mm trunking as shown on the drawing and then to install separate conduits from the trunking up to each row of lights and along each row of lights, fixing the conduit to the roof structure.

Step 3: Calculate lengths of trunking, conduit and cable required

You measure these from the drawing and calculate the actual distance using the scale provided (1:50). You will also need to know the height of the building, which is not shown on the layout diagram.

For the purpose of this exercise only, we will assume the height of the warehouse to be 7 metres, switch mounting height to be 1500 mm, DB mounting height to be 2000 mm and that 1.5 mm² cable will be acceptable for the lighting installation. The luminaires are to be suspended 5 metres above the finished floor level.

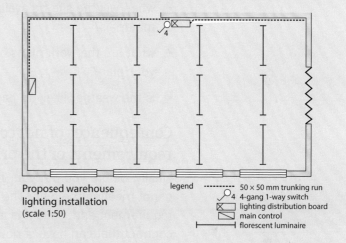

Proposed warehouse lighting installation (scale 1:50)

legend
- ---------- 50 × 50 mm trunking run
- 4-gang 1-way switch
- lighting distribution board
- main control
- florescent luminaire

Figure 2.16: The scale layout drawing

Step 4: Include accessories, fixings, etc.

You will need to allow back boxes and hook-and-chain arrangements at each luminaire, and to order sufficient fixings (screws, bolts, saddles for conduit, etc.) of various types for the installation.

Step 5: Consider special access equipment

Do you need special ladders, scaffolding, etc.? It's no use having the materials if you can't get to the right places.

Planning work allocations, operative duties and co-ordination with other services and personnel

In to the work programme, we need to consider the estimators' quantities and times, health and safety requirements and their maintenance, site access, waste removal, access arrangements, any specialist guidance and related employment legislation.

However, as an employer, there are still more things to consider before we can commit to a plan. Some of the key points would be:

- the ability of your staff (Are they skilled in the areas of work that the installation requires?)

- the availability of your staff (Are they working on another site or on holiday?)

- the availability of material and equipment (Does specialist equipment need to be ordered?)

- when will the site be available, safe and secure enough to receive labour and materials?

- what are the work plans of the other contractors involved and how do they affect your plan?

- is the weather likely to have an adverse effect?

Consequences of not completing work on time or meeting requirements of the programme of work

Finally, before you put your plan on paper, you need to consider the consequences of not meeting the plan. The production of a work programme is a contractual requirement and, once it is issued, failure to comply with it constitutes a breach of contract that can have serious cost implications if someone feels they have incurred damages.

Remember that all a client wants is their project completed to specification. That said, if something goes wrong, isn't operating properly or is delayed, the client will want a solution.

General damages (also known as unliquidated damages) are one of the most important remedies for a breach of contract but they require that the non-defaulting party proves that it has incurred actual loss as a result of the breach.

A liquidated damages clause in the contract avoids this requirement, as the non-defaulting party only needs to prove that a breach has occurred and the money calculation is based on an estimate of the costs resulting from that breach. This establishes some predictability involving costs so that, when planning, you can balance the cost of your anticipated performance against the cost involved should you breach the contract.

Remember also the effect that variations to a contract can bring. A small Variation Order may only require a small amount of extra electrical work, but it may involve other trades causing the effect to become cumulative, thereby affecting overall completion times.

Some typical problems and their consequences are shown in Table 2.5.

Problem	Consequences
Not completing work in time	The effect of this may only be to create a minor inconvenience. However, if your delay affects others, you run the risk that all parties make a claim against you.
	Some contracts where loss of business can be reasonably predicted have a liquidated damages clause in excess of £1 million per week if the project isn't completed on time.
Not meeting the requirements of the work programme	The work programme will be drawn up to make the best use of time, skills and resources. If you do not meet the requirements of the programme in some way, you could be responsible for adding costs, delaying work or even the failure of the structure.
Using incorrect materials and equipment	If you use, without gaining approval, incorrect or unspecified materials or equipment you could face the costs (both financial and time) of having to replace them with the correct thing.
	If that delays project progress, it could lead to not completing work on time.
Not installing materials and equipment as required	The effect here could be a low-quality piece of work, or a job where elements do not function properly. However, the outcome could be worse: rectifying faults could be very inconvenient and costly and, at worst, very dangerous.

Table 2.5: Typical problems when completing work programmes and their consequences

---

Working life

You are working in some student accommodation and an additional stage to the contract has been identified. This involves fitting powered showers in several areas. Variation Orders have been issued to cover the altered work. You clearly see the impact on the programme, as the work involves both the plumbing contractor and your company installing wiring to the showers.

- What considerations need to be checked for the operatives working on these circuits?
- What items will you need to check before committing to any plan of work?
- How could the plumbers' work affect your programme?

Producing and illustrating work programmes

Everyone on site has responsibilities and we should always check that working conditions are safe and that the proposed work will not put others at risk before work begins. The key to achieving safe working conditions is to ensure health and safety issues are planned, organised, controlled, understood, monitored and reviewed.

Remember that planning has to consider changes to the site as it develops – from the initial welfare arrangements at the set-up stage, through installation to **snagging** work and the dismantling and removal of site cabins at the end of the contract.

Key term

Snagging – a list of omissions, normally prepared by the Consulting Engineer, that require correction before an installation can be classed as complete

The person supervising the work must be adequately trained, experienced and able to manage health and safety procedures on site. The same applies to staff on site and, before setting them to work, the supervisor should be aware of any training workers have received and their experience of safe working practice.

Risk assessment and method statements aim to prevent some of the risk from hazards and we covered those earlier in this book (see page 62).

Once work has started, the team should continually monitor all situations as circumstances can change quickly during an installation. All storage areas should be kept secure and tidy, whether in an agreed storage area or on the site itself. Where possible, deliveries should be planned so that the amount of materials on site are kept to a minimum.

In addition to drawings and specifications, charts and reports can be used to show and communicate information and data on the above points. Therefore, in order to prepare a work programme and monitor progress against it, you must be able to interpret the data contained in a chart. The charts you will see in the following section can be created using Excel®, a spreadsheet programme that easily suits this purpose.

Charts

Charts can often make information easier to understand and allow the user to see clearly what they need to know. The most popular chart used within construction work is the bar chart. When it shows activities against time, it is sometimes referred to as a Gantt chart, after its inventor, Robert Gantt.

Figure 2.17: is a bar chart that shows several activities and when they are due to happen. The chart helps the supervisor keep an eye on how the contract is progressing compared to the original plan. Main contractors often use this sort of bar chart to show when individual trades should be on site at any time during the contract.

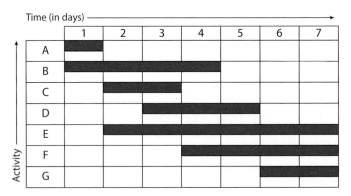

Figure 2.17: Bar Chart 1

Looking at Figure 2.17: you can see that:

- Activity A should take 1 day

- Activity B starts on the same day, and lasts 4 days

- Activity C lasts 2 days, but doesn't start until the second day, and so on.

Bar charts can provide additional information by adding colours, codes and symbols.

Figure 2.18: gives another example of a bar chart. Here the activities are the same as before, but the actual progress against each one is shown by the shaded blue area beneath the original bars. The chart shows progress to the end of Day 3. It is easy to see which activities have been completed, and which ones are lagging behind.

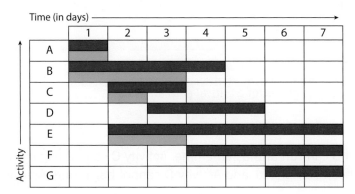

Figure 2.18: Bar Chart 2

Critical path analysis

In larger projects, many tasks must be completed before the project is finished. Not all of these activities can be done at the same time, and some can't begin until others have been completed. You need a way of working out the best way to organise the project efficiently, and critical path analysis (CPA) offers one solution.

Critical path networks (CPNs) are diagrams that represent each task and how they relate to one another. The critical path is the sequence of activities that fix the duration of a project; if you know the time needed for each activity, you can calculate the overall project completion time. CPA helps you to see what happens if a task is delayed unexpectedly.

Figure 2.19: represents an activity (A), which lasts for 2 days. The circles are 'events'; they have no duration but simply represent the point at which the activity starts or finishes. The arrow represents the activity, and always goes from left to right. It starts and ends with an event.

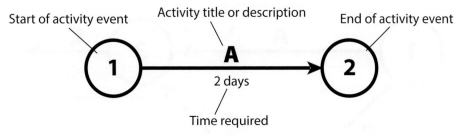

Figure 2.19: An example of a critical path diagram

The first step in constructing a CPN is to list all the activities, what must be done before they can start (the sequence) and the expected time needed for each.

You then build the network by linking the activities from left to right at their start and end events.

One rule of CPA is that no two activities can begin and end on the same two events. To explain this, we'll use an example.

Activity	Activities that need to be done before this activity
A	None
B	None
C	A and B
D	B

Table 2.6: Sequence of activities for a critical path analysis

In Table 2.6 you have four activities (A, B, C and D) to complete.

Activities A and B can run at the same time. Activity C cannot begin until Activities A and B have been completed, and Activity D cannot begin until Activity B has been completed.

As the first two activities (A and B) can begin at the same time, the temptation would be to draw them as shown in Figure 2.20.

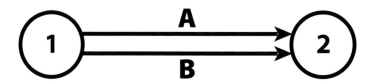

Figure 2.20: Timing of Activities A and B

However, to comply with the rule that no two activities can start and end on the same events, we introduce what is called a 'dummy activity'. Shown as a dotted line, a dummy activity doesn't take any time. This means that the correct drawing becomes what is shown in Figure 2.21.

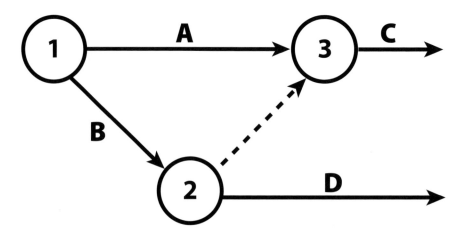

Figure 2.21: Introducing a dummy activity

This drawing shows that Activity C can only start at Event 3, when both A and B are complete.

Now let's look at a more detailed example, where the information is shown as both a bar chart and as a CPN.

This is the information we have about the activities.

- Activity A starts on Day 1 and lasts 2 days.
- Activity B starts on Day 1 and lasts 3 days.
- Activity C can only begin once Activity B is complete and lasts 3 days.
- Activity D can only begin once Activity C is complete and lasts 3 days.
- Activity E cannot start until Activity A is complete; it will take 5 days.
- Activity F can start at any time and lasts 2 days.

The question is: how long will it take to complete the project? Figure 2.22: shows the information represented as a bar chart.

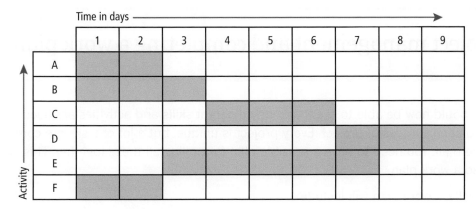

Figure 2.22: Activities shown as a bar chart

You can see that the project will finish at the end of Day 9. Figure 2.23: now shows the same information represented by a CPN.

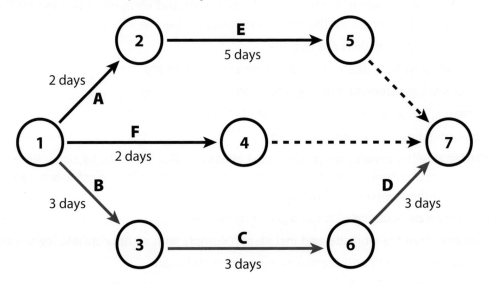

This may need a little careful study to see how it all fits together.

The minimum time for project completion is taken as the longest time path through the network. In this example it is through points 1, 3, 6 and 7, giving us a project time of nine days.

Figure 2.23: Activities shown as a critical path network

In a CPN, the shortest time it will take to complete a project is found by taking the longest time path through the network. If you follow the red line through events 1, 3, 6 and 7 in the diagram in Figure 2.23, you can see that the project lasts for 9 days.

You may feel that the bar chart is easier to understand, but it can't readily show when several activities have to be completed before another can begin. Using the critical path method gives you greater control over establishing when activities may start.

Bar charts, spreadsheets and CPNs will help you to see which activities affect your work and how your work fits in with everyone else's, so you can:

- plan which areas to work in
- see when you can start each activity
- make sure you have the correct materials and equipment ready at the right time
- avoid working unsafely around other trades
- avoid causing delays to others and to the overall contract.

Project management and completing a work plan

You should now be able to see that many different skills and activities are needed to complete a successful project. Every project is unique, but a lot of tasks are common to them all. You need to have a sensible plan for pulling all these together. This is called a work plan.

Typically, a work plan will include:

- checking the drawings, instructions and specifications
- identifying the tasks to be done
- checking that the work area and environment are suitable and safe at all times
- using scaled drawings, listing the tools, materials and equipment needed for the project and making sure that they are available when required
- establishing what skills are required
- allocating work in line with skills, experience and ability
- establishing responsibility levels for staff
- creating a logical sequence for the work activities
- co-ordinating with other contractors
- managing the installation process cost effectively (for example, by using time sheets and delivery notes to track materials and time used against estimated costs, without waste or incurring costs)
- ensuring compliance with the work programme
- making sure the worksite and installation comply with all appropriate legislation
- inspecting, testing and commissioning the installation
- ensuring the project has been completed to specified requirements and handing over to the client.

Depending on the size of the project, one person or many may have the responsibility for devising and monitoring the work plan. On a large project, contract managers and engineers, project engineers, safety officers and site supervisors may all be involved.

For a small project, many of these tasks (if not all) may fall to the electrician on site. This might include producing drawings and specifications.

Figure 2.24: Teamwork and communication is an important part of project management

All the tools you have covered in this chapter – including communication skills, bar charts, time sheets, critical path networks, requisitions, delivery records, day-work sheets, letters and reports, and Variation Orders – will help you to complete a project successfully.

Rescheduling work

Bear in mind that some jobs may have their start dates delayed. This could be caused by a number of factors, such as an overrun on a previous contract, changes to the design of the installation or the availability of specialist materials.

If this happens, it is important to review the overall project and study the critical path to see if any changes can be made in the project management or plan for the work in order to make up the time.

An important part of project management is checking if there is a way of keeping the project on target.

Working life

Your company is involved in a major refurbishment programme to an office block. The following form part of the contract:
- new distribution cables to each floor
- new lighting and power circuits in each office
- new luminaires to all office areas
- new data circuits and computers to install
- replacement showers in washrooms
- redecorating of all areas
- new workstations to be fitted for computers
- replacement pipework in washrooms.

1. Consider the tasks that are required and show on a plan a suitable order for them to be completed.

2. How would you maintain electrical safety if the new pipework was to be completed after all of the electrical work was finished?

3. What would your company need to do if the computing workstations were delayed from the manufacturers?

Summary

1. Why as an electrician is it important for you to be able to see that many different skills and activities are needed to complete a successful project, especially on a small project?
2. Give a reason why a start date of a project may be delayed.
3. What could be used to aid in the organisation of getting the project back up to date?

Industry standards and legislation relevant to the installation of electrotechnical systems and equipment

There is a great deal of legislation that employers need to be familiar with in order to successfully plan and run their businesses. Where it related to health and safety, such legislation was covered in Chapter 1 'Understand health, safety and environmental considerations'. However, we also need to consider:

*   specialist guidance
*   employment legislation.

Specialist guidance

IEC 60617

The IEC 60617 is the European standard that details the standard electrical graphical symbols to be used on layout drawings and circuit diagrams. The most common installation symbols were shown in Figure 2.15: on page 155.

BS.7671

Also known as the IET Wiring Regulations and currently in their 18th edition, these Regulations are not mandatory but compliance with them affords compliance with other mandatory legislation such as the HASAWA and EAWR. The Regulations are intended to be applied to electrical installations in general but, for example, do not apply to systems for the distribution of electricity to the public, railways, installations on board ships or aircraft, and mines.

Hazardous area installations

Hazardous areas are defined in the Dangerous Substances and Explosive Atmospheres Regulations 2002 (DSEAR), as 'any place in which an explosive atmosphere may occur in quantities such as to require special precautions to protect the safety of workers'. The 'special precautions' referred to in the definition are best taken as relating to the construction, installation and use of apparatus, as given in BS EN 60079 Part 10.

Within such hazardous areas there exists the risk of explosions and/or fires occurring due to electrical equipment 'igniting' the gas, dust or flammable liquid. These areas are not included in BS.7671 but are covered by IEC Standard BS EN 60079 as follows:

- BS EN 60079 Part 10 – Classification of hazardous areas

- BS EN 60079 Part 14 – Electrical apparatus for explosive gas atmospheres

- BS EN 60079 Part 17 – Inspection/maintenance of electrical installations in hazardous areas.

The BS EN 60079 has been in place since 1988, replacing the old BS 5345. However, many installations obviously still exist that were completed in accordance with BS 5345 and new European Directives (ATEX) address safety where there is a danger from potentially explosive atmospheres.

Other statutory regulations such as the Petroleum Regulation Acts 1928 and 1936 and local licensing laws govern storage of petroleum.

Zoning

Area classification is a method of analysing and classifying the environment where explosive gas atmospheres may occur. The main purpose is to facilitate the proper selection and installation of apparatus to be used safely in that environment, taking into account the properties of the flammable materials that will be present. DSEAR specifically extends the original scope of this analysis to take into account non-electrical sources of ignition and mobile equipment that creates an ignition risk.

Hazardous areas are classified into zones based on an assessment of the frequency of the occurrence and duration of an explosive gas atmosphere, as follows:

- Zone 0 – an area in which an explosive gas atmosphere is present continuously or for long periods

- Zone 1 – an area in which an explosive gas atmosphere is likely to occur in normal operation

- Zone 2 – an area in which an explosive gas atmosphere is not likely to occur in normal operation and, if it occurs, will only exist for a short time.

Various sources have therefore tried to place time limits on these zones, but none have been officially adopted. The most common values used are:

- Zone 0 – explosive atmosphere for more than 1000 hours/year

- Zone 1 – explosive atmosphere for more than 10, but less than 1000 hours/year

- Zone 2 – explosive atmosphere for less than 10 hours/year, but still sufficiently likely as to require controls over ignition sources.

Where people wish to quantify the zone definitions, these values are the most appropriate, but for the majority of situations a purely qualitative approach is adequate. When the hazardous areas of a plant have been classified, the remainder will be defined as non-hazardous, and sometimes referred to as 'safe areas'.

Key terms

Here are some of the key terms used in BS EN 60079.

Explosive limits – the upper and lower percentages of a gas in a given volume of gas/air mixture at normal atmospheric temperature and pressure that will burn if ignited

Lower explosive limit (LEL) – the concentration below which the gas atmosphere is not explosive

Upper explosive limit (UEL) – the concentration of gas above which the gas atmosphere is not explosive

Ignition energy – the spark energy that will ignite the most easily ignited gas/air mixture of the test gas at atmospheric pressure; hydrogen ignites very easily, whereas butane or methane require about ten times the energy

Flash point – the minimum temperature at which a material gives off sufficient vapour to form an explosive atmosphere

Ignition temperature or auto-ignition temperature – the minimum temperature at which a material will ignite and sustain combustion when mixed with air at normal pressure, without the ignition being caused by any spark or flame (note: this is not the same as flash point, so don't confuse them)

Selection of equipment

DSEAR sets out the link between a zone and the equipment that may be installed in that zone. This applies to new or newly modified installations. The equipment categories are defined by the ATEX equipment directive, set out in UK law as the Equipment and Protective Systems for Use in Potentially Explosive Atmospheres Regulations (EPS) 1996.

Standards set out different protection concepts, with further subdivisions for some types of equipment according to gas group and temperature classification. Most of the electrical standards have been developed over many years and are now set at international level, while standards for non-electrical equipment are only just becoming available from CEN (Comité Européen de Normalisation), which translates as the European Committee for Standardisation.

The DSEAR ACOP describes the provisions concerning existing equipment. There are different technical means (protection concepts) of building equipment to the different categories. These, the standard current and the letter giving the type of protection are listed below.

Correct selection of electrical equipment for hazardous areas requires the following information.

- Temperature class or ignition temperature of the gas or vapour involved as shown in Table 2.7.

Temperature classification	Maximum surface temperature °C	Ignition temperature of gas or vapour °C
T1	450	>450
T2	300	>300
T3	200	>200
T4	235	>135
T5	100	>100
T6	85	>85

Table 2.7: Temperature class or ignition temperature

- Classification of the hazardous area, as in zones shown in Table 2.8.

Zone 0	Zone 1	Zone 2
Category 1	Category 2	Category 3
'ia' intrinsically safe EN 50020, 2002	'd' flameproof enclosure EN 50018 2000	Electrical Type 'n' EN 50021 1999 Non electrical EN 13463-1, 2001
Ex's' – special protection if specially certified for Zone 0	'p' pressurised EN 50016 2002	
	'q' powder filling EN 50017, 1998	
	'o' oil immersion EN 50017, 1998-	
	'e' increased safety EN 50019, 2000	
	'ib' intrinsic safety EN 50020, 2002	
	'm' encapsulation EN 50028, 1987	
	's' special protection	

Table 2.8: Classification of hazardous areas

If several different flammable materials may be present within a particular area, the material that gives the highest classification dictates the overall area classification. The IP (International Protection) code considers specifically the issue of hydrogen containing process streams as commonly found on refinery plants.

Consideration should be shown for flammable material that may be generated due to interaction between chemical species.

Ignition sources – identification and control

Ignition sources may be:

- flames

- direct fired space and process heating

- use of cigarettes/matches etc.

- cutting and welding flames

- hot surfaces

- heated process vessels such as dryers and furnaces

- hot process vessels

- space heating equipment

- mechanical machinery

- electrical equipment and lights

- spontaneous heating

- friction heating or sparks

- impact sparks

- sparks from electrical equipment

- stray currents from electrical equipment

- electrostatic discharge sparks

- lightning strikes

- electromagnetic radiation of different wavelengths

- vehicles (unless specially designed or modified, these are likely to contain a range of potential ignition sources).

Sources of ignition should be effectively controlled in all hazardous areas by a combination of design measures, and systems of work:

- using electrical equipment and instrumentation classified for the zone in which it is located; new mechanical equipment will need to be selected in the same way (see above)

- earthing of all plant/equipment (see Technical Measures Document on Earthing)

- elimination of surfaces above auto-ignition temperatures of flammable materials being handled/stored (see above)

- provision of lightning protection

- correct selection of vehicles/internal combustion engines that have to work in the zoned areas (see Technical Measures Document on Permit to Work Systems)

- correct selection of equipment to avoid high intensity electromagnetic radiation sources, e.g. limitations on the power input to fibre optic systems, avoidance of high intensity lasers or sources of infrared radiation

- prohibition of smoking/use of matches/lighters

- controls over the use of normal vehicles

- controls over activities that create intermittent hazardous areas, such as tanker loading/unloading

- control of maintenance activities that may cause sparks/hot surfaces/naked flames through a Permit to Work System.

Petrol-filling stations

The primary legislation controlling the storage and use of petrol is the Petroleum (Consolidation) Regulations 2014 (PCR). This requires anyone who keeps petrol to obtain a licence from the local Petroleum Enforcement Authority (PEA).

The licence may be, and usually is, issued subject to a number of licence conditions. The PEA sets the licence conditions, but they must be related to the safe keeping of petrol.

The Local Authority Co-ordinating Body on Food and Trading Standards (LACOTS) has issued a set of standard licence conditions. Most, if not all, PEAs apply these to their sites.

Installations within petrol filling stations are effectively also covered by BS EN 60079 Parts 10, 14 and 17. There is also industry-developed guidance for this sector in the form of the electrical section of the APEA's 'Guidance for Design, Construction, Modification, Maintenance and Decommissioning of Filling Stations' (2011), affectionately known as 'the blue book'.

Figure 2.25: Petrol filling station

Employment legislation

Within England and Wales, the law regarding employment both protects and imposes obligations on employees, during their employment and after it ends. The law sets certain minimum rights and an employer cannot give you less than what the law stipulates. The principal rights and obligations imposed on employers and employees arise from three sources:

- common law, which governs any contract of employment between employer and employee, and includes the body of law created by historical practice and decisions

- UK legislation

- European legislation and judgements from the European Court of Justice (ECJ).

UK employment law has been heavily influenced by European law, particularly in the areas of equal pay and equal treatment; many of our statutory minimum rights began their life in European legislation.

Here are just some of the most relevant pieces of legislation.

The Employment Rights Act 1996 and The Employment Act 2008

Subject to certain qualifications, employees have a number of statutory minimum rights (such as the right to a minimum wage). The main vehicle for employment legislation is the Employment Rights Act 1996 – Chapter 18. If you did not agree certain matters at the time of commencing employment, your legal rights will apply automatically.

The Employment Rights Act 1996 deals with many matters such as:

- the right to statement of employment
- the right to pay statement
- minimum pay
- minimum holidays
- maximum working hours
- the right to maternity/paternity leave.

The Employment Act 2008, amended the 1996 Act to make provision for statutory rights to paternity and adoption leave and pay. The Act makes provision for the resolutions of employment dispute including compensation for financial loss, enforcement of minimum wage and of offences under the Employment Agencies Act 1973, and the right of Trade Unions to expel members due to membership of political parties.

Employment Relations Act 1999 and 2004

The 1999 Act is based on the measures proposed in the White Paper: Fairness at Work (1998), which was part of the Government's programme to replace the notion of conflict between employers and employees with the promotion of partnership.

As such it comprises changes to the law on trade union membership, to prevent discrimination by omission and the blacklisting of people on grounds of trade union membership or activities; new rights and changes in family-related employment rights, aimed at making it easier for workers to balance the demands of work and the family; and a new right for workers to be accompanied in certain disciplinary and grievance hearings.

The Employment Relations Act 2004 is mainly concerned with collective labour law and trade union rights. It implements the findings of the review of the Employment Relations Act 1999, announced by the Secretary of State in July 2002, with measures to tackle the intimidation of workers during recognition and de-recognition ballots and provisions to increase the protections against the dismissal of employees taking official, lawfully organised industrial action.

The Human Rights Act 1998

The Human Rights Act 1998 covers many different types of discrimination – including some not covered by other discrimination laws. However, it can be used when one of the other 'articles' (the specific principles) of the Act applies, such as the right to 'respect for private and family life'.

Rights under the Act can only be used against a public authority (such as the police or a local council) and not a private company. However, court decisions on discrimination will generally have to take into account what the Human Rights Act says.

The main articles within this Act are:

- Article 2: Right to life
- Article 3: Freedom from torture and inhuman or degrading treatment
- Article 4: Freedom from slavery and forced labour
- Article 5: Right to liberty and security
- Article 6: Right to a fair trial
- Article 7: No punishment without law
- Article 8: Respect for your private and family life, home and correspondence
- Article 9: Freedom of thought, belief and religion
- Article 10: Freedom of expression
- Article 11: Freedom of assembly and association
- Article 12: Right to marry and start a family
- Article 13: If people's rights are violated they are able to access effective remedy. This means they can take their case to court to seek a judgment
- Article 14: Protection from discrimination in respect of these rights and freedoms

Equality Act 2010

From 1 October 2010, The Equality Act 2010 legally protects people from discrimination in the workplace and in wider society. It replaced previous anti-discrimination laws with a single act, making the law easier to understand and interpret. The Equality Act strengthens protection in some situations and also sets out the different ways in which it is unlawful to treat someone.

The nine main pieces of previous legislation that merged to create the Equality Act are:

- The Equal Pay Act 1970
- The Sex Discrimination Act 1975
- The Race Relations Act 1976
- The Disability Discrimination Act 1995
- The Employment Equality (Religion or Belief) Regulations 2003
- The Employment Equality (Sexual Orientation) Regulations 2003
- The Employment Equality (Age) Regulations 2006
- The Equality Act 2006, Part 2
- The Equality Act (Sexual Orientation) Regulations 2007.

Equality Act provisions that came into force include:

- the basic framework of protection against direct and indirect discrimination
- protection against harassment and victimisation in services and public functions, work, education, associations and transport
- extended protection against indirect discrimination of disability
- making it unlawful to discriminate against, harass or victimise workers because of religion, or religious or similar philosophical belief.

Protection from Harassment Act (PHA) 1997

Harassment is defined as any form of unwanted or unwelcome behaviour (ranging from mildly unpleasant remarks to physical violence) that causes alarm or distress by a course of conduct on more than one occasion (note that it doesn't have to be the same course of conduct).

The PHA is the main criminal legislation dealing with harassment, including stalking, racial or religious motivation and certain types of anti-social behaviour such as playing loud music. Significantly, the PHA gives emphasis to the target's perception of the harassment rather than the perpetrator's alleged intent.

The General Data Protection Regulation (GDPR)

Effective from May 2018, the GDPR is a new set of rules which have been created to allow people greater control over their personal data and to produce simpler regulations for businesses to follow. This means both people and businesses can benefit from an economy that is increasingly based on digital technologies.

The introduction of GDPR is important because nearly every part of our lives now involves data. Think about posts that are made on social media and online shopping transactions, both actions generate personal data. Most services we use now collect and analyse our personal data, which is then stored by organisations. Because so much data is collected and stored, data breaches happen. This is when information is lost or stolen, usually by people with malicious intentions.

The GDPR dictates that organisations must ensure personal data is collected legally. Those responsible for collecting and managing data are required to protect it from misuse, and to respect the rights of data owners. People who fail to adhere to these terms will face penalties.

Racial and Religious Hatred Act 2006

The Racial and Religious Hatred Act 2006 makes inciting hatred against a person on the grounds of their religion an offence in England and Wales. The House of Lords passed amendments to the Bill that effectively limit the legislation to 'a person who uses threatening words or behaviour, or displays any written material which is threatening… if they intend thereby to stir up religious hatred.' This removes the abusive and insulting concept, and requires the intention – rather than just the possibility – of stirring up religious hatred.

Child Protection and Safeguarding

Safeguarding means keeping children, young persons and vulnerable adults safe from harm (physical or psychological distress or injury) and abuse (physical, sexual or emotional abuse or injury). The United Nations Convention on the Rights of the Child 1989 set out minimum standards for all children up to the age of 18.

There is no single piece of legislation that covers 'child protection' or 'safeguarding' in the UK, but instead a number of laws that are continually being amended, updated or revoked.

The Children's Act 1989 provides a comprehensive framework for the care and protection of children and centres on the welfare of children up to their 18th birthday. It defines parental responsibility and encourages partnership working with parents. Interagency co-operation is encouraged.

The Children's Act 2004 supplemented the 1989 Act and reinforced the message that all organisations working with children have a duty in helping to safeguard and promote the welfare of children.

Underpinned by the Children's Act 2004, 'Working Together to Safeguard Children 2015' is a government initiative that tries to address concerns about child protection and states that all agencies and individuals should aim to proactively safeguard and promote the welfare of children.

Discrimination and victimisation

Under current law, there are two main forms of discrimination: direct and indirect.

Direct discrimination

Direct discrimination occurs when someone is treated less favourably because of their sex, race or **disability**. With regard to employment, this could happen if an employer treats a job applicant or existing employee less favourably on the grounds of their sex, race or disability. In law, the applicable test is if someone would have been treated differently, or more favourably, had it not been for their sex, etc. This definition is expected to continue under future legislation.

An example of direct discrimination could be a woman of superior qualifications and experience being denied promotion in favour of a less experienced and less qualified man.

Indirect discrimination

Indirect discrimination occurs where the effect of certain requirements, conditions or practices imposed by an employer disproportionately disadvantages one group more than another. Courts tend to consider three factors:

- the number of people from a racial group or of one sex that can meet the job criteria is considerably smaller than the rest of the population

- the criteria cannot actually be justified by the employer as being a real requirement of the job, so an applicant who could not meet the criteria could still do the job as well as anyone else

- because the person cannot comply with these criteria, they have actually suffered in some way (this may seem obvious, but a person cannot complain unless they have lost out in some way).

With cases of indirect discrimination, employers may argue that there may be discrimination, but that it is actually required for the job. For example, one individual claimed indirect discrimination on religious grounds against his employer as he was requested to shave off his beard. The court agreed that discrimination had been applied, but as the employer was a factory involved in food preparation, the particular case was rejected on the grounds of hygiene.

Disability discrimination

Disability discrimination relies on the same basic principles, but the complainant must be treated less favourably due to their disability. A person has a disability if they have a physical or mental impairment that has a substantial and long-term effect on their ability to carry out normal everyday activities.

Victimisation

This is where an employee is singled out for using their workplace complaints procedures or exercising their legal rights: for example, making a complaint of discrimination or giving evidence and information on behalf of another employee who has brought proceedings for discrimination.

Key term

Disability – a physical or mental impairment that has a substantial and long-term effect on a person's ability to carry out normal everyday activities

Key term

Genuine Occupational Requirements – where an employer can demonstrate that there is a genuine identified need for someone of a specific race or gender to the exclusion of others (for example, a film company needs an Indian actor for a film set in India, or a modelling agency needs a woman to model female clothes)

Positive discrimination and positive action

Positive discrimination occurs when someone is selected to do a job purely on the basis of their gender or race, and not on their ability to do the job. This is illegal under both the Sex Discrimination Act and the Race Relations Act and is generally unlawful other than for what are called '**Genuine Occupational Requirements**'.

Positive action is activity to increase the numbers of men, women or minority ethnic groups in a workforce where they have been shown to be under-represented. This may be in proportion to the total employed by the employer or in relation to the profile of the local population.

An example of positive action might be carefully targeted advertising and courses to develop the careers of those from under-represented groups who are already employed by an organisation. Positive action is legal and is designed to help employers achieve a more balanced workforce.

Summary

1. Name the three sources that are imposed on employers and employees with regards principal rights and obligations.
2. What Act aims to protect disabled people and disability discrimination?
3. What does the Data Protection Act say must be done to ensure information is handled properly?

3. Requirements for organising the provision and storage of required resources

By now you should have gained an insight into what needs to be considered when planning an installation.

The key factors you need to remember are:

- interpreting the installation specification and work programme to identify the exact resource requirements for the work to be undertaken
- interpreting the schedule to confirm that the materials available are correct, fit for purpose, in the correct quantity and suitable for the work to be completed efficiently and to cost
- using the correct storage and transportation requirements for all work, materials, tools and equipment
- following procedures to ensure the safe and effective storage of materials, tools and equipment by:
  - ensuring that deliveries are allocated suitable times and access arrangements
  - ensuring that you have suitable staff available to receive deliveries
  - designating suitable storage areas for plant, materials, waste, flammable liquids, gases and other substances
  - not storing things where they could prove to be an obstruction
  - carefully storing easily damaged materials and equipment (considering temperatures, and ingress of moisture and dust if so required)
  - making sure that storage arrangements are secure.

Working life

In the refurbishment task in the previous Working life feature on page 165, you and a colleague are tasked with ensuring all materials are securely stored on site. This is to ensure they are readily available and accessible when required. All equipment is delivered at ground level.

- Explain what you need to consider to ensure everyone is fully supplied with materials at the correct time in the programme.
- Will any specialist equipment be required to move the stored material to the points of installation?
- How will you store the equipment materials to ensure breakages are kept to a minimum?

Getting ready for assessment

EAL	City & Guilds
For this unit you will need to complete the following assessments: • 45 question multiple choice online exam covering units 03 and 04. • 1 centre marked EAL design project(04a) covering units 03 and 04 criteria not covered in the exam.	For this unit you will need to complete the following assessments: • Multiple choice online exam. • Task A centre marked planning project.

▶ Preparing for this assessment:

- For EAL this unit will only form a small part of the 03/04 exam and project.
- The topics covered in the exam will not appear in the project. This will help break the unit down and make it easier to revise and ultimately understand.
- Your on-site experience will help in this unit as you will recognise things that have been done on-site.
- When you answer questions on the projects make sure you are clear in your answers and include all key words that you think the assessor will be looking for. These will most likely be in the learning outcomes or the unit criteria.
- Instead of thinking about what is happening during the installation, remember this unit focuses on what needs to be completed or taken into consideration before work starts.
- If you are allowed to use resources for the projects, this book would be a good start as well as the internet or study notes. Remember though do not directly copy any work and claim it as your own!

▶ Worked examples

This section will help you to understand some of the key concepts in this chapter. The answers show some of the best practice, and supply guidance to help you understand the reasons behind each of these concepts.

A. There are two main categories for sources of information, what are these?

The two main categories for sources of information are:

1. Functional information – this can include information such as user instructions, including when your professional expertise may be called on to advise a customer.

2. Technical information – this can include information such as; installation and equipment specifications, manufacturers date and instructions or test information.

B. Diagrams and drawings are an important part of planning a job as without these we may not know any dimension or know what something is meant to look like. Name seven different types of diagrams and drawings that could be used and describe how these could be used.

- Block Diagrams – Used to relate information about a circuit without giving details of components or the way they are connected.

> Remember this information may be portrayed in various formats, it may not always be on a piece of paper it may be that you must provide information verbally or by showing the customer how they would actually physically do something.

- Circuit Diagram – Uses symbols to represent all the circuit components and shows how they are connected.
- Schematic Diagrams – These are used to show how the circuit is meant to work.
- Wiring Diagrams – These show the physical layout of the circuit and are used to help the electrician install the cables and know the correct connections.
- Assembly Drawings – Used to show how the individual part of a product fit together.
- Layout Drawings – Used to show where everything must go on the job. Each item will be shown as a symbol and a scale will be used with this drawing.
- Record Drawings – These are used to record what has been fitted which will help with fault finding and maintenance of equipment.

Sample answers

If you are shown a picture in the exam and asked to say which one of the above it is, there are some easier ways to remember some of them.

1. *A block diagram will do what it says and just look like a load of blocks in a certain order.*

2. *A circuit diagram and a wiring diagram will be similar in some ways but if you struggle to recognise the difference remember a circuit diagram will use symbols and a wiring diagram will show how the installation is meant to look like, so will show specific connections.*

3. *A Schematic diagram is easy to recognise as the lines will go from the top to the bottom of the page with the components in-between.*

4. *Assembly drawings will look like the instruction drawings you receive with a certain well known flat pack shop.*

5. *A layout drawing will show the outline of the building or room and the way in which doors will open, symbols for these can be found in the on-site-guide.*

C. The development of a team is very important to how smoothly a job will run. What are the four main stages of team development?

1. Forming – when a team has just come together. At this stage they will not know each other and will rely strongly on a leader. The team's roles at this stage may be unclear.

2. Storming – this is when the members of the team may compete to secure positions. At this stage the leader receives challenges, the task becomes clearer, small groups may form and the leader will be required to become more of a coach.

3. Norming – this is a more peaceful stage where agreements are reached, roles become clearer and big decisions are made by the whole team. The team will begin to enjoy each other's company and may even socialise together, with leadership roles being shared.

4. Performing – there is now little or no input from the leader, there is no need for instruction, members will look after each other and disagreements will be dealt with positively.

Think about what happened when you first started your training. You will probably have been put into a group of similar learners. Over time you will recognise when some of these stages will have been reached as a group, when you work together.

Check your knowledge

1. Which of the following would not usually be included in a site visitors book?

   a) Date

   b) Name

   c) Time out

   d) Car colour

2. Which of the following documents is mainly used for alterations to the original contract?

   a) Day work sheet

   b) Variation order

   c) Time sheet

   d) Purchase order

3. Critical path networks allow site managers to see:

   a) How much the contract will cost

   b) The length of time tasks takes

   c) The profitability of the contract

   d) The number of suppliers utilised

4. What diagram would show how a circuit works and is mainly used for larger more complicated systems?

   a) Circuit diagram

   b) Wiring diagram

   c) Block diagram

   d) Schematic diagram

5. The organisation with the main responsibility for the agreement of an electricians national working conditions and wage rates is called the:

   a) JIB

   b) HSE

   c) NICEIC

   d) PASMA

6. What is the name of the person who designs the appearance and construction of a building so that is fulfils its proper function?

   a) Client

   b) Clerk of works

   c) Architect

   d) Employer

7. The person responsible for managing and controlling costs for building projects is called:

   a) The client

   b) The architect

   c) The clerk of works

   d) The quantity surveyor

8. When building a working relationship with a customer which one of the following is something you should not do?

   a) Bad mouth your employer

   b) Be honest

   c) Be neat and tidy

   d) Show enthusiasm

9. Which one of these is not a normal method of instruction?

   a) Visual

   b) Reading

   c) Demonstration

   d) Written examination

10. Team development can best be described using which steps of order?

    a) Form-storm-norm-perform

    b) Form -norm-perform-advance

    c) Form-storm- perform-norm

    d) Storm-form-norm-perform

CHAPTER 3
Electrical scientific principles and technologies

As part of being a competent electrician, you need to know how and why things work. Therefore, the purpose of this chapter is to look at the principles of mathematics, electrical science and electronics necessary to support the installation and maintenance of electrical systems and equipment.

This chapter will cover the following learning outcomes.

1. Mathematical principles appropriate to electrical installation, maintenance and design work.

2. Units of measurement used in electrical installation, maintenance and design work.

3. Basic mechanics and the relationship between force, work, energy and power.

4. The relationship between resistance, resistivity, voltage, current and power.

5. Fundamental principles which underpin the relationship between magnetism and electricity.

6. Types, applications and limitations of electronic components in electrical systems and equipment.

7. Electrical supply systems.

8. How different electrical properties can affect electrical circuits, systems and equipment.

9. The operating principles and applications of DC machines and AC motors.

10. The operating principles of electrical components.

11. The principles and applications of electrical lighting systems.

12. The principles and applications of electrical heating.

1 and 2. Units of measurement and mathematical principles appropriate to electrical installation, maintenance and design work

It is impossible to know what people are talking about unless you understand the language they are speaking. In science and engineering, mathematics is the language that is used to explain how things work. To work with all things electrical, we need to understand and be able to communicate using this universal language and therefore this section will cover the following topics:

- SI units: how we describe basic measurement quantities
- powers of 10: mega, pico and the decimal system
- basic rules: getting the right answer
- fractions and percentages: working with parts of the whole
- algebra: formulas for all
- indices: powers of anything
- transposition: re-arranging equations
- triangles and trigonometry: angles on reading
- the sines
- statistics: ways of showing data.

SI units

Imagine if each country had a different idea of how long a metre is, or how much beer you get in a pint. What if a kilogram in Leeds was different from one in London?

A common system for defining properties such as length, temperature and time is essential if people in different places are to work together.

Most countries have adopted an agreed international system of units for measuring different properties, known as the SI (Système Internationale) system. It has seven base units from which all other units are derived and a set of decimal prefixes to the unit names and symbols that may be used when specifying multiples and fractions of units.

Table 3.1 shows the seven base units.

Base unit	Symbol	Base quantity
metre	m	length
kilogram	kg	mass
second	s	time
ampere	A	electric current
kelvin	K	thermodynamic temperature
mole	mol	amount of substance
candela	cd	luminous intensity

Table 3.1: SI units

The most common derived units you will deal with are shown in Table 3.2.

Derived unit	Symbol	Derived quantity
hertz	Hz	frequency
newton	N	force, weight
pascal	Pa	pressure, stress
joule	J	energy, work, heat
watt	W	power
coulomb	C	electric charge or quantity of electricity
volt	V	voltage (electrical potential), electromotive force
farad	F	capacitance
ohm	Ω	resistance, impedance, reactance
siemens	S	electrical conductance
weber	Wb	magnetic flux
tesla	T	magnetic flux density
henry	H	inductance
degree Celsius	°C	temperature relative to 273.15 K
lumen	lm	luminous flux
lux	lx	illuminance

Table 3.2: Most common derived units

SI unit prefixes

Often we want to deal with quantities that are much larger or smaller than the base units. If we could only use the base units, the numbers would become clumsy and it would be easy to make mistakes. For example, the diameter of a human hair is about 0.0009 m and the average distance of the Earth from the Sun is around 150 000 000 000 m.

To make life easier, we can alter the symbols (and the quantities they represent) by adding another symbol in front of them (known as a prefix) and these represent the base units multiplied or divided by one thousand, one million, etc. Table 3.3 shows the most common ones:

Multiplier	Name	Symbol prefix	As a power of 10
1 000 000 000 000	Tera	T	1×10^{12}
1 000 000 000	Giga	G	1×10^{9}
1 000 000	Mega	M	1×10^{6}
1 000	kilo	k	1×10^{3}
1	unit		
0.001	milli	m	1×10^{-3}
0.000 001	micro	μ	1×10^{-6}
0.000 000 001	nano	n	1×10^{-9}
0.000 000 000 001	pico	p	1×10^{-12}

Table 3.3: Common prefixes

Here are some common examples of using the prefixes with the unit symbol:

- km (kilometre = one thousand metres)
- mm (millimetre = one thousandth of a metre)
- MW (megawatt = one million watts)
- μs (microsecond = one millionth of a second).

Later in this unit you will see SI units applied to a wide range of electrical variables:

- resistance
- resistivity
- power
- frequency
- current
- voltage
- energy
- impedance
- inductance and inductive reactance
- capacitance and capacitive reactance
- power factor
- actual power
- reactive power
- apparent power.

Identify and apply appropriate mathematical concepts

Basic rules

Unless we all carry out calculations using the same basic rules, we will all get different answers to the same question. Try working out the sum in the example.

Example

Work out the answer to the following sum.

$(42 \times 4) + (6 \div 3) - 2 = ?$

We asked three apprentices. Andy says it's 56, but Mo says it's 420, and Ali says it's 168.

So who's right? What do you think?

The problem is that each apprentice followed their own set of rules.

Andy simply worked from left to right:	Mo worked from right to left:	Ali did the multiplications first, then the divisions, then the addition and subtraction:
$42 \times 4 = 168$	$3 - 2 = 1$	$42 \times 4 = 168$
$168 + 6 = 174$	$6 \div 1 = 6$	$6 \div 3 = 2$
$174 \div 3 = 58$	$4 + 6 = 10$	$168 + 2 = 170$
$58 - 2 = \mathbf{56}$	$10 \times 42 = \mathbf{420}$	$170 - 2 = \mathbf{168}$

Mathematics needs rules, and we need to know them if we are to get the correct answers. The three main ones are as follows.

Basic Rule 1

'All numbers are positive unless told otherwise.'

All numbers are either positive or negative (except 0, of course). Since most things we deal with are positive numbers, we don't usually bother to put a positive sign (+) sign in front of them, but we must put a minus sign (–) in front of any negative numbers.

Basic Rule 2

'Like signs add, unlike signs subtract.'

For example:

$4 + (+5) = 4 + 5 = \ 9$ (Like signs add)

$4 + (–5) = 4 – 5 = –1$ (Unlike signs subtract)

$4 – (+5) = 4 – 5 = –1$ (Unlike signs subtract)

$4 – (–5) = 4 + 5 = \ 9$ (Like signs add)

The same applies when multiplying and dividing: 'Like signs give positive results, unlike signs give negative results.'

For example:

$+4 \times -5 = -20$ (Unlike signs give negative results)

$-4 \times +5 = -20$ (Unlike signs give negative results)

$-4 \times -5 = 20$ (Like signs give positive results)

$20 \div +5 = 4$ (Like signs give positive results)

$-20 \div +5 = -4$ (Unlike signs give negative results)

$20 \div -5 = -4$ (Unlike signs give negative results)

$-20 \div -5 = 4$ (Like signs give positive results)

Basic Rule 3

'BODMAS rules!'

BODMAS is what we call an '**acronym**' and BODMAS represents the order in which we must tackle a calculation.

This is where BODMAS comes in to help you, as it stands for:

Brackets **O**ther operations **D**ivision **M**ultiplication **A**ddition **S**ubtraction

So the order you should do your calculations in is:

- **B**rackets (*Always calculate what's in them first*)

- **O**ther operations (*Such as powers or square roots*)

- **D**ivision and **M**ultiplication (*Start on the left and work them out in the order that you find them*)

- **A**ddition and **S**ubtraction (*When only addition and subtraction are left in the sum work them out in the order you find them, starting from the left of the sum and working towards the right*)

In BODMAS, division and multiplication have the same priority, as do addition and subtraction. Let's look at some examples.

Key term

Acronym – an abbreviation of several words in such a way that the abbreviation itself forms a pronounceable word (e.g. BODMAS); this often helps you to remember a topic

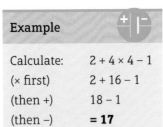

Example	
Calculate:	$2 + 4 \times 4 - 1$
(× first)	$2 + 16 - 1$
(then +)	$18 - 1$
(then −)	**= 17**

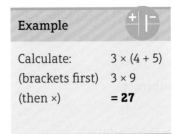

Example	
Calculate:	$3 \times (4 + 5)$
(brackets first)	3×9
(then ×)	**= 27**

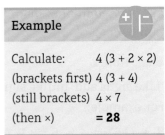

Example	
Calculate:	$4 (3 + 2 \times 2)$
(brackets first)	$4 (3 + 4)$
(still brackets)	4×7
(then ×)	**= 28**

We'll show this final example step-by-step to confirm the process.

Example	
Calculate	$(4-2)^2 \times 2 \times 5$
(brackets first)	$(4-2)^2 \times 2 \times 5$
	$2^2 \times 2 \times 5$
(next operations)	$2^2 \times 2 \times 5$
	$4 \times 2 \times 5$
(next × work L to R)	$4 \times 2 \times 5$
(next × work L to R)	8×5
(next ×)	8×5
Answer	**40**

Having looked at these examples, we should note two further things:

When there is a number in front of the brackets, but no operator (e.g. +, −, ×, ÷) after it, then a multiplication symbol is always assumed.

So for example, 5 (3 + 9) is the same as saying 5 × (3 + 9) where the result is 5 × 12 = 60.

In this example, you could also multiply all the numbers inside the bracket by the number outside, and then do the calculation.

In other words: 5 (3 + 9)

$$= (5 \times 3) + (5 \times 9)$$

$$= 15 + 45 = \mathbf{60}$$

Powers of 10

So far so good, but what happens when you want to do some arithmetic with several quantities?

For instance, speed is calculated by dividing the distance covered by the time taken. So an energetic spider might cover 1 m in 1 s, and its speed would therefore be 1 m/s (metre per second).

But how do we express the speed of a bullet that travels 3 km in 50 ms?

This is where an understanding of powers of 10 will help us.

When we write down any calculation, the position of the figures shows their size relative to the decimal point, e.g. units, tens, hundreds, thousands, etc. The purpose of the decimal point is to separate whole numbers from parts of numbers. Therefore, we can say 1.5 is 1 and 5 tenths, the same as one and a half.

As an example, the number 4123.4 tells us that we have:

Thousands	Hundred	Tens	Units	Decimal point	Tenths
4	1	2	3	.	4

We could also look at it like this.

Example	
The number 4123.4 means:	
4 times one thousand	4000.0
Plus 1 times one hundred	100.0
Plus 2 times ten	20.0
Plus 3 units	3.0
Plus 4 times one-tenth	0.4
Total	**4123.4**

In both the above examples we can see that going left from the decimal point, each column is 10 times greater than the previous one. Going right from the decimal point, each column is 10 times less or one-tenth of the previous one.

The example has included zeros to make sense of a column of figures, but extra zeros added does not change the number. 4123.4 is exactly the same as 4123.40 or 4123.400.

When adding, always line up the decimal points and each column when writing them down, then you are sure of adding the number of 10s in one number to the number of 10s in another number and so on.

It can help if you draw straight lines, which helps keep your calculations easy to understand when checking answers!

Let's look at adding 24.01 to 110

Here is another example.

Example	
	32 456.24
+	123.51
Total	**32 579.75**

The fact that each column is either ten times bigger or one-tenth of the previous column also makes it easy to multiply and divide by 10, as all you need to do is move all the digits one jump to the right to divide by 10, and one jump to the left to multiply by 10.

To multiply 123.4 by 10 (note the position of the decimal point) we move the decimal point one place to the right.

Therefore, 123.4 × 10 = 1234.0

Division sees the decimal point move in the other direction; so

$4321.0 \div 10 = 432.1$

4321.0 becomes 432.10

Similarly, multiplying or dividing by 100 means moving the decimal point two places to the left or right. Multiplying or dividing by 1000 then just means moving the decimal point three places to the left or right.

In other words, we are moving the same amount as there are zeros in the number:

10 = has one zero, therefore we move the decimal point one place

1000 = has three zeros, therefore we move the decimal point three times

6789.345×100 (00)	=	6789.345	=	$678\,934.5$
$6789.345 \div 1000$ (000)	=	6789.345	=	$6.789\,345$

Other powers of numbers

We have a shorthand way of showing a number multiplied by itself.

For example 25, which is 5×5, can be written as 5^2, which we say as 'five to the power of two', or 'five squared'. (We call it 5 squared because we find the area of a square from its two dimensions L × W or 5 × 5).

We can multiply any number by other powers. So for example, 125 which is $5 \times 5 \times 5$, can be written as 5^3, which we say is '5 to the power of 3' or '5 cubed'. (We call it 5 cubed because we find the volume of a cube from its 3 dimensions L × W × D or 5 × 5 × 5).

The power can take any value, for example

$10\,000 = 10 \times 10 \times 10 \times 10 = 10^4$

$1\,000\,000 = 10 \times 10 \times 10 \times 10 \times 10 \times 10 = 10^6$

We can also have negative powers. If there is a minus sign in front of the power, this represents our number divided by the power.

So $\quad 10^{-1} = 1 \div 10^1 \quad (1 \div 10) \quad = 0.1$

And $\quad 10^{-3} = 1 \div 10^3 \quad (1 \div 1000) = 0.001$

All scientific calculators have a 'powers' button for working with large powers. Figure 3.1 shows the button that is normally used.

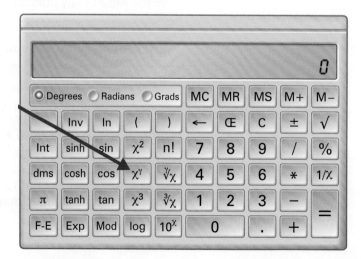

Figure 3.1: Calculator

Try it with a calculation that you know the answer of (e.g. 2^4) to check that you can use your calculator correctly.

To find 7^8 we would use the following key sequence:

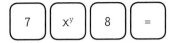

The answer should be **5 764 801**

Multiplying and dividing with powers

When we multiply two numbers with powers together, we add the powers.

For example, we know that $5^3 = 5 \times 5 \times 5 = 125$, therefore $5^3 \times 5^3$ will be $125 \times 125 = \textbf{15 625}$

Adding the powers we get $5^{3+3} = 5^6$ which also equals **15 625**.

Although the powers can be different, i.e. $5^3 \times 5^2$ it must be the same number (in this case 5) that we are applying the powers to. This method would not work for $4^2 \times 5^2$.

When it comes to division we subtract the powers.

For example, we know that 3^3 is 27 and that 3^2 is 9 and that $27 \div 9 = 3$.

Therefore, when written as powers this would be $3^{3-2} = 3^1$

When we have a number raised to the power of 1, it is simply the original number; in other words, 3^1 is just 3.

However, when you see any number raised to the power of 0, then the result is always 1.

This can be explained by looking at what happens when we divide a number by itself.

Example

$5 \div 5 = 1$ (as 5 goes into 5 once)
Having established that 5^1 means 5, we could also write this as $5^1 \div 5^1 = 1$
Remember that when dividing we subtract the powers
So we can also write $5^{1-1} = 5^0$
So the value of any number to the power of 0 will be the number 1

Most commonly we see powers of 10 used to express very large numbers.

Example

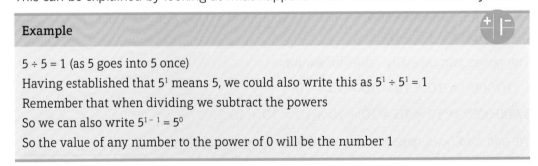

$$123\,456.0 \quad = \quad 12\,345.6 \times 10 \qquad \text{or} \qquad 12\,345.6 \times 10^1$$
$$= \quad 1234.56 \times 100 \qquad \text{or} \qquad 1234.56 \times 10^2$$
$$= \quad 1.234\,56 \times 10\,000 \quad \text{or} \qquad 1.234\,56 \times 10^5$$

Note: Every time the decimal point moves a place to the left, the power goes up by 1.

The same can be done for very small numbers.

Example

$$0.000\,123 = 0.001\,23 \times \frac{1}{10} \quad \text{or} \quad 0.001\,23 \times 10^{-1}$$

$$\qquad\quad = 1.23 \times \frac{1}{1000} \quad \text{or} \quad 1.23 \times 10^{-4}$$

It is important to understand that in all the previous examples, the value of the numbers did not change, only the way we wrote them down.

In science we can use any power, but in engineering we normally use only powers of 10 in multiples of 3, e.g. 10^{-3}, 10^3, 10^6 and we do this because they match the prefixes we use such as milli, kilo or Mega.

If you look back to Table 3.3, you should now be able to see how the powers of ten relate to them:

Mega (M) = 1 000 000 times, which is the same as 10^6

micro (μ) = 0.000 001 times, or 10^{-6}

So, just how fast was that speeding bullet?

Well... to recap, we said it was travelling 3 km in 50 ms.

We also said that we calculate speed by using the following formula:

$$\text{Speed} = \frac{\text{Distance travelled}}{\text{Time taken}}$$

3 km = 3×10^3 m ... in other words 3000 m

And 50 ms = 50×10^{-3} s ... in other words 0.05 s

So the speed of the bullet is:

$\frac{3\,\text{km}}{50\,\text{ms}}$ which we can write as $\frac{3 \times 10^3}{50 \times 10^{-3}}$ which gives us

$$\frac{3000\,\text{m}}{0.05\,\text{s}} = \textbf{60\,000 m/s}$$

Our answer could also be written as 60×10^3 m/s which we could also say as 60 km/s.

It is important to practise using these different ways of expressing numbers as, although a calculator is a great help, it is easy to make a mistake. Being comfortable with numbers and always being able to check that the result looks correct is very useful.

Fractions

We often need to do calculations with parts of a whole unit and so far we have used the decimal system for this. However, another method is to use fractions.

A fraction is simply the result of dividing something (the whole thing) into smaller, equal parts.

Consider a cake that hasn't been cut up and so we have the whole thing. There is one part available and we've got it.

However, you wish to cut it into 4 equal pieces and so divide the whole thing into 4 parts.

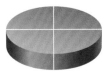

If we do this and then put one piece aside, that piece (shown in blue) will be one quarter of the original cake. That leaves three pieces remaining of the original 4 that made up the whole cake.

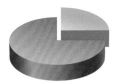

Our small piece of cake is one bit out of the 4 bits that were available, and we would write it as:

$\frac{1}{4}$ one part out of four available. This leaves 3 parts out of four left, in order words $\frac{3}{4}$.

The same blue piece of cake could also be described with decimals as 0.25 of the cake; it doesn't make any difference to the size of the piece. Sometimes we use fractions, sometimes decimals, it often depends on which is easiest.

Adding and subtracting fractions

To become an electrician you will need to know how to handle arithmetic involving different fractions.

For example, how do you add

$\frac{1}{4} + \frac{3}{7} = ?$

So, how do we add quarters to sevenths?

We need to express each of the two fractions with the same common denominator (the number under the line) so we can add like to like.

So, to add or subtract fractions, follow these steps:

1. Choose a new common denominator (the number under the line) for both fractions. To do this, we find the lowest possible number that both denominators will go into. Quite often the easiest method is to multiply the two numbers together, in this **4 × 7 = 28**.

$$\frac{1}{4} + \frac{3}{7}$$

(28)

2. Now change each fraction into values of the new common denominator. We do this by multiplying the top part of each fraction (the numerator) by the number of times that the original denominator divides into our new common denominator. So, in our example, in the first fraction $\left(\frac{1}{4}\right)$, 4, goes into 28 seven times, so we need to multiply the top of our first fraction (1) by 7. For the second fraction $\left(\frac{3}{7}\right)$, because 7 goes into 28 four times, we multiply the top of our fraction (3) by 4.

$$\frac{1}{4} + \frac{3}{7}$$

$$28$$

Now our sum will look like this:

$\frac{7 + 12}{28}$ which gives us $\frac{19}{28}$

3. One last step might be needed. If the numerator is bigger than the denominator, this means there's more than one whole thing. It is correctly called an improper fraction.

For example $\frac{3}{2}$ means you have 'three halves' which you would normally say was 'one and a half'.

When this happens, we simply find how many times the denominator will go into the numerator (this gives us the amount of whole numbers we have) and then what's left becomes the numerator (top number) of the fractional part.

For example $\frac{29}{12}$

12 goes into 29 twice, with 5 left over, so this is $2\frac{5}{12}$ as a mixed number.

Multiplying fractions

Multiplying fractions is easier than adding and subtracting. You simply multiply all the top numbers together to get a new numerator and then multiply all the bottom ones together to get a new denominator.

So, for example: $\frac{1}{4} \times \frac{3}{7}$ becomes $\frac{1 \times 3}{4 \times 7} = \frac{3}{28}$

And $\frac{3}{4} \times \frac{4}{5}$ becomes $\frac{12}{20} = \frac{3}{5}$

Dividing fractions

Dividing fractions is nearly as easy. First turn the second fraction upside down and then treat the problem as though it was a multiplication.

So for example:

$\frac{1}{4} \div \frac{3}{7}$ becomes $\frac{1}{4} \times \frac{7}{3} = \frac{7}{12}$

And

$\frac{1}{2} \div \frac{1}{4}$ becomes $\frac{1}{2} \times \frac{4}{1} = \frac{4}{2} = 2$

Percentages

Percentages are based upon a fraction where we assume that the whole thing has 100 parts to it. The name comes from the Latin word 'Centum', meaning 100 – think of a 'century' break in snooker, or the number of American 'cents' in a dollar and you'll see it's still being used within words today.

Per cent means parts out of a hundred, which means that 1 per cent (%) is one part out of a hundred. We can use a grid of squares to show this.

1	2	3	4	5	6	7	8	9	10
11	12	13	14	15	16	17	18	19	20
21	22	23	24	25	26	27	28	29	30
31	32	33	34	35	36	37	38	39	40
41	42	43	44	45	46	47	48	49	50
51	52	53	54	55	56	57	58	59	60
61	62	63	64	65	66	67	68	69	70
71	72	73	74	75	76	77	78	79	80
81	82	83	84	85	86	87	88	89	90
91	92	93	94	95	96	97	98	99	100

Our green square is one out of the 100 available, in other words $\frac{1}{100}$ or 1%.

The blue row has 10 squares: in other words, 10 out of the 100 available, or $\frac{10}{100}$ or 10%.

1	2	3	4	5	6	7	8	9	10
11	12	13	14	15	16	17	18	19	20
21	22	23	24	25	26	27	28	29	30
31	32	33	34	35	36	37	38	39	40
41	42	43	44	45	46	47	48	49	50
51	52	53	54	55	56	57	58	59	60
61	62	63	64	65	66	67	68	69	70
71	72	73	74	75	76	77	78	79	80
81	82	83	84	85	86	87	88	89	90
91	92	93	94	95	96	97	98	99	100

In this second grid, the orange squares make up 76 of the 100 available: in other words, 76%.

Hopefully, by looking at these examples, you can see that fractions and percentages are simply different ways of expressing the same thing. If we introduce decimals, we should be able to see how it all fits together – something often referred to as 'number bonding'.

Table 3.4 demonstrates this by showing two common fractions and how they link to decimals and percentages.

Fraction	Said as	Meaning	Calculator	Decimal	Observation	Alternative fraction	Meaning	Percentage (%)	Calculator again	Decimal
$\frac{1}{2}$	One half	The whole has been divided into two parts and we've got one of them.	key 1 ÷ 2	0.5	If the whole has 100 parts, then we have 50 of them.	$\frac{50}{100}$	We have 50 parts out of 100.	50	key 50 ÷ 100	0.5
$\frac{3}{4}$	Three quarters	The whole has been divided into four parts and we've got three of them.	key 3 ÷ 4	0.75	If the whole has 100 parts, then we have 75 of them.	$\frac{75}{100}$	We have 75 parts out of 100.	75	key 75 ÷ 100	0.75

Table 3.4: Linking fractions to decimals and percentages

If someone says they are 100 per cent happy, we can assume they are completely or wholly happy. In other words, we are saying that the whole thing has 100 parts to it.

We can say 100%; 100 parts out of the 100 available; 100 divided by 100 equals 1; the whole thing – they all mean the same thing.

Let's look at some calculations with percentages.

Example 1

What is 35% of £18 000?

$\frac{35}{100} \times 18\,000$ gives us 0.35 × 18 000 = **£6300**

Or we could say:

If percentages mean assuming that the 'whole thing' has 100 parts to it, then £18 000 (the whole thing in this example) has 100 parts to it.

This would mean that if we divide £18 000 by 100 we will know what one hundredth, or in other words 1%, of £18 000 is.

£18 000 ÷ 100 = £180

Now we know what 1% is (£180), we can find 35% by simply multiplying £180 by 35, which comes to **£6300**.

We can very quickly check this without the use of a calculator.

35% is made up of 3 × 10% plus 5%

10% of £18 000 is one tenth of £18 000, so divide £18 000 by 10 and you get £1800. We need three of these (because 3 tenths is 30%).

5% is half of 10%, which is £1800 ÷ 2 or £900.

So, 3 × £1800 (3 × 18 comes to 54) must therefore come to £5400.

Now add our 1 × £900 to £5400 and we have a grand total of **£6300**.

And now to introduce one final skill…approximation or, in other words, a rough check.

We know that 75% is three quarters, 50% is a half and 33.3% is one third.

A third of £18 000 (dividing 18 000 by 3) comes to £6000.

As we know that 33% is just under the 35% we are looking for, the real answer must be slightly larger than £6000 and it is at £6300.

So, remember approximation. It can be a very useful tool when checking examination answers.

Example 2

I have a restaurant bill of £72 and want to leave the staff a 10% tip. How much will this be?

10% is 10 ÷ 100 which gives us a tenth, or as a decimal 0.1.

0.1 × £72 is **£7.20**

Again, we don't need a calculator.

10% of £72 is one tenth of £72 and to find a tenth we divide by ten.

To divide by ten we move the decimal point from its place at the end of £72 (£72.00), one place to the left, giving us £7.20.

Example 3

At the beginning of December, you notice that a store has increased the price of a Blu-ray player by 5% to make a bigger Christmas profit. However, at the beginning of January there is a sale in the store. All unsold items, including the Blu-ray player are now labelled 5% off. Would you now be paying the same, more, or less than if you had bought the item in November?

As we aren't given any actual numbers in this question, simply choose an easy one to work with and then apply the question accordingly.

Let's assume that the Blu-ray player cost £200 in November.

In December, the store increased the price by 5%.

5% is half of 10%, 10% of £200 would be £20 and therefore 5% must be £10.

Therefore, the December price must be £210.

Then in January, the store sale offered 5% off the advertised price.

Remember that the advertised price is now £210.

As before, 5% is half of 10% and 10% of £210 is £21; therefore 5% must be half of that, which is £10.50.

So, in January, the sale price works out as £210 – £10.50 = £199.50

We can see that you would actually pay slightly less if you bought the player in the January sale.

Algebra

People often think that algebra is very difficult, but it is actually just a way of writing down calculations without using specific numbers. Instead, we use letters or symbols to represent different quantities. Using algebra, we can write down relationships between different things, and then later we can replace the symbols with real numbers when we know them.

As a simple example, let's say we have 'x' girls in a class and 'y' boys in the same class. At the moment, it doesn't matter what numbers 'x' and 'y' represent. However, if someone asked you to find the total number of students in the class, which we can call 'z', then you know that you must add the total number of boys and girls together.

Written as an algebra equation this is $z = x + y$

If we are then told that x = 11 and y = 15, then by substituting the real numbers into the above equation, we can establish that z must = 26.

Rules for algebra

In algebra, we don't bother with the multiplication sign. So (D × E) × F is written as (DE)F.

In addition and multiplication, it doesn't matter which symbol comes first. So, D + E means exactly the same as E + D, and DE could be written as ED.

There are several ways of writing the same thing. So D(E + F) could be written as D × (E + F) or D(F + E). We could also write it as (D × E) + (D × F).

As another example $\frac{D}{E} + \frac{E}{F}$ by cancellation, is the same as saying $\frac{D}{F}$.

Here's an example to demonstrate some of these rules.

Example 1

Work out the value of the expression 8DE − 2EF + DEF when D = 1, E = 3 and F = 5.

We must do the multiplications first, so we'll rewrite the expression with '×' signs and brackets to show what we're going to do:

8 × D × E − 2 × E × F + D × E × F without brackets

8 × (D × E) − 2 × (E × F) + (D × E × F) with brackets

Now we replace the letters with the correct numbers:

8 × (1 × 3) − 2 × (3 × 5) + (1 × 3 × 5)

= 8 × (3) − 2 × (15) + (15)

= 24 − 30 + 15

= **9**

Indices

If you remember, a few pages ago we talked about some little numbers that were called 'powers'.

A power, or an index to use its proper name, is used when we want to multiply a number by itself several times. The plural of index is indices. In other words, powers and indices are one and the same thing. However, it would be wise to cover the topic in a slightly different way to make sure we fully understand it and other related concepts.

If we multiply two identical numbers together, say 5 and 5, the answer is 25 and the process is usually expressed as: 5 × 5 = 25

However, we could express the same calculation as: $5^2 = 25$

The upper ^{2} is referred to as the index and the number it is applied to, in this case the number 5, is called the base. We can therefore say that the index is the number of times that the base is written down with multiplication signs between them.

Using the example above, sometimes this is referred to as five raised to the power of two, and using this logic we can therefore say that 5^3 means five written down 3 times with multiplication signs between them. In other words:

$5 \times 5 \times 5 = 125 = 5^3$

Be careful – Do not make the mistake of thinking $5^3 = 5 \times 3$. It is not!

Some other examples of using indices are shown below.

Example 2

$3^3 = 3 \times 3 \times 3 = \mathbf{27}$ $8^3 = 8 \times 8 \times 8 = \mathbf{512}$ $6^2 = 6 \times 6 = \mathbf{36}$

A number by itself, say 4, actually has an index of 1, but this is not normally shown.

And how about multiplying two numbers together that both have indices?

Consider $4^2 \times 4^2$

This could be shown as $4 \times 4 \times 4 \times 4$ or as 4^4, which would mean that the indices ^{2} and ^{2} have simply been added together.

So the rule is: When multiplying numbers with indices simply add the indices together.

Here is an example to illustrate both points.

Example 3

$4 \times 4^2 = 4^1 \times 4^2$ $5 \times 5^3 \times 5^2 = 5^1 \times 5^3 \times 5^2$

Add the indices

$= 4^3$ $= 5^6$

$= 4 \times 4 \times 4$ $= 5 \times 5 \times 5 \times 5 \times 5 \times 5$

$= \mathbf{64}$ $= \mathbf{15\,625}$

Let us now move on to the situation where we are dividing numbers that have indices.

Example 4

$\dfrac{2^5}{2^3} = \dfrac{2 \times 2 \times 2 \times 2 \times 2}{2 \times 2 \times 2}$ which if we check by multiplying out is $\dfrac{(32)}{(8)}$

If we cancel out the twos:

$\dfrac{2^5}{2^3} = \dfrac{\mathbf{2 \times 2} \times 2 \times 2 \times 2}{\cancel{2} \times \cancel{2} \times \cancel{2}} = 2 \times 2$

This leaves us with,

$2 \times 2 = \mathbf{2^2}$ **or 4** ($32 \div 8$ does indeed equal 4)

So the rule is: When dividing numbers with indices simply subtract the indices.

Example 5

$\dfrac{5^3 \times 1}{5^2}$ As anything multiplied by 1 remains the same, we could instead say $\dfrac{5^3}{5^2}$

This means that the indices can now be subtracted. Therefore, subtracting the indices (i.e. $3 - 2$) gives us:

$\dfrac{5^3}{5^2} = 5^1$ and as we don't write the index of 1, our answer is **5**.

In the above example we subtracted the indices ($3 - 2$).

But 3 subtract 2 ($3 - 2$) can also be written as 3 add -2.

If you remember, the addition of indices belongs to multiplication of numbers with indices. So from this we can see that 5^3 divided by 5^2 will actually be the same as 5^3 multiplied by 5^{-2}.

We can further say that: $\frac{1}{5^2}$ is the same as $1 \times 5^2 = 5^{-2}$

Further examples of this could be:

$\frac{1}{4^3} = 4^{-3}$ and $\frac{1}{2^6} = 2^{-6}$

Where we can now see that indices can be moved above or below the line, but they will have an opposite value (i.e. 2^6 became 2^{-6}).

Example 6

$$\frac{5^6 \times 5^7 \times 5^{-3}}{5^4 \times 5^2} = \frac{5^{13} \times 5^{-3}}{5^6} = \frac{5^{10}}{5^6} = 5^{10} \times 5^{-6} = 5^4 = 5 \times 5 \times 5 \times 5 = \mathbf{625}$$

Transposition

Transposition is a method that uses the principles of mathematics to allow you to rearrange a formula or equation so that you can find an unknown quantity.

There is however one important rule that must always be followed ... **without fail!**

What you do to one side of the equation, you must do to the other side.

Let's work through an example.

Example 1

Transpose (rearrange) the following formula to make Y the subject (the one we want):

$X = Y + Z$

First, think of the equation as being a pair of scales and remember that each side of the scales (each side of the equals sign) must be balanced.

Second, when we want to remove something, we perform an opposite operation. In doing so, remember that if there is no + or – sign in front of a number, then the number is positive.

We have to find Y; so to get Y by itself, we must remove Z.

As Z has been added to Y we need to perform 'an opposite operation'.

We need to subtract Z from both sides of the equation to keep it balanced.

So: $X = Y + Z$ now becomes: $X - Z = Y + Z - Z$

As $+ Z - Z = 0$, you are left with: $\mathbf{X - Z = Y}$

Note that when something moves from one side of the equal sign to the other, it becomes the opposite value (+Z became –Z).

You can check your understanding of this new concept by using numbers instead of letters.

In our example   X = Y + Z   could become   8 = 6 + 2

When rearranged   X − Z = Y   would therefore be   8 − 2 = 6

Example 2

Transpose A = R − LS so that R is the subject of the equation.

To get R by itself, we need to get rid of LS. This is being subtracted from R, so we need to add it to both sides.

So: A + LS = R − LS + LS

Remember that −LS + LS cancels out.

By completing the calculation we have an answer of: **R = A + LS**

The previous examples showed how a formula made up of addition and subtraction can be changed around. Equally, we can view multiplication and division in much the same way. For example:

Example 3

Transpose the formula   V = I × R   to make I the subject.

We can see that I has been multiplied by R. Therefore, to leave I by itself, we must divide by R on both sides.

So V = **I** × R now becomes $\dfrac{V}{R} = \dfrac{\mathbf{I} \times R}{R}$

Cancel $\dfrac{V}{R} = \dfrac{\mathbf{I} \times R}{R}$ and we are left with an answer of: $\mathbf{I = \dfrac{V}{R}}$

Again, note that when something moves from one side of the equal sign to the other, it becomes the opposite value (V = I × R ended up as I = V ÷ R).

Here is another example:

Example 4

This equation describes how resistance is related to length, area and type of material in a conductor (you will come across this equation later in this section).

$R = \dfrac{\rho L}{A}$ Transpose to find L

First we need to get rid of the A.

As it is currently divided into ρL, we need to multiply both sides by A.

Therefore: $R = \dfrac{\rho L}{A}$

Becomes: $R \times A = \dfrac{\rho L \times A}{A}$

Giving us: R × A = ρL

We now need to get rid of the symbol ρ.

This is currently multiplying L, so we must divide by ρ on both sides.

Therefore: R × A = ρL

Becomes: $\dfrac{R \times A}{\rho} = \dfrac{\rho L}{\rho}$

The two ρ on the right side cancel.

Giving us: $\mathbf{\dfrac{R \times A}{\rho} = L}$

Triangles and trigonometry

There are areas of electrical science and even practical installation work where knowledge of triangles and trigonometry is very useful. This section covers some basic principles.

Angles

An angle is the size of the opening between two lines.

Both lines start at point O, and the length of the lines makes no difference to the angle. Even if line B was twice as long as line A, the angle between them would be the same.

If we rotate line A (with one end still fixed to point O) anticlockwise, the angle will get bigger. Eventually, it will be on top of line B, and the angle will be zero. We divide this complete turn into 360 parts, called degrees, represented by the symbol '°' after the number (e.g. 360°).

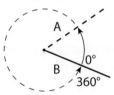

Figure 3.2 shows some common types of angle.

 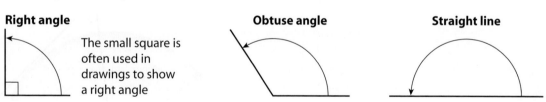

Acute angle   **Right angle**   **Obtuse angle**   **Straight line**

The small square is often used in drawings to show a right angle

Figure 3.2: Types of angle

Angles on a straight line

In the diagrams so far, you can see that we can think of a straight line as an angle of 180° (which is not surprising as there are 360° in a full circle).

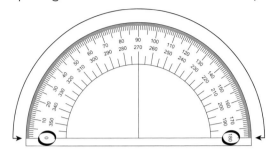

You can see this clearly on a protractor. Starting at one side and moving round, we end up at the 180° point.

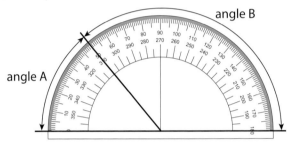

If we have two angles drawn on a straight line, then they must add up to 180°. In our diagram, angle A is 50°, and angle B is 130°, which add up to 180°.

Angle sum of a triangle

In any triangle there are three internal angles at the corners and these must add up to 180°. This means that, if we are given two of the angles, we can easily find the third one. For example, if one angle is 40° and another is 60° (40 + 60 = 100), then the third must be 80° (100 + 80 = 180).

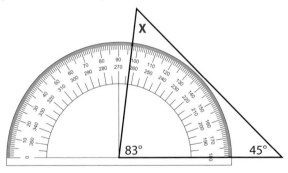

In this diagram, one angle is 83° the other is 45° and so the third, 'X', must be **52°**.

Triangles

There are five types of triangle as shown in Figure 3.3.

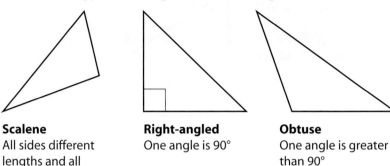
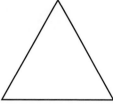

Scalene
All sides different lengths and all angles differ

Right-angled
One angle is 90°

Obtuse
One angle is greater than 90°

Isosceles
Two sides are the same length and two angles are the same

Equilateral
All sides are equal length and all angles are 60°

Figure 3.3: Types of triangle

This brings us to one of the most useful formulas that you will ever be given: one that is seen in everyday use. Its name is **Pythagoras' Theorem**.

Pythagoras' Theorem

Pythagoras' Theorem states that:

> *For a right-angled triangle, the square of the hypotenuse is equal to the sum of the squares on the other two sides.*

This means that if you know the length of two of the sides, you can find out the length of the third.

Let's have a look at the right-angled triangle in Figure 3.4.

We can see that the right angle (represented with a square in the corner) is like an arrowhead and it always points at the longest side, which is called the hypotenuse. For ease, let's call the hypotenuse side (A) and the other sides (B) and (C). Remember the formula:

$A^2 = B^2 + C^2$

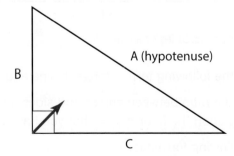

Figure 3.4: Right-angled triangle

We said that it could be used every day

Well, how do they get the sides of a building straight?

If you know that one side wall is 30 metres long and the other is 40 metres, then if you use Pythagoras' Theorem to work out the diagonal (hypotenuse) you can get both walls exactly straight by checking they form a right-angled triangle.

Using the formula:

$A^2 = B^2 + C^2$

$A^2 = 30^2 + 40^2$

$A^2 = 900 + 1600$

Therefore $A^2 = 2500$

Therefore $A = \sqrt{2500}$

Therefore $A = \mathbf{50\,m}$

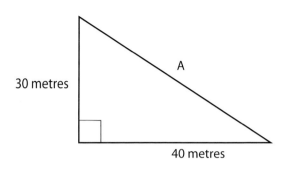

Trigonometry

Trigonometry is about the relationship between the angles and sides of triangles, and on the previous page we discovered that in a right-angled triangle, we call the long side the hypotenuse and the right angle 'points' at it. The names of the other two sides will depend on the angle that we have to find, or intend to use!

The side which is opposite the angle being considered is called the opposite, and the side which is next to the angle under consideration and the right angle is called the adjacent.

Well, if placed on to a drawing we would have the following and in the drawing, (Ø) is the angle to be considered.

So, think of it as being like a torch and the beam is shining on to the opposite side.

We already know that the longest side is the hypotenuse, so the one that is left must be the adjacent.

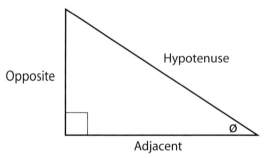

Figure 3.5: Sides of a triangle

The next step relates to the following terms: tangent, sine and cosine.

These are used to show the ratio between angles and sides and you choose which one you need depending upon the information that you have been given.

You need to know the following formulae:

$$\textbf{S}\text{ine } Ø = \frac{\textbf{O}\text{pposite}}{\textbf{H}\text{ypotenuse}} \qquad \textbf{C}\text{osine } Ø = \frac{\textbf{A}\text{djacent}}{\textbf{H}\text{ypotenuse}} \qquad \textbf{T}\text{angent } Ø = \frac{\textbf{O}\text{pposite}}{\textbf{A}\text{djacent}}$$

To help you remember them, try to remember the following name: **SOHCAHTOA**.

It's another mnemonic and represents the letters that we have highlighted in each formula below:

SOH (**S**ine = **O**pposite over **H**ypotenuse)

CAH (**C**osine = **A**djacent over **H**ypotenuse)

TOA (**T**angent = **O**pposite over **A**djacent)

Figure 3.6: Using a calculator for trigonometry

Let us have a look at some examples. Remember that the formula you will use will depend on the information that you have been given. Figure 3.6 shows the relevant keys on a calculator that you will need to use and which we refer to in the examples.

Example 1

From the diagram, what is the value of angle Ø?

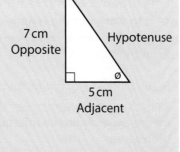

Because in this example we are given details about the opposite and adjacent sides, we will therefore use the tangent formula.

$$\text{Tangent } Ø = \frac{\text{Opposite}}{\text{Adjacent}}$$

$$\text{Tangent } Ø = \frac{7}{5} = 1.4$$

We have now found that the angle has a tangent of 1.4. Use your calculator to find the angle by pressing the (SHIFT) key and then the (TAN) key (which accesses the Tan⁻¹ function) then enter 1.4 (=).

The answer will be 54.562 which we will round up to become 54.5°.

Example 2

From the diagram, what is the value of angle Ø?

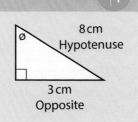

This time we have information about the opposite and hypotenuse and so we use the sine formula.

$$\text{Sine } Ø = \frac{\text{Opposite}}{\text{Hypotenuse}}$$

$$\text{Sine } Ø = \frac{3}{8} = 0.375$$

Use your calculator to find the angle by pressing the (SHIFT) key and then the (SIN) key (which accesses the Sin⁻¹ function) then enter 0.375 (=).

The answer will be 22.024, which we will round down to 22°.

Example 3

From the diagram, what is the value of angle Ø?

This time we have information about the adjacent and hypotenuse and so we use the cosine formula.

$$\text{Cosine } Ø = \frac{\text{Adjacent}}{\text{Hypotenuse}}$$

$$\text{Cosine } Ø = \frac{9}{11} = 0.81818$$

Now find the angle that has a cosine of 0.81818. Use your calculator to find the angle by pressing the (SHIFT) key and then the (COS) key (which accesses the Cos⁻¹ function) then enter 0.81818 (=).

The answer will be 35.1°.

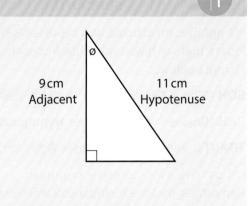

In the previous examples we were using trigonometry to find an angle. We can also use it to work out the length of a side of a triangle.

Example 4

In the following diagram, find the length of side **x**.

As in the previous examples, the formula that we use depends on the information that we have been given.

In this question, we have been told to find the length of side **x** and this is opposite the angle that we have been given.

We are also told that the adjacent side is 5 cm. Remember, if we are given details about the opposite and adjacent sides, then we use the Tangent formula.

$$\text{Tangent } 25° = \frac{\text{Opposite}}{\text{Adjacent}}$$

$$\text{Tangent } 25° = \frac{\text{Side } \mathbf{x}}{5}$$

We therefore now need to transpose the formula to make **x** the subject.

Doing so gives: **x** = Tangent 25° × 5 cm

Now using your calculator, press the (TAN) key, enter 25 and then (=). This will give you 0.4663.

Now multiply this by 5 and the answer should be 2.331 and so side **x** of the triangle is **2.33 cm** long.

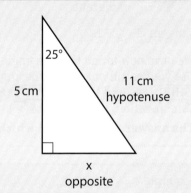

The area of a triangle

One last thing about triangles is how to calculate their area. Remember when you're looking at this that a right-angled triangle will be half the area of a rectangle.

The formula is: Area (A) = $\frac{1}{2}$ base × height   or $\frac{base × height}{2}$

Here's an example using both formulae, noting that the large triangle we are trying to find the area of effectively contains two right-angled triangles. An example is shown below.

Example 5

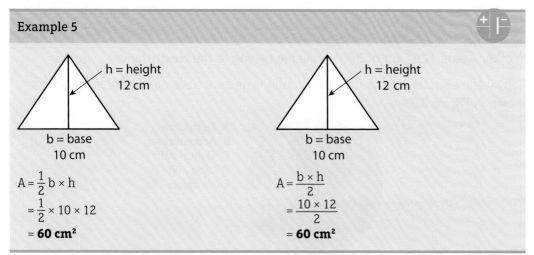

$A = \frac{1}{2} b \times h$

$= \frac{1}{2} \times 10 \times 12$

$= \textbf{60 cm}^2$

$A = \frac{b \times h}{2}$

$= \frac{10 \times 12}{2}$

$= \textbf{60 cm}^2$

Statistics

Charts

There are many ways to record and display **data** and in this section we will look at some of the basic techniques. We'll start with some data about an electrical company and then show how we can graphically represent the information.

Table 3.5 shows data that has been gathered about the workforce of an electrical contractor who employs a total of 40 people.

Key term

Data – factual information and statistics used as a basis for discussion, calculation or analysis

Type of staff	Ref code	Number employed	Percentage of total workforce (%)
Electricians	A	14	35% (14 ÷ 40 × 100)
Apprentices	B	12	30% (12 ÷ 40 × 100)
Clerical staff	C	8	20% (8 ÷ 40 × 100)
Labourers	D	4	10% (4 ÷ 40 × 100)
Managers	E	2	5% (2 ÷ 40 × 100

Table 3.5: Electrical contracting company staffing statistics

Having given each type of job a reference code, we can now represent this information pictorially and here are the two most common methods.

The pie chart

As the name suggests, this type of diagram shows the information as sections of a pie. To be able to do this we first have to convert information into angles. As we know that a full circle has 360°, this will represent our total number (100%).

In our data, this is a total of 40 employees. Therefore, we now need to find what angle represents each occupation.

We know that electricians (A) make up 14 out of the 40 and therefore for electricians the angle is:

$\frac{14}{40} \times 360 = 126$

In other words 126° out of 360° available belong to the electricians.

Repeat the exercise for the other occupations and we have our complete chart, as shown in Figure 3.7.

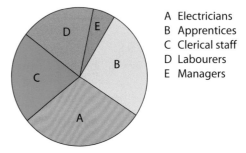

A Electricians
B Apprentices
C Clerical staff
D Labourers
E Managers

Figure 3.7: Pie chart of contracting company staffing statistics

The bar chart

A bar chart uses rectangular bars with lengths proportional to the values that they represent and it is the height of the bar that shows its magnitude.

Bar charts are used for comparing two or more values and the bars can be shown horizontally or vertically.

Figure 3.8 shows all our employer data using this method.

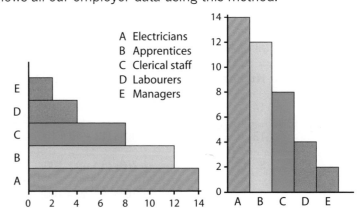

A Electricians
B Apprentices
C Clerical staff
D Labourers
E Managers

Figure 3.8: Bar chart of contracting company staffing statistics

Frequency distribution and tally charts

A frequency distribution is a representation of the number of counts of something (e.g. objects or responses), that is usually shown in the form of a table or graph.

Tally marks are a simple counting system that lets us record how many times something happens. The tally system works by drawing a vertical line every time something happens and every fifth occurrence a fifth line is drawn diagonally across the previous four lines to indicate a bunch of five.

If I was counting some bananas, here's how it would work:

1 I   2 II   3 III   4 IIII

And when I got to the fifth banana I would mark it down like this: ⅲ

This makes working out an amount a lot easier, as it is easy to count in groups of five.

Here you will see both techniques in a worked example.

Example

Imagine that a company manufactures screws. A box that contains 100 screws is checked, the lengths of the screws are different and their lengths are shown in Figure 3.9.

A customer needs screws that can only be 15 mm long for some specialist equipment and the manufacturer needs to know how many of each size there are. This is where the tally mark system can be used.

Using the tally system to count the various screws, gives Figure 3.10.

15.02	15.00	15.00	15.01	15.01
15.01	14.99	14.99	15.00	14.99
15.01	15.01	14.99	14.98	15.03
15.01	15.00	15.00	15.02	15.03
15.01	15.00	14.98	15.02	15.04
14.98	14.97	14.99	15.00	14.98
15.00	15.00	14.98	14.99	15.00
14.98	15.00	14.99	14.97	15.01
15.01	15.00	15.03	14.98	14.98
15.01	14.99	15.00	15.02	15.00
14.98	14.98	15.00	14.96	14.99
15.03	15.02	15.01	15.03	15.01
14.99	15.04	15.02	15.01	15.01
15.01	15.01	14.98	15.02	14.99
15.01	15.01	14.99	15.02	15.00
15.03	14.97	14.97	15.00	15.00
14.99	15.00	14.99	14.99	14.99
15.02	15.00	15.00	15.00	15.03
15.01	14.99	15.00	14.96	14.99
15.01	14.99	15.03	15.01	14.99

Figure 3.9: Lengths of screws

Length (mm)	Number of screws with this length	Frequency
14.96	II	2
14.97	IIII	4
14.98	ⅲ I	11
14.99	ⅲ ⅲ ⅲ ⅲ	20
15.00	ⅲ ⅲ ⅲ ⅲ III	23
15.01	ⅲ ⅲ ⅲ ⅲ I	21
15.02	ⅲ IIII	9
15.03	ⅲ III	8
15.04	II	2

Figure 3.10: The tally system

From the tally chart we can see that there are 23 15 mm screws and the customer can be supplied. It is easy to see on the tally chart how many we have of something (the frequency distribution); it can be easier and more useful if we portrayed the information pictorially.

The histogram

As we just said, frequency distribution becomes clearer if we draw a diagram and we would normally do this using a histogram.

A histogram is a type of bar chart where it is the area, rather than the height, of each bar that is representative of the frequency. The histogram provides a measure of spread and the bars always touch.

Figure 3.11 shows the information from the tally chart expressed as a histogram.

When you look at the histogram, the pattern of the variation in screw size is easy to understand, most of the values are grouped near the centre of the diagram with a few values more widely scattered.

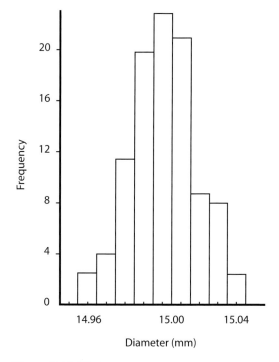

Figure 3.11: Histogram

This shows that the company generally make screws of the right length (15 mm) but that the accuracy could improve. There is possible waste of materials with longer ones and the shorter ones may be unusable.

Statistical averages

One last aspect of statistics involves the calculation of averages. There are three common types of average:

Mean

This is the commonest type of average and it is determined by adding up all the items in the set and dividing the result by the number of items:

$$\text{Mean} = \frac{\text{The sum total of items}}{\text{The number of items}}$$

Example

The marks of an apprentice in four examinations were 86, 72, 68 and 78. Find the mean of his marks.

$$\text{Mean} = \frac{86 + 72 + 68 + 78}{4}$$

$$\text{Mean} = \frac{304}{4} = \textbf{76}$$

Median

If a distribution is arranged so that all the items are in ascending (or descending) order of size, then the median is the value that is half-way along the series. Generally there will be an equal number of items below and above the median. If there is an even number of items the median is found by taking the average of the two middle items.

Example

The median of 3, 4, 4, 5, **6**, 8, 8, 9, 10 is 6

The median of 3, 3, 5, **7, 9**, 10, 13, 15 is therefore $\frac{(7 + 9)}{2} = \mathbf{8}$

Mode

The observation or item which occurs most frequently in a distribution, is called the mode.

In the data set 3, 3, 5, 7, 9, 10, 13, 15 the number 3 occurs most often, so 3 is the mode.

Summary

1. What is the acronym used to tackle a calculation and what does it stand for?
2. What is the result of dividing something into smaller equal parts?
3. What is the main rule when you rearrange a formula and what is the process called?

3. Basic mechanics and the relationship between force, work, energy and power

The human race is very inventive. We have devised many means of overcoming simple problems, such as lifting a heavy object and moving it from one place to another. Now that we understand the basics behind mathematical procedures, we need to start applying these to some of the scientific and mechanical concepts you will be dealing with as an electrician.

The difference between mass and weight

We need to understand a very important concept: the difference between weight (a force) and mass.

Mass

This is simply the amount of stuff or matter contained in an object. Assuming we do not cut or change the object, the mass of an object will stay the same wherever we are.

The unit of mass is the kilogram (kg)

Weight

This is a force and depends on how much gravity pulls on a mass. This can vary according to where we are (the higher above sea level you go, the gravitational pull of the Earth is less and so you weigh less).

This change in weight is tiny but can be measured with very sensitive and expensive scientific equipment.

The unit of weight (and all other forces) is the newton (N)

On Earth, if we disregard the effect of height above sea level, the weight acting on 1 kg of mass is equal to 9.81 newtons (N). So, **1 kg weighs 9.81 N**. In many situations this can be rounded up to 10 N.

Principles of basic mechanics

A simple machine is a device that helps us to perform our work more easily when a force is applied to it. A screw, wheel and axle and lever are all simple machines.

A machine also allows us to use a smaller force to overcome a larger force and can also help us change the direction of the force and work at a faster speed. The most common simple machines are shown as follows.

Levers

Levers let us use a small force to apply a larger force to an object. They are grouped into three classes, depending on the position of the fulcrum (the pivot).

Class 1

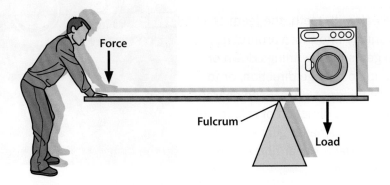

The fulcrum is between the force and the load, like a seesaw.

Class 2

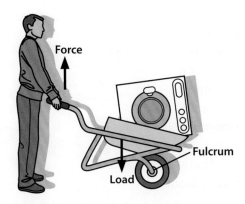

The fulcrum is at one end, the force at the other end, and the load is in the middle. A wheelbarrow is a good example.

Class 3

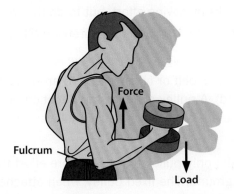

The fulcrum is at one end, the load at the other end and the force in the middle, like a human forearm.

A small force at a long distance will produce a larger force close to the pivot:

$10 \times 2 = F \times 0.5$

$F = \frac{10 \times 2}{0.5} = \frac{20}{0.5} = 40\,N$

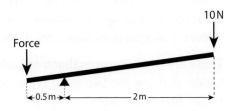

Figure 3.12: Large force close to pivot

Gears

Gears are wheels with teeth; the teeth of one gear fit snugly into those around it. You can use gears to slow things down or speed them up, to change direction, or to control several things at once. Each gear in a series changes the direction of rotation of the previous gear. A smaller gear will always turn faster than a larger gear and in doing so, turns more times.

Figure 3.13: Gears

The inclined plane

The inclined plane is the simplest machine of all, as it is basically a ramp or sloping surface. The shortest distance between two points is a straight line, but it is easier to move a heavy object to a higher point by using stairs or a ramp. If you think of the height of a mountain, the shortest distance is straight up from the bottom to the top. However, we usually build a road up a mountain as a slowly-winding inclined plane from bottom to top.

As an electrician, you will use the inclined plane in the form of a screw, which is simply an inclined plane wound around a central cylinder.

So the inclined plane works by saving effort, but to do this you must move things a greater distance.

Pulleys

A pulley is made with a rope, belt or chain wrapped around a wheel and can be used to lift a heavy object (load). A pulley changes the direction of the force, making it easier to lift things. There are two main types of pulleys: the single fixed pulley and the moveable pulley.

A **single fixed pulley** is the only pulley that uses more effort than the load in order to lift the load from the ground. The fixed pulley, when attached to an unmoveable object, e.g. a ceiling or wall, acts as a class 1 lever with the fulcrum being located at the axis but with a minor change – the bar becomes a rope. The advantage of the fixed pulley is that you do not have to pull or push the pulley itself up and down. The disadvantage is that you have to apply more effort than the load.

A **moveable pulley** is one that moves with the load. The moveable pulley allows the effort to be less than the weight of the load. The moveable pulley also acts as a class 2 lever. The load is between the fulcrum and the effort.

There are many combinations of pulleys, the most common being the block and tackle, that use the two main types as their principle of operation. The example shows how these work.

Example

Let us look at examples of the two main types of pulleys to understand their operating principles. Imagine that you have the arrangement of a 2 kg weight suspended from a rope, but actually resting on the ground as shown in the diagram.

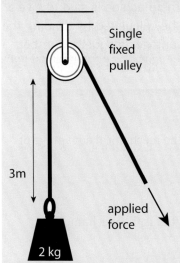

Single fixed pulley

3m

applied force

2 kg

If we want to have the 2 kg load suspended in the air above the ground, then we have to apply an upward force of 20 N (1 kg will exert a force of approximately 10 N) to the rope in the direction of the arrow. If the rope was 3 m long and we wanted to lift the weight up 3 m above the ground, we would have to pull in 3 m of rope to do it.

Now imagine that we add a single fixed pulley to the scenario, as shown in the diagram. The only thing that has changed is the direction of the force we have to apply to lift the load. We would still have to apply 20 N of force to suspend the load above the ground, and would still have to reel in 3 m of rope in order to lift the weight 3 m above the ground. This type of system gives us the convenience of pulling downwards instead of lifting.

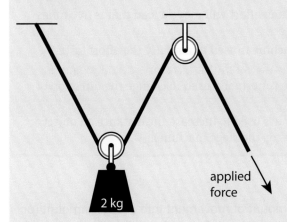

applied force

2 kg

This diagram shows the arrangement if we add a second, moveable pulley. This new arrangement now changes things in our favour because effectively the load is now suspended by two ropes rather than one. That means the weight is split equally between the two ropes, so each one holds only half the weight, or 10 N. That means that if you want to hold the weight suspended in the air, you only have to apply 10 N of force (the ceiling exerting the other 10 N of force on the other end of the rope). However, if you want to lift the weight 3 m above the ground, then you have to reel in twice as much rope – i.e. 6 m of rope must be pulled in.

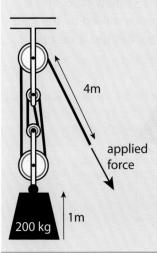

4m

applied force

200 kg

1m

The more pulleys we have the easier it is to lift heavy objects. As rope is pulled from the top pulley wheel, the load and the bottom pulley wheel are lifted. If 2 m of rope are pulled through, the load will only rise 1 m (there are two ropes holding the load and both have to shorten by the same amount).

With pulley systems, to calculate the effort required to lift the load, we divide the load by the number of ropes (excluding the rope connected to the effort). The diagram shows a four-pulley system, where the person lifting a 200 kg mass or 2000 N load has to exert a pull equal to only 500 N (i.e. 2000 N divided by 4 ropes).

Mechanical advantage

The common theme behind all of these machines is that because of the machine we can increase our ability and gain an advantage. This is a relationship between the effort needed to lift something (input) and the load itself (output) and we call this ratio the mechanical advantage.

When a machine can put out more force than is put in, the machine is said to give a good mechanical advantage. Mechanical advantage can be calculated by dividing the load by the effort. There are no units for mechanical advantage, it is just a number.

Mechanical Advantage (MA) = $\frac{\text{Load}}{\text{Effort}}$

Example

Using the final diagram from the earlier example, what is the mechanical advantage of the pulley system?

$$\textbf{MA} = \frac{\text{Load}}{\text{Effort}} = \frac{2000\,\text{N}}{500\,\text{N}} = \textbf{4}$$

In a lever, an effort of 10 N is used to move a load of 50 N. What is the mechanical advantage of the lever?

$$\textbf{MA} = \frac{\text{Load}}{\text{Effort}} = \frac{50}{10} = \textbf{5}$$

This effectively means that for this lever, any effort will move a load that is five times larger. To summarise:

- **Where MA is greater than 1:** The machine is used to magnify the effort force (e.g. a class 1 lever).
- **Where MA is equal to 1:** The machine is normally used to change the direction of the effort force (e.g. a fixed pulley).
- **Where MA is less than 1:** The machine is used to increase the distance an object moves or the speed at which it moves (e.g. the siege machine).

Velocity ratio

Sometimes machines translate a small amount of movement into a larger amount (or vice versa). For example, in Figure 3.14, a small movement of the piston causes the load to move a much greater distance. This property is known as the velocity ratio, and is found by dividing the distance moved by the effort by the distance moved by the load (in the same period of time). There are no units for velocity ratio, it is just a number.

Velocity ratio (VR) = $\frac{\text{Distance moved by effort}}{\text{Distance moved by load}}$

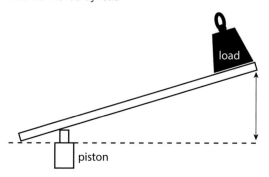

Figure 3.14: Velocity ratio

Example

In the diagram, the piston moves 1 m to move the load 5 m. The velocity ratio is:

$$\text{VR} = \frac{\text{Distance moved by effort}}{\text{Distance moved by load}} = \frac{1}{5} = \mathbf{0.2}$$

Main principles and calculating values of force, work, energy, power and efficiency

Force

Force is a push or pull that acts on an object. If the force is greater than the opposing force, the object will change motion or shape. Obvious examples of forces are gravity and the wind. Force is measured in newtons.

The presence of a force is measured by its effect on a body, e.g. a heavy wind can cause a stationary football to start rolling; or a car colliding with a wall causes the front of the car to deform and the occupants of the car to be forced forwards towards the windscreen (hence the use of seat belts).

Equally, gravitational force will cause objects to fall towards the Earth. Therefore, a spring will extend if we attach a weight to it, because gravity is acting on the weight.

As the force of gravity acts on any mass, that mass tends to accelerate. This acceleration due to gravity is universally taken to be 9.81 m/s² at sea level and therefore a mass of 1 kg will exert a force of 9.81 N.

Expressed as a formula:

Force (N) = Mass × Acceleration

(Note: In calculations, the value of acceleration is often taken as 10 m/s² to simplify the calculations.)

Work

If an object is moved, then work is said to have been done. The unit of work done is the joule. (This is also the unit for energy.) Work done is a relationship between the effort (force) used to move an object and the distance that the object is moved. Expressed as a formula:

Work done (J) = Force (N) × Distance (m)

> **JTL tip**   JTL
>
> Mass and weight are **not** the same thing. Mass is the amount of material in an object. Weight is a force – e.g. a person who weighs a certain amount on Earth would weigh less on the Moon due to the decreased gravitational force, but they would still have the same mass.

> **JTL tip**   JTL
>
> Do not assume that the acceleration due to gravity is = 10 m/s². It is 9.81 m/s². Only take it as 10 m/s² if you are told to do so in a question, or if you are doing a rough calculation for your own purposes.

Example

A distribution board has a mass of 50 kg. How much work is done when it is moved 10 m?

Work = Force × Distance

$= (50 \times 9.81) \times 10$

$= 490.5 \times 10$

$= \mathbf{4905\ J}$

Energy

Energy, measured in joules, is the ability to do work, or to cause something to move or the ability to cause change. Machines cannot work without energy and we are unable to get more work out of a machine than the energy we put into it.

Energy is wasted in a machine because of **friction**. Friction occurs when two substances rub together. Try rubbing your hands together. Did you feel them get warmer?

Work produced (output) is usually less than the energy used (input). Energy can be transferred from one form to another, but energy cannot be created or destroyed.

The energy lost by friction is converted into heat.

There are many forms of energy, but there are only two types:

*   **potential energy** (energy of position or stored energy)
*   **kinetic energy** (energy due to the motion of an object).

Some forms of energy are: solar, electrical, heat, light, chemical, mechanical, wind, water, muscles and nuclear.

Potential energy

Anything may have stored energy, giving it the potential to cause change if certain conditions are met. The amount of potential energy something has depends on its position or condition. A brick on the top of scaffolding has potential energy because it could fall under the influence of gravity. The bow used to propel an arrow has no energy in its resting position, but drawing the bow back requires energy and this is then stored as elastic potential energy. A change in its condition (releasing it) can cause change (propelling the arrow).

Potential energy due to height above the Earth's surface is called gravitational potential energy, and the greater the height, the greater the potential energy.

There is a direct relation between gravitational potential energy and the mass of an object; more massive objects have greater gravitational potential energy. There is also a direct relation between gravitational potential energy and the height of an object. The higher an object is above the Earth, the greater its gravitational potential energy. These relationships are expressed by the following equation:

PE_{grav} = mass of an object × gravitational acceleration × height

PE_{grav} = m × g × h = mgh

Another example of potential energy is the spring inside a clockwork watch. The wound spring transforms potential energy to kinetic energy of the wheels and cogs etc. as it unwinds.

Kinetic energy

Kinetic energy is energy in the form of motion and the greater the mass of a moving object, the more kinetic energy it has.

The formula is $KE = \frac{1}{2}mv^2$

Power

When we do work in a mechanical system, the energy we put into the system does not appear all at once. It takes a certain time to move an object, lift a weight etc. As a result, the power that we put into a system must depend not only on the amount of work we do but also how fast we carry out the work.

To try to understand this, think of a 100 metre runner and a marathon runner. The sprinter has a burst of energy for maybe 10 seconds or so whereas the marathon runner may use a similar amount of energy but at a much slower pace. Let's face it, both events would leave you feeling shattered, but it is usual to say that the sprinter had greater power because he used his energy very quickly.

We usually say that:

Power = the rate of doing work

In terms of equations we can say that:

Power (P) $= \dfrac{\text{Work done (W)}}{\text{Time taken to do the work (t)}}$

or

Power (P) $= \dfrac{\text{Energy used (E)}}{\text{Time taken to do the work (t)}}$

Energy or work is measured in joules (J) and time is measured in seconds (s). Power is measured in joules per second or J/s, also known as watts (W).

1000 watts (W) = 1 kilowatt (kW).

The power of an electrical device is also measured in Watts or kW.

Example

A distribution board has a mass of 50 kg and it is moved 10 m.

Work = Force × Distance = (50 × 9.81) × 10 = 490.5 × 10 = 4905 J

Now what if it took 20 s to move the distribution board by 10 m. How much power did we put into moving it?

In this case:

$$P = \frac{\text{Work done in moving the distribution board by 10 m (W)}}{\text{The time it took to move the distribution board (t)}}$$

Now, W = 4905 J, and t = 20 s. So:

$$P = \frac{4905}{20}$$

Therefore: **P = 245.25 W**

Efficiency

We often think of machines as having an input and an output. A machine actually has two outputs, one that is wanted and one that is not and is therefore wasted (as frictional heat, noise etc.). The greater the unwanted component, the less efficient the machine is.

In all machines, the power at the input is greater than the power output, because of losses that occur in the machine such as friction, heat or vibration. This difference, expressed as a ratio of output power over input power, is called the efficiency of the machine. The symbol sometimes used for efficiency is the Greek letter η (eta).

That is:

$$\text{Efficiency} = \frac{\text{Output power}}{\text{Input power}}$$

To give the efficiency as a percentage, which is usually more convenient and understandable, we can say that

$$\% \text{ efficiency} = \frac{\text{Output power}}{\text{Input power}} \times 100$$

We will now follow a series of steps to end up with a final equation for efficiency. It is quite complicated and the most important thing is to remember the final formula.

Now, for any machine:

Work done at the input = Effort × Distance the effort moves

(force × distance)

and

Work done at the output = Load × Distance the effort moves

(force × distance)

Dividing these two equations gives us:

$$\frac{\text{Work at output}}{\text{Work at input}} = \frac{\text{Load}}{\text{Effort}} \times \frac{\text{Distance moved by load}}{\text{Distance moved by effort}} = \text{Efficiency}$$

Now you know already that

$$\text{Mechanical advantage (MA)} = \frac{\text{Load}}{\text{Effort}}$$

And that:

$$\text{Velocity ratio (VR)} = \frac{\text{Distance moved by effort}}{\text{Distance moved by load}}$$

So:

$$\frac{1}{\text{VR}} = \frac{\text{Distance moved by effort}}{\text{Distance moved by load}}$$

So:

$$\text{Efficiency} = \frac{\text{Work at output}}{\text{Work at input}} = \frac{\text{Load}}{\text{Effort}} \times \frac{\text{Distance moved by load}}{\text{Distance moved by effort}} = \frac{\text{MA}}{\text{VR}} \times 1$$

Which can be rewritten as:

$$\textbf{Efficiency} = \frac{\textbf{Mechanical advantage}}{\textbf{Velocity ratio}} = \frac{\textbf{MA}}{\textbf{VR}} \textbf{ or \% Efficiency} = \frac{\textbf{MA}}{\textbf{VR}} \times \textbf{100}$$

If a machine has low efficiency, this does not mean it is of limited use. A car jack, for example, has to overcome a great deal of friction and therefore has a low efficiency, but it is still a very useful tool as a small effort allows us to lift the whole weight of a car to change a tyre.

JTL tip

The unit of velocity (m/s) and acceleration (m/s²) are also written as ms^{-1} and ms^{-2}.

Let us look at a couple of examples that will illustrate these concepts.

Example 1

In the following diagram, a trolley containing lighting fittings is pulled at constant speed along an inclined plane to the height shown. Assume that the value of the acceleration due to gravity is 10 m/s².

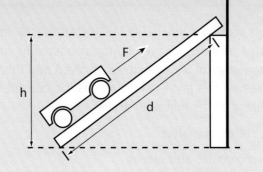

If the mass of the loaded cart is 3.0 kg and the height shown is 0.45 m, then what is the potential energy of the loaded cart at the height shown?

PE = m × g × h

PE = 3 × 10 × 0.45

PE = 13.5 J

If a force of 15.0 N was used to drag the trolley along the incline for a distance of 0.90 m, then how much work was done on the loaded trolley?

W = F × d

W = 15 × 0.9

W = 13.5 J

Example 2

A motor control panel arrives on site. It is removed from the transporter's lorry using a block and tackle that has five pulley wheels. Establish the percentage efficiency of this system given that the effort required to lift the load was 200 N, the panel has a mass of 80 kg and acceleration due to gravity is 10 m/s².

The load = Mass × Acceleration due to gravity

= 80 × 10

= 800 N

$$\text{Mechanical Advantage} = \frac{\text{Load}}{\text{Effort}} = \frac{800}{200} = 4$$

Remembering that velocity ratio is equal to the number of pulley wheels

Velocity Ratio = the number of pulley wheels = 5

$$\text{Efficiency} = \frac{\text{Mechanical advantage}}{\text{Velocity ratio}} = \frac{4}{5} = 0.8$$

So, % efficiency = 0.8 × 100 = 80%

Therefore the system is 80% efficient.

Summary

1. What is the difference between mass and weight?
2. Levers have different classes; how many are there?
3. In a lever, an effort of 15 N is used to move a load of 45 N. What is the mechanical advantage of the lever?
4. If a machine has low efficiency, does this mean it is of limited use? Explain your answer.

4. The relationship between resistance, resistivity, voltage, current and power

This section is where we really start to look at electricity and electrical circuits in detail. You cannot even consider becoming an electrician unless you have a sound knowledge of the principles involved and this starts with the atomic theory of matter and how this gives rise to an electric current. In this section we will therefore be looking at the following areas:

- states of matter
- molecules and atoms
- the electric circuit
- the causes of an electric current
- the effects of an electric current
- resistance.

Basic principles of electron theory

States of matter

It has in the past been thought that there were three states of matter, solid, liquid and gas. However, with advances in science and technology it is currently felt that there are five main states of matter: solid, liquid, gas, plasma and Bose-Einstein condensate.

We can think of each of these states as being a phase that matter can move from and to when affected by other things such as temperature. The effect of temperature is an easy one to see as if we apply enough heat to a block of metal it melts. In other words the metal has moved from a solid state to a liquid state.

Matter can change from one phase to another but it is still the same substance.

As an example consider a solid block of ice. If we apply gentle heat it will become a liquid pool of water. If we apply more heat to our pool of water it will evaporate into a gas.

However, through all the changes of phase, it is still water and always has the same chemical properties.

(A chemical change would be needed to change the water into something completely new.)

The three classic states of matter

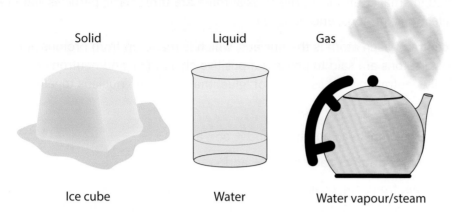

Solid	Liquid	Gas
Ice cube	Water	Water vapour/steam

Molecules are always in a state of rapid motion, but when they are densely packed together, this movement is restricted and the substance formed by these molecules is solid. When the molecules of a substance are less tightly bound, there is a great deal of free movement and the substance is a liquid. Finally, when the molecule movement is almost unrestricted, the substance can expand and contract in any direction and is a gas.

Molecules and atoms

As a starting point for understanding these, we can say that particles of matter are used to create atoms. Atoms are then used to create molecules and elements are used to create molecules.

Molecules are electrically neutral groups of at least two atoms held together by a chemical bond. A molecule may consist of atoms of a single chemical element such as oxygen (O), or of different elements such as water (two hydrogen atoms and one oxygen atom H_2O).

Atoms have a nucleus that is made of protons and neutrons, with very small electrons orbiting around it (rather like planets revolving round the Sun).

Protons and neutrons are now known to be made from even smaller particles called nucleons and quarks. You may know that nuclear chemists and physicists work together using particle accelerators such as the Large Hadron Collider, 17 miles in circumference and buried 150 metres underground in Switzerland, to study these sub-atomic particles.

Figure 3.15: The Large Hadron Collider is the most powerful particle accelerator in the world

Structure of the atom

Even though smaller atomic particles exist there are three basic particles within an atom: electrons, protons, and neutrons.

At the centre of each atom is the nucleus, which is made up from protons and neutrons. Protons are said to possess a positive charge (+), and neutrons are electrically neutral and act as a type of 'glue' that holds the nucleus together.

You probably already know that:

*   Like charges repel each other (+ and + or – and –).

*   Unlike charges attract each other (+ and –).

So without neutrons, the positively charged protons would repel each other and the nucleus would fly apart. The neutrons hold the nucleus together. However, as neutrons are electrically neutral, they play no part in the chemical or electrical properties of atoms.

The remaining particles in an atom are electrons and these circulate in orbits of varying radius around the nucleus and have a negative charge (–).

There are many different kinds of atoms, one for each type of element, and there are currently 118 different known elements (such as oxygen).

For any particular atom the number of electrons is usually the same as the number of protons. If the numbers are the same, the atom is seen as balanced, with the positive and negative charges being cancelled out thus leaving the atom electrically neutral.

The simplest atom is a hydrogen atom which has one proton and one neutron balancing each other.

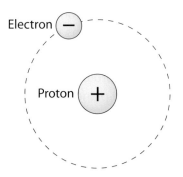

Figure 3.16: Hydrogen atom

Electrons in orbit nearest the nucleus are generally held tightly in place. However, those furthest away are more loosely attached and in some cases it is possible to remove or add an electron to a neutral atom. This leaves the atom with a net positive or negative charge. Such 'unbalanced' atoms are known as ions.

Since all atoms 'want' to be balanced, the atom that is unbalanced will attract a 'free' electron to fill the place of the missing one or lose an extra electron to return to its neutral state. These are wandering or 'free' electrons moving about the molecular structure of a material that give rise to what we refer to as electricity.

Electricity is the movement of free electrons along a suitable material (conductor). A material that does not allow the easy movement of free electrons is an insulator.

Identifying and differentiating between insulators and conductors

Insulators

We need to protect ourselves and contain the flow of electricity otherwise we would get an electric shock every time we used a piece of electrical equipment. The materials that we use to do this are called insulators. Insulators are poor conductors of electricity. They do not allow free passage of electrons through them. Surprisingly, one insulator that is used in cable manufacture is paper. Some others are shown in Table 3.6.

Rubber/plastic	Very flexible Easily affected by temperature Used in cable insulation
Impregnated paper	Stiff and **hygroscopic** Unaffected by moderate temperature Used in large cables
Magnesium oxide	Powder, therefore requires a containing sheath Very hygroscopic Resistant to high temperature Used in cables for alarms and emergency lighting
Mica	Unaffected by high temperature Used for kettle and toaster elements
Porcelain	Hard and brittle Easily cleaned Used for carriers and overhead line insulators
Rigid plastic	Less brittle and less costly than porcelain Used in manufacture of switches and sockets

Table 3.6: Common insulators

Key term

Hygroscopic – the ability to absorb water

Conductors

Conductors have a molecular/atomic structure that allows electrons to move freely through them, meaning they have a low resistance to electron flow. Many are metals but graphite (carbon) and some liquids also conduct electricity.

Gold and silver are among the best conductors, but cost inhibits their use. Table 3.7 is a guide to the most common conductors and their uses.

Aluminium (Al)	Low cost and weight Not very flexible Used for large power cables
Brass (an alloy of copper and zinc)	Easily machined Corrosion resistant Used for terminals and plug pins
Carbon (C)	Hard Low friction in contact with other materials Used for machine brushes
Copper (Cu)	Good conductor Soft and ductile Used in most cables and busbar systems
Iron/steel (Fe)	Good conductor Corrodes Used for conduit, trunking and equipment enclosure
Lead (Pb)	Flexible Corrosion resistant Used as an earth and as a sheath of cable
Mercury (Hg)	Liquid at room temperature Quickly vaporises Used for contacts Vapour used for lighting lamps
Sodium (Na)	Quickly vaporises Vapour used for lighting lamps
Tungsten (W)	Extremely ductile Used for filaments in light bulbs

Table 3.7: Common conductors

Applying electron theory to electrical circuits

Measuring electricity

Electricity is invisible, so what exactly do we measure?

Electricity is simply the flow of free electrons along a conductor, so it would seem obvious to count the number of electrons moving along the conductor. However, the electron is far too small to be seen or counted. So we measure the number of larger groups of electrons moving along.

These groups are coulombs, and contain an unimaginable 6 240 000 000 000 000 000 electrons or 6.24×10^{18} (give or take a couple).

A plumber will measure the amount of water flowing in gallons not drops, as drops are too small to measure. If the plumber wishes to know how much water is being used at any one time, in other words 'the rate of flow' of the water, this would be measured in gallons or litres per second.

This movement of the water can be thought of as its current.

Similarly, the electrician may wish to know the amount of electrons flowing at any one time (rate of flow of electrons). In electricity, just as with water, this rate of flow of electrons is called the current and is defined as being one coulomb (an imaginary 'bucket-full') of electrons passing by every second.

If one coulomb of electrons passes along the conductor every second, we say that the current flowing along is a current of one ampere.

We use the letter I to represent current.

JTL tip

One ampere equals one coulomb of electrons passing by every second.

The electric circuit

We now know that electricity is the movement of electron charges along a conductor and that the rate of flow is known as the current. But what makes the electron charges move?

Battery

In this circuit (Figure 3.17), the battery cell has an internal chemical reaction that provides what is known as an electromotive force (e.m.f. for short), that will push the electrons along the conducting wire and into the lamp. The electrons will then pass through the lamp filament, causing it to heat up and glow and then leave via the second conductor, returning to the battery and thus completing the circuit.

In other words, a battery is a chemically fuelled electron pump and, like every other pump in the world, the battery does not supply the electrons that it pumps. When a battery runs down it is because its chemical 'fuel' is exhausted, not because any charges have been lost.

Figure 3.17: A simple battery

Electron flow and conventional current flow

An electromotive force (e.m.f.) is needed to cause the flow of electrons. This has the symbol E and the unit symbol V (volt). Any apparatus which produces an e.m.f. (such as a battery) is called a power source and as we saw in Figure 3.17, will require wires or cables to be attached to its terminals to form a basic circuit.

If we take two dissimilar metal plates and place them in a chemical solution (an electrolyte) a reaction will take place in which electrons from one plate travel through the electrolyte and collect on the other plate.

One plate now has an excess of electrons, which will make it more negative than positive. The other plate will now have an excess of protons, which makes it more positive than negative. This process is the basis of how a simple battery or cell works.

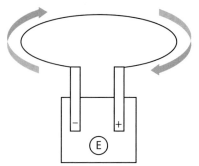

Figure 3.18: Electron flow through an electrolyte

Now select a piece of wire as a good conductor and connect this wire to the ends of the plate as shown in Figure 3.18.

Since unlike charges are attracted towards each other and like charges repel each other, you can see that the negative electrons will move from the negative plate, through the conductor towards the positive plate.

This drift of free electrons is what we know as electricity and this process will continue until the chemical action of the battery is exhausted and there is no longer a difference between the plates.

As we can see, the actual electron flow is from positive to negative inside the battery and then from negative to positive through the conductor.

Note that early science actually thought the opposite and that flow ran externally from positive to negative. This is called conventional current flow.

Potential difference

The chemical energy within a battery is used to do work on a charge in order to move it from the negative terminal, out through a conductor and then returning to the positive terminal.

To do this, the battery is raising the potential of the electrons.

If you hold a stone and raise your hand in the air, the stone has a potential energy. The higher up it is, the higher the potential and we measure that potential against a reference point.

If you now let go of the stone it will fall towards that reference point losing potential along the way.

(It may be easier to understand if I said the reference point was your head and potential means the stone's ability to hurt you. The higher it is above your head the more likely it is to hurt you.)

In a battery, the electric charges at the negative terminal have more potential energy than they will have when they get to the positive terminal, in other words they can 'fall downhill' from the negative terminal to the positive terminal via the conductor that makes up the circuit. The electrons then pick up energy in the cell of the battery which pushes it out to the components of the circuit. At the point when they return to the cell, they have given up all the energy they gained.

We can therefore say that potential difference (p.d.) is the difference in electrical potential energy between any two points in a circuit, p.d. is therefore also measured in volts.

We measure an amount of charge in a unit called a coulomb so we could also say that potential difference is a measure of the amount of joules of work required to push one coulomb along the circuit between our two points. The units of this would be measured in joules/coulomb more commonly referred to as the volt.

Therefore **One volt = One joule/coulomb**

Our battery is therefore acting as an energy conversion system, converting chemical energy into electric potential energy. This work increases the potential energy of the charge and thus its electric potential. By chemical reaction the charge is moved from a 'low potential' terminal to a 'high potential' terminal inside the internal circuit of the battery. Once there it will then move through the external circuit (the conductor and equipment), before returning to the low potential terminal. The difference between our terminals is referred to as the potential difference and without it there can be no flow of charge.

As the charge moves through the external circuit, it can pass through different types of component each of which acts as an energy conversion system, for example, the lamp in Figure 3.17. Here the moving charge is doing work on the lamp filament to produce different forms of energy: heat and light. However, in doing so it is losing some of its electric potential energy and therefore on leaving the lamp, it is less energised.

Looking again at Figure 3.17, we can see that at a point just prior to entering the lamp (or any circuit component) we have a higher electric potential compared to a point just after leaving the lamp. This loss of potential across any circuit component is also called the volt drop and we will discuss this later on page 241.

Controlling a circuit

In Figure 3.17 we have a complete circuit connected across a healthy battery and the lamp is therefore lit.

However, if either of the two wires becomes broken or disconnected the flow of electricity will be interrupted and the lamp will go out.

It is this principle that we use to control electricity in a circuit.

As we can see in Figure 3.19, by inserting a switch into one of the wires connected to the lamp, we can physically 'break the circuit' with the switch and thus switch the lamp off and on.

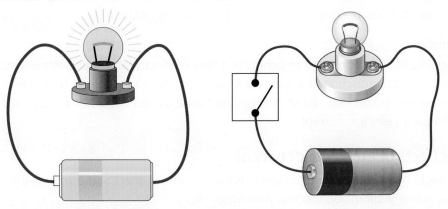

Figure 3.19: Simple battery circuit and broken circuit

To summarise, for practical purposes a working circuit should:

- have a source of supply (such as the battery)
- have a device (fuse/MCB) to protect the circuit
- contain conductors through which current can flow
- be a complete circuit
- have a load (such as a lamp) that needs current to make it work
- have a switch to control the supply to the equipment (load).

Chemical and thermal effects of electrical currents

The causes of an electric current

We need an electromotive force (e.m.f.) to drive electrons through a conductor. The principal sources of an e.m.f. that will cause current to flow can be classed as being as follows.

Chemical

When we take two electrodes of dissimilar metal and immerse them in an electrolyte, we have effectively created a battery. So as we have seen earlier, the chemical reactions in the battery cause an electric current to flow.

Thermal

When a closed circuit consists of two junctions, each junction made between two different metals, a potential difference will occur if the two junctions are at different temperatures. This is known as the Seebeck effect, based upon Seebeck's discovery of this phenomenon in 1821.

If we now connect a voltmeter to one end (the cold end) and apply heat to the other, then our reading will depend upon the difference in temperature between the two ends. When we have two metals arranged like this, we have a thermocouple.

We can apply this to measure temperatures, with the 'hot end' being placed inside the equipment (such as an oven or hot water system) and the 'cold end' connected to a meter that has been located in a suitable remote position.

Magnetic

A magnetic field can be used to generate a flow of electrons. We call this situation electromagnetic induction. If a conductor (wire) is moved through a magnetic field, then an e.m.f. will be induced in it. Provided that a closed circuit exists, this e.m.f. will then cause an electric current.

The effects of an electric current

The effects of an electric current are categorised in the exact same way as the causes, namely chemical, thermal and magnetic.

Looking at the circuit in Figure 3.20 we can see a DC supply enters a contactor. When we close the switch on the contactor the coil is energised and becomes an electromagnet, this attracts anything in the magnetic field that contains iron towards it. Once the circuit is made then the main supply flows through to the distribution centre.

From the distribution centre a supply is taken to a change-over switch. In its current position, this switch allows current to flow into the electrolyte (dilute sulphuric acid and water) via one of the two lead plates. The current returns to the distribution centre via the other lead plate.

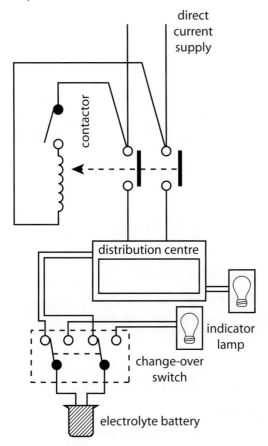

Figure 3.20: DC supply

Also fed from the distribution centre is a filament lamp. We could have equally used an electric fire. This is because when current flows through a conductor heat is generated. The amount of heat varies according to circumstances, such as the conductor size. If sized correctly, we can make the conductor glow white-hot (a lamp) or red-hot (a fire).

If we run the system like this for a few minutes and then switch off the contactor, obviously we would see our filament lamp go out. However, if we now move our change-over switch into its other position, we would see that our indicator lamp would glow for a short while.

If we were to look at the lead plates, we would see that one of the plates has become discoloured. This is because the current has caused a chemical reaction, changing the lead into an oxide of lead. In this respect the plates acted as a form of rechargeable battery, also known as a secondary cell.

Table 3.8 indicates how various pieces of equipment use these effects of current as their principle of operation.

Chemical effect	Heating effect	Magnetic
Cells	Filament lamp	Bell
Batteries	Heater	Relay
Electro-plating	Cooker	Contactor
	Iron	Motors
	Fuse	Transformers
	Circuit-breaker	Circuit-breaker
	Kettle	

Table 3.8: Principles of operation

Summary

1. What are the five main states of matter?
2. What are the three main particles within an atom?
3. What is the difference between an insulator and a conductor?

Resistance and resistivity in relation to electrical circuits

So far we have considered the amount of electron charges flowing in a conductor every second and the force that pushes them along the conductor. But does anything interfere with this flow?

If we turn our minds back to our marathon runners again, would they rather be running on a brand new athletics track or through a field of sticky mud four feet deep?

Obviously the new track would be the easiest to run on as it is least likely to affect their ability to run.

Or, in other words, the new track will offer a lower resistance to their progress than the muddy field.

In electrical circuits, just like the muddy field, electrical conductors, connections and known resistors will offer a level of resistance to the electrons trying to flow through them.

You could also think of resistance as hurdles that electrons have to jump over on their way around the circuit, and the more hurdles there are, then the longer it will take to get around the circuit. Watch the Olympics if you need further proof!

There is a scientific law that we can apply to resistance.

Ohm's Law

So far we have established that **current** is the amount of electrons flowing by every second in a conductor and that a force known as the e.m.f. (or **voltage**) is pushing them. We now also know that the conductor will try to oppose the current, by offering a **resistance** to the flow of electrons.

Ohm's Law was named after the nineteenth-century German physicist G.S. Ohm who researched how current, potential difference and resistance are related to each other. It's probably the most important electrical concept you will need to understand and is stated as follows:

> *The current flowing in a circuit is directly proportional to the voltage applied to the circuit, and indirectly proportional to the resistance of the circuit, provided that the temperature affecting the circuit remains constant.*

However, in simple language we could re-write Ohm's Law as follows: The amount of electrons passing by every second will depend upon how hard we push them, and what obstacles are put in their way.

We can prove this is true, because if we increase the voltage (push harder), then we increase the number of electrons that we can get out at the other end.

Try flicking a coin along the desk. The harder you flick it, the further it travels along the desk. This is what we mean by **directly proportional**. If one thing goes up (voltage), then so will the other thing (current).

Equally we could prove that if we increase the resistance (put more obstacles in the way), then this will reduce the amount of electrons that we can get along the wire.

This time put an obstacle in front of the coin before you flick it. If flicked at the same strength, it will obviously not go as far as it did before. This is what we mean by indirectly proportional. If one thing goes up (resistance), then the other thing will go down (current).

Ohm's Law is therefore expressed by the following formula:

$$\text{Current (I)} = \frac{\text{Voltage (V)}}{\text{Resistance (R)}}$$

Resistivity

Take away all resistors from a circuit and you still have some resistance there – caused by the conductor itself. Electrons find it easier to move along some materials than others and each material has its own resistance to the electron flow. This individual material resistance is called resistivity, represented by the Greek symbol rho (ρ) and measured in micro ohm millimetres ($\mu\Omega$mm).

But in considering a conductor there are also some other factors at work!

How long is it? Would you rather run for 100 metres or 25 miles?

The shorter distance of course. So would the electron!

What is its cross-sectional area (CSA)?

Which is easier, to walk along a 3-metre high corridor, or to crawl along a 1-metre high pipe on your stomach?

Walking, of course.

To summarise: The amount of electrons that can flow along a conductor will be affected by how far they have to travel, what material they have to travel through and how big the object is that they are travelling along.

As an electrical formula, this is expressed as follows:

$$\text{Resistance} = \frac{\text{Resistivity} \times \text{Length}}{\text{Cross-sectional area}} = R = \frac{\rho \times L}{a}$$

We find the value of resistivity for each material, by measuring the resistance of a 1 metre cube of the material. Then, as cable dimensions are measured in square millimetres (e.g. $2.5\,mm^2$), this figure is divided down to give the value of a 1 millimetre cube.

This resistivity, as we found out earlier, is given in $\mu\Omega mm$, or in other words we will encounter a resistance of so many millionths of an ohm for every millimetre forward that we travel through the conductor.

The accepted value for copper is $17.8\,\mu\Omega mm$ and the accepted value for aluminium is $28.5\,\mu\Omega mm$.

Let us now look at a typical question involving resistivity.

Example 1

Find the resistance of the field coil of a motor where the conductor cross-sectional area (CSA) is $2\,mm^2$, the length of wire is 4000 m and the material resistivity is $18\,\mu\Omega mm$.

$$R = \frac{\rho \times L}{a}$$

$$\qquad \textit{Problem 1} \quad \textit{Problem 2}$$

$$R = \frac{18}{1\,000\,000} \times \frac{4\,000\,000}{2}$$

What has happened here?

Problem 1: The value of ρ is given in millionths of an ohm millimetre. If we have $18\,\mu\Omega mm$, then we have 18 millionths of an ohm and we therefore write it as 18 divided by one million, or:

$$\frac{18}{1\,000\,000}$$

Problem 2: Remember, when doing calculations, all units must be the same. Here the length is in metres, but everything else is in millimetres. Therefore, note that 4000 m has now become 4 000 000 mm.

So back to the calculation:

$$R = \frac{18}{1\,000\,000} \times \frac{4\,000\,000}{2} = \frac{72\,000\,000}{2\,000\,000} = 36\,\Omega$$

Another way of doing this calculation, **without the calculator**, would have been to cancel the zeros down (division):

$$R = \frac{18}{1\,\cancel{000\,000}} \times \frac{4\,\cancel{000\,000}}{2}$$

$$R = \frac{18 \times 4}{2} = \mathbf{36\,\Omega}$$

Example 2

A copper conductor has a resistivity of $17.8\,\mu\Omega mm$ and a CSA of $2.5\,mm^2$. What will be the resistance of a 30 m length of this conductor?

$$R = \frac{\rho \times L}{A} \quad \text{then} \quad R = \frac{17.8 \times 30\,000}{1\,000\,000 \times 2.5} = \frac{534\,000}{2\,500\,000} \quad \text{so} \quad \mathbf{R = 0.2136\,\Omega}$$

Example 3

A copper conductor has a resistivity of 17.8 $\mu\Omega$mm and is 1.785 mm in diameter. What will be the resistance of a 75 m length of this conductor?

We must first convert the diameter into the CSA. This is carried out by using one of the following formulas, which you may remember from school.

(a) $CSA = \dfrac{\pi d^2}{4}$　　Where d = diameter

Or:

(b) $CSA = \pi r^2$　　Where r = radius and π = 3.142

Using the first formula:

$CSA = \dfrac{\pi d^2}{4}$

Step 1: Put in the correct values:　　**Step 2:** Multiply the top line:　　**Step 3:** Divide by 4

$CSA = \dfrac{3.142 \times 1.785 \times 1.785}{4}$　　$CSA = \dfrac{10.01}{4}$　　$CSA = \textbf{2.5 mm}^2$

Therefore, using this method, the CSA is 2.5 mm².

Using the second formula:

$CSA = \pi r^2$

Step 1: Put in the correct values:　　**Step 2:** Multiply out

$CSA = 3.142 \times 0.8925 \times 0.8925$　　$CSA = \textbf{2.5 mm}^2$

Using the second method, the CSA is still 2.5 mm². We can now proceed with the example:

$R = \dfrac{\rho \times L}{a}$

Step 1: Put in the correct values:　　**Step 2:** Calculate out the top line:

$R = \dfrac{17.8 \times 10^{-6} \times 75 \times 10^3}{2.5}$　　$R = \dfrac{17.8 \times 10^{-3} \times 75}{2.5}$

Which is the same as:

$R = \dfrac{17.8 \times 75}{2.5 \times 10^3}$

So:

$R = \dfrac{1335}{2500}$

Therefore: **R = 0.534 Ω**

Current, voltage and resistance in parallel and series circuits

We have now started looking seriously at circuits in terms of what is in them and how current, resistance and potential difference are all related. However, a circuit can contain many resistors and they can be connected in many ways. In this section, we will be applying Ohm's Law and looking at:

- series circuits
- parallel circuits
- parallel-series circuits
- voltage drop.

Series circuits

If a number of resistors are connected together end to end and then connected to a supply, as shown in Figure 3.21, the current can only take one route through the circuit. We call this type of connection a series circuit.

Features of a series circuit

- The total circuit resistance (R_t) is the sum total of all the individual resistors. In Figure 3.21, this means:

$R_t = R_1 + R_2 + R_3$

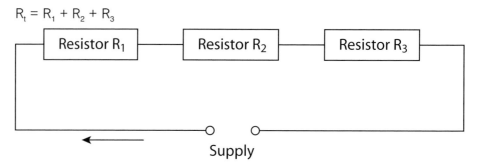

Figure 3.21: Series circuit

- The total circuit current (I) is the supply voltage divided by the total resistance. This is Ohm's Law:

$I = \dfrac{V}{R}$

- The current will have the same value at every point in the circuit.

- The potential difference across each resistor is proportional to its resistance. If we think back to Ohm's Law, we use voltage to push the electrons through a resistor. How much we use depends upon the size of the resistor. The bigger the resistor, the more we use. Therefore:

$V_1 = I \times R_1 \qquad V_2 = I \times R_2 \qquad V_3 = I \times R_3$

- The supply voltage (V) will be equal to the sum of the potential differences across each resistor. In other words, if we add up the p.d. across each resistor (the amount of volts 'dropped' across each resistor), it should come to the value of the supply voltage. We show this as:

$V = V_1 + V_2 + V_3$

- The total power in a series circuit is equal to the sum of the individual powers used by each resistor.

Calculation with a series circuit

Example

Two resistors of 6.2 Ω and 3.8 Ω are connected in series with a 12 V supply as shown in Figure 3.22. We want to calculate:

(a) total resistance

(b) total current flowing

(c) the potential difference (p.d.) across each resistor.

(a) Total resistance

For series circuits, the total resistance is the sum of the individual resistors:

$R_t = R_1 + R_2 = 6.2 + 3.8 =$ **10 Ω**

(b) Total current

Using Ohm's Law:

$I = \dfrac{\text{Voltage}}{\text{Resistance}} = \dfrac{12}{10} =$ **1.2 A**

(c) The p.d. across each resistor

$V = I \times R$, therefore:

Across R_1: $V_1 \quad = I \times R_1 \quad = 1.2 \times 6.2 =$ **7.44 V**

Across R_2: $V_2 \quad = I \times R_2 \quad = 1.2 \times 3.8 =$ **4.56 V**

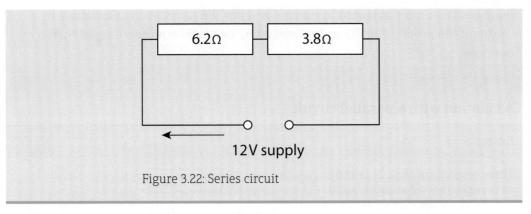

Figure 3.22: Series circuit

Parallel circuits

If a number of resistors are connected together as shown in Figure 3.23, so that there are two or more routes for the current to flow, then they are said to be connected in parallel.

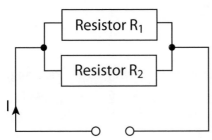

Figure 3.23: Parallel circuit

In this type of connection, the total current splits up and divides itself between the different branches of the circuit. However, note that the pressure pushing the electrons along (voltage), will be the same through each of the branches. Therefore any branch of a parallel circuit can be disconnected without affecting the other remaining branches.

Explanation

If we think about the definition of Ohm's Law, we know that the amount of electrons passing by (current) depends upon how hard we are pushing.

In a parallel circuit, the voltage is the same through each branch. Try to push two identical pencils in the same direction as the current flow towards a point on the circuit where the two branches split (shown as black circles in Figure 3.23). When they reach that point, one pencil will travel towards R_1 and the other towards R_2, but look how the force pushing the pencils has stayed the same.

However, how easily a pencil can then pass through a branch will depend upon the size of the obstacle in its way (the resistance of a resistor).

Features of a parallel circuit

The total circuit current (I) is found by adding together the current through each of the branches:

$$I = I_1 + I_2 + I_3$$

The same potential difference will occur across each branch of the circuit:

$$V = V_1 = V_2 = V_3$$

Where resistors are connected in parallel and, for the purpose of calculation, it is easier if the group of resistors is replaced by one total equivalent resistor (R_t). Therefore:

$$\frac{1}{R_t} = \frac{1}{R_1} + \frac{1}{R_2} + \frac{1}{R_3}$$

Calculation with a parallel circuit

Example

Three resistors of 16 Ω, 24 Ω and 48 Ω are connected across a 240 V supply. There are two ways to find out the total circuit current.

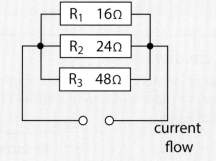

current flow

Method 1

Find the equivalent resistance, then use Ohm's Law:

$$\frac{1}{R_t} = \frac{1}{R_1} + \frac{1}{R_2} + \frac{1}{R_3}$$

Therefore: And therefore: Giving us: Rearranging the equation:

$$\frac{1}{R_t} = \frac{1}{R_1} + \frac{1}{R_2} + \frac{1}{R_3} \qquad \frac{1}{R_t} = \frac{3+2+1}{48} \qquad \frac{1}{R_t} = \frac{6}{48} \qquad R_t = \frac{48}{6}$$

and thus, $R_t = 8\ \Omega$

Now using the formula: We can say that: And therefore:

$$I = \frac{V}{R} \qquad\qquad I = \frac{240}{8} \qquad\qquad \mathbf{I = 30\ A}$$

Method 2

Find the current through each resistor and then add them together.

Now, for R_1:   **Gives:**   **So:**

$$I_1 = \frac{V}{R_1} \qquad\qquad I_1 = \frac{240}{16} \qquad I_1 = 15\ A$$

For R_2:   **Gives:**   **So:**

$$I_2 = \frac{240}{16} \qquad\qquad I_2 = \frac{240}{24} \qquad I_2 = 10\ A$$

For R_3:   **Gives:**   **So:**

$$I_3 = \frac{V}{R_3} \qquad\qquad I_3 = \frac{240}{48} \qquad I_3 = 5\ A$$

As: **Then:**

$$I_t = I_1 + I_2 + I_3 \qquad I_t = 15 + 10 + 5 = \mathbf{30\ A}$$

Please note that there is a second method of calculating R_t, namely, convert the fractions to decimals by diving the top number (1) by the respective bottom number (the value of the resistor). Using our example above, it would look like this:

$$\frac{1}{R_t} = \frac{1}{16}\ (0.0625) + \frac{1}{24}\ (0.0417) + \frac{1}{48}\ (0.0208)$$

$$0.0625 + 0.0417 + 0.0208 = 0.125$$

$$\frac{1}{R_t} = \frac{1}{0.125} \text{ therefore } R_t = \mathbf{8\ \Omega}$$

Series/parallel circuits

This type of circuit combines the series and parallel circuits as shown in the diagram in the example below. To calculate the resistance of the parallel group (R_p). Then, having found the equivalent value for the parallel group, we simply treat the circuit as being made up of series connected resistors and now add this value to any series resistors in the circuit, thus giving us the total resistance (R_t) for the whole of the network.

Here is a worked example.

Example 1

Calculate the total resistance of this circuit and the current flowing through the circuit, when the applied voltage is 110 V.

R₁ 10Ω R₂ 20Ω R₃ 30Ω R₄ 10Ω

Step 1: Find the equivalent resistance of the parallel group (R_p):

$$\frac{1}{R_p} = \frac{1}{R_1} + \frac{1}{R_2} + \frac{1}{R_3}$$

$$\frac{1}{R_p} = \frac{1}{10} + \frac{1}{20} + \frac{1}{30}$$

$$\frac{1}{R_p} = \frac{6 + 3 + 2}{60}$$

$$\frac{1}{R_p} = \frac{11}{60}$$

Therefore $R_p = \frac{60}{11} = \textbf{5.45 }\Omega$

Step 2: Add the equivalent resistor to the series resistor R_4:

$R_t = R_p + R_4$

$R_t = 5.45 + 10$

$R_t = \textbf{15.45 }\Omega$

Step 3: Calculate the current:

$$I = \frac{V}{R_t} = \frac{110}{15.45} = \textbf{7.12 A}$$

Using the rules we have learned, what appear to be complicated diagrams of interconnected resistors can be resolved to a single value.

The following example shows the process step by step.

Example 2

Calculate the total resistance (R_t) of the resistor arrangement shown in the following diagram.

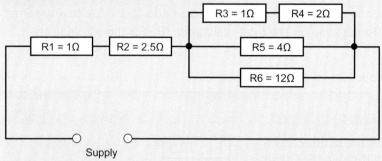

Start by reducing the branch with resistors R_3 and R_4. As they are series connected we can add the resistances together meaning that we could now redraw the diagram as follows:

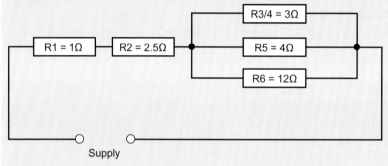

Now we can reduce down the parallel group (R_p) of resistors $R_{3/4}$, R_5 and R_6.

Therefore: $\dfrac{1}{R_p} = \dfrac{1}{3} + \dfrac{1}{4} + \dfrac{1}{12}$ which gives us $\dfrac{4+3+1}{12} = \dfrac{8}{12}$

Therefore: $R_p = \dfrac{12}{8}$ so $\mathbf{R_p = 1.5\,\Omega}$

We can now redraw the circuit again to reflect this:

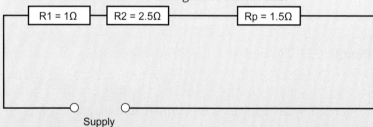

We now have three series connected resistors. This means our final calculation will be:

$R_t = R_1 + R_2 + R_p = 1 + 2.5 + 1.5$

Therefore $\mathbf{R_t = 5\,\Omega}$

Voltage drop

Cables in a circuit are also resistors, in that the longer a conductor is, the higher its resistance becomes and thus the greater the voltage drop will be. We can calculate this by using Ohm's Law.

To determine voltage drop quickly in circuit cables, BS 7671 and cable manufacturer data include tables of voltage drop in cable conductors. The tables list the voltage drop in terms of (mV/A/m) and are listed as conductor feed and return, e.g. for two single-core cables or one two-core cable.

BS 7671 states that the voltage drop between the origin of the installation (usually the supply terminals) and any load point should not exceed 3% for lighting and 5% for power.

For a 230 V lighting circuit	For a 230 V power circuit
$\frac{3}{100} \times 230 = 6.9\,V$	$\frac{5}{100} \times 230 = 11.5\,V$

Table 3.9: Voltage drop in circuits

Power

We know that electrons are pushed along a conductor by a force called the e.m.f. Now consider the electrical units of work and power. Because energy and work are interchangeable (we use up energy to complete work) they have the same units, joules. Both can be measured in terms of force and distance.

If a force is required to move an object some distance, then work has been done and some energy has been used to do it. The greater the distance and the heavier the object, then the greater the amount of work done.

We already know that:

Energy (or Work done) = Distance moved × Force required

Power is, 'the rate at which we do work' and it is measured in watts. So:

$$\text{Power} = \frac{\text{Energy (or work done)}}{\text{Time taken}}$$
$$= \frac{\text{Distance moved} \times \text{Force required}}{\text{Time taken}}$$

For example, we could drill two holes in a wall – one using a hand drill, and the other with an electric drill. When we have finished, the work done will be the same in both cases, there will be two identical holes in the wall, but the electric drill will do it more quickly because its power is greater.

If power is therefore considered to be the ratio of work done against the time taken to do the work, we may express this as follows:

$$Power = \frac{Work\ done\ (W)}{Time\ taken\ (t)} = \frac{Energy\ used}{Time}$$

The units are:

$$watts = \frac{joules}{seconds}$$

Earlier in this unit, we considered the e.m.f. and defined it as being the amount of joules of work necessary to move one coulomb of electricity around the circuit, measured in joules per coulomb, also known as the volt.

Noting that 1 volt = 1 joule/coulomb and rearranging the formula, this could be expressed as:

joules = volt × coulombs and since:

coulombs = amperes × seconds

We can substitute this to get:

joules = volts × amperes × seconds

And, since joules are the units of work:

Work = V × I × t (joules)

Taking this one step further, we can show how we arrive at some of our electrical formulae. It goes as follows.

If:

$$Power = \frac{work}{time}$$ this means: $$P = \frac{V \times I \times t}{t}$$

So cancelling gives:

P = V × I **or** P = I × V

In Ohm's Law:

V = I × R

Therefore by showing V as (I × R):

P = I × (I × R) **thus P = I² × R**

Also in Ohm's Law:

$$I = \frac{V}{R}$$

Therefore by showing I as $\left(\frac{V}{R}\right)$

$P = \frac{V}{R} \times V$ **thus $P = \frac{V^2}{R}$**

Simple when you know how!

And when you have practised changing equations dozens of times!

Some examples of power calculations

Example 1

Two 100 Ω resistors are connected in series to a 100 V supply. What will be the total power dissipated?

Firstly find the total resistance, which for a series circuit is $R_t = R_1 + R_2$

Therefore $R_t = 100 + 100 = 200\,Ω$

Power can be found by $\frac{V^2}{R}$ Therefore: $P = \frac{100^2}{200} = \frac{10\,000}{200}$

Therefore **P = 50 W**

Example 2

How much energy is supplied to a 100 W resistor that is connected to a 150 V supply for one hour?

$P = \frac{V^2}{R}$ therefore: $\frac{150 \times 150}{100} = $ **225 W**

Now:

$E = P \times t$

Firstly, convert one hour into seconds as 60 minutes × 60 seconds = 3600

Then:

E = energy supplied = 225 × 3600 = **810 000 joules**

Power calculations for a parallel circuit are essentially the same as those used for the series circuit.

Since power dissipation in resistors consists of a heat loss, power dissipations will be additive irrespective of how the resistors are connected in the circuit and the total power is equal to the sum of the power dissipated by each individual resistor.

Example 3

Three resistors are connected in parallel as shown.

Calculate the power dissipated by each resistor and in total.

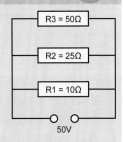

Power for R_1 $P = \frac{V^2}{R} = \frac{50^2}{10} = \frac{2500}{10} = $ **250 W**

Power for R_2 $P = \frac{V^2}{R} = \frac{50^2}{25} = \frac{2500}{25} = $ **100 W**

Power for R_3 $P = \frac{V^2}{R} = \frac{50^2}{50} = \frac{2500}{50} = $ **50 W**

As power dissipation is additive, total power = 250 + 100 + 50 = **400 W**

An alternative method to find the total power would be to collapse the parallel network to an equivalent resistance.

In which case our calculation would be:

$\frac{1}{R_t} = \frac{1}{R_1} + \frac{1}{R_2} + \frac{1}{R_3}$ therefore $\frac{1}{R_t} = \frac{1}{10} + \frac{1}{25} + \frac{1}{50}$ which gives us $\frac{1}{R_t} = \frac{5 + 2 + 1}{50} = \frac{8}{50}$

If $\frac{1}{R_t} = \frac{8}{50}$ then $R_t = 50 \div 8 = 6.25\,Ω$

If $P = \frac{V^2}{R}$ then gives us $\frac{50^2}{6.25} = \frac{2500}{6.25}$ therefore again, P = **400 W**

Kilowatt hour

It should be noted that the joule is far too small a unit for sensible energy measurement. For most applications, we use something called the kilowatt hour.

The kilowatt hour is defined as the amount of energy used when one kilowatt (1000 watts) of power has been used for a time of 1 hour (3600 seconds).

From this we can see that:

1 joule (J) = 1 watt (W) for 1 second (s)

1000 joules (J) = 1 kilowatt (kW) for 1 second

In 1 hour there are 3600 seconds. Therefore:

3600 s × 1000 J = 1 kW for 1 hour (kWh) So:

1 kWh = 3.6 × 10⁶ J

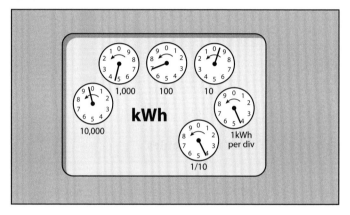

Figure 3.24: Typical electric meter dials

The kilowatt hour is the unit used by the electrical supply companies to charge their customers for the supply of electrical energy. Have a look in your house. You will see that the electric meter is measuring in kWh. However, these are more often referred to as Units by the time they appear on your bill!

Example

If a small house has the following items connected to the supply each day, calculate how much energy would be consumed over a seven day period.

- Four 100 W light fittings each used for 2 hours.
- One 3 kW electric fire used for 2 hours.
- One 3 kW kettle for a total of 1 hour.

Remembering that E = P × t and applying this to each load:

Lights = (4 × 100) × 2 = 800 = 0.8 kWh

Fire = 3 × 2 = 6 kWh

Kettle = 3 × 1 = 3 kWh

This gives a total daily consumption of 9.8 kWh

Therefore over seven days the consumption will be 9.8 × 7 = **68.6 kWh**

Efficiency

We have looked at efficiency in the mechanics section. The calculations and theory for efficiency applied to electrical circuits are very similar.

You already know that:

Percentage efficiency $= \dfrac{\text{Output}}{\text{Input}} \times 100$

Let us have a look at two examples.

Example 1

Calculate the efficiency of a water heater if the output in kilowatt hours is 25 kWh and the input energy is 30 kWh.

Efficiency (%) $= \dfrac{\text{Output}}{\text{Input}} \times 100 = \dfrac{25}{30} \times 100 =$ **83.33%**

Example 2

The power output from a generator is 2700 W and the power required to drive it is 3500 W. Calculate the percentage efficiency of the generator.

Efficiency (%) $= \dfrac{\text{Output}}{\text{Input}} \times 100 = \dfrac{2700}{3500} \times 100 =$ **77.1%**

Instruments and measurement

As electricians we are often responsible for the measurement of different electrical quantities. Some must be measured as part of the inspection and testing of an installation (e.g. insulation resistance). However, of the remainder, the most common quantities that we are likely to come across are shown in Table 3.10.

Property	Instrument
Current	Ammeter
Voltage	Voltmeter
Resistance	Ohmmeter
Power	Wattmeter

Table 3.10 Electrical quantities

We will look at the different instruments that we use to measure these quantities in the following section. But before we ever use a meter, we must always ask ourselves:

- Have we chosen the correct instrument?
- Is it working correctly?
- Has it been set to the correct scale?
- How should it be connected?

Measuring current (ammeter)

An ammeter measures current by series connections. Although we know that we can use a multimeter on site, the actual name for an instrument that measures current is an ammeter. Ammeters are connected in series so that the current to be measured passes through them. The circuit diagram in Figure 3.25(a) illustrates this. Consequently, they need to have a very low resistance or they would give a false reading.

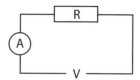

Figure 3.25(a): Ammeter in circuit

If we now look at the same circuit, but use a correctly set multimeter, the connections would look as in Figure 3.25(b).

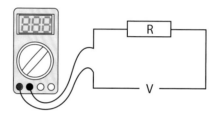

Figure 3.25(b): Multimeter in circuit

Measuring voltage (voltmeter)

On site or for general purposes, we can use a multimeter to measure voltage, but the actual device used for measuring voltage is called a voltmeter. It measures the potential difference between two points (for instance, across the two connections of a resistor). The voltmeter must be connected in parallel across the load or circuit to be measured as shown in Figure 3.26(a).

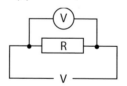

Figure 3.26(a): Voltmeter in circuit

If we now look at the same circuit, but use our correctly set multimeter, the connections would look as in Figure 3.26(b). The internal resistance of a voltmeter must be very high if we wish to get accurate readings.

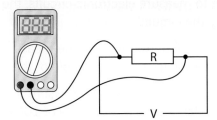

Figure 3.26(b): Multimeter measuring voltage

Measuring resistance (ohmmeter)

There are many ways in which we can measure resistance. However, in the majority of cases we do so by executing a calculation based on instrument readings (ammeter/voltmeter) or from other known resistance values. Once again we can use our multimeter to perform the task, but we refer to the actual meter as being an ohmmeter.

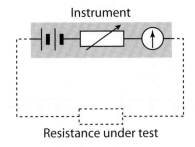

Figure 3.27: Ohmmeter

The principle of operation involves the meter having its own internal supply (battery). The current, which then flows through the meter, must be dependent upon the value of the resistance under scrutiny.

However, before we start our measurement, we must ensure that the supply is off and then connect both leads of the meter together and adjust the meter's variable resistor until full-scale deflection (zero) is reached.

The dotted line in Figure 3.27 indicates the circuit under test. All other components are internal to the meter.

Using an ammeter and voltmeter

If we consider the application of Ohm's Law, we know that we can establish resistance by the following formula:

$$R = \frac{V \text{ (voltmeter)}}{I \text{ (ammeter)}}$$

If we therefore connect an ammeter and voltmeter in the circuit, then by using a known supply (battery) we can apply the above formula to the readings that we get.

In practice, we invariably find that we need a long 'wandering' test lead to perform such a test. Where this is the case, we must remember to deduct the value of the test lead from our circuit resistance.

Loading errors

Connecting a measuring instrument to a circuit will invariably have an effect on that circuit. In the case of the average electrical installation, this effect can largely be ignored. But if we were to measure electronic circuits, the effect may be drastic enough to actually destroy the circuit.

We normally refer to these errors introduced by the measuring instrument as loading errors, and in Figure 3.28 we will look at an example of this.

Let's assume in (a) that we have been asked to measure the voltage across resistor B in the circuit, where both items have a resistance of 100 kΩ. Note that in this arrangement, the potential difference (p.d.) across each resistor will be 115 V.

Our instrument, a voltmeter, has an internal resistance of 100 kΩ and would therefore be connected as in Figure 3.28.

In effect, by connecting our meter in this way, we are introducing an extra resistance in parallel into the circuit. We could, therefore, now draw our circuit as in Figure 3.28(b).

Now, if we find the equivalent resistance of the parallel branches:

$$\frac{1}{R_t} = \frac{1}{R_1} + \frac{1}{R_2} = \frac{1+1}{100} = \frac{2}{100} \, k\Omega$$

Therefore:

$$R_t = \frac{100}{2} = 50 \, k\Omega$$

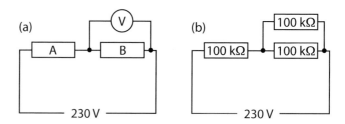

Figure 3.28: Loading errors

And then if we treat the parallel combination as being in series with 100 kΩ resistor A then total resistance:

$$R = R_A + R_t = 100 \, k\Omega + 50 \, k\Omega = 150 \, k\Omega$$

If you applied Ohm's Law again, we would find we now have a current of 0.001 53 A (1.53 mA) flowing in the circuit. This in turn would give a p.d. across each resistor of 76 V and not the 115 V we would expect to see.

The problem is caused by the amount of current that is flowing through the meter, and this is normally solved by using meters with a very high resistance (as resistance restricts current). So you now see why we said earlier that voltmeters must have a high internal resistance in order to be accurate.

Meter displays

There are two types of display, **analogue** and **digital**. Analogue meters have a needle moving around a calibrated scale, whereas digital tend to show results, as numeric values, via a liquid crystal or LED display.

For many years electricians used the analogue meter and indeed it is still common for continuity/insulation resistance testers to be of the analogue style. However, their use is slowly being replaced by the digital meter. Most modern digital meters are based on semiconductors and consequently have very high impedance, making them ideal for accurate readings and good for use with electronic circuits.

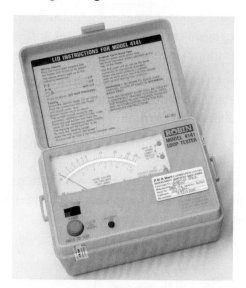

Figure 3.29: Analogue meter

Figure 3.30: Digital meter

Generally speaking, as they have no moving parts they are also more suited to rugged site conditions than the analogue style.

What sort of meter will I need?

Although instruments exist to measure individual electrical quantities, most electricians will find that a cost-effective solution is to use a digital multimeter similar to the one pictured. Meters like this are generally capable of measuring current, resistance and voltage, both in AC and DC circuits and across a wide range of values.

Is the meter working correctly?

It is important to check that your meter is functioning correctly and physically fit for purpose. There are commercially available proving units that will help. However, on site it is more normal to use a known supply as the means of proving voltage measurement and the shorting/separating of leads to prove operation.

Measuring power

In a DC circuit it is possible to measure the power supplied by using a voltmeter and an ammeter. Then by using the formula $P = V \times I$ we can arrive at the power in watts.

However, in an AC circuit, this method only produces the apparent power, a figure that will not be accurate unless we have unity power factor. This is because components such as capacitors and inductors will cause the current to lead or lag the voltage.

For a single-phase AC circuit we therefore use the formula:

$P = V \times I \times \cos \emptyset$

This indicates how we would connect measuring instruments to establish power. For a single-phase resistive load, we can use the ammeter and voltmeter, but for a circuit containing capacitance or inductance we must use a wattmeter.

Figure 3.31 indicates how a wattmeter is connected into a single-phase circuit. Just like Ohm's Law, a wattmeter also requires values for voltage and current, a wattmeter also requires values of voltage and current.

The instrument shown in Figure 3.31 has a current coil, indicated between W_1 and W_2, that is wired in series with the load, and a voltage coil, shown between P_1 and P_2, wired in parallel across the supply. This can be used to measure the power in a single-phase circuit or in a balanced three-phase load, where the total power will be equal to three times the value measured on the meter.

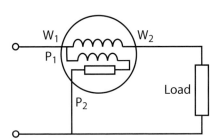

Figure 3.31: Wattmeter connected

Measuring power in a three-phase, four-wire balanced load – one-wattmeter method

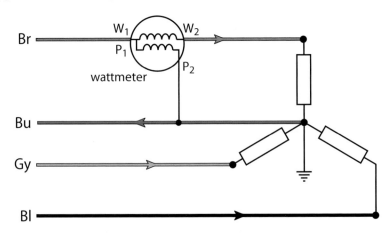

Figure 3.32: One-meter method

Measuring power in a three-phase balanced load–two-wattmeter method

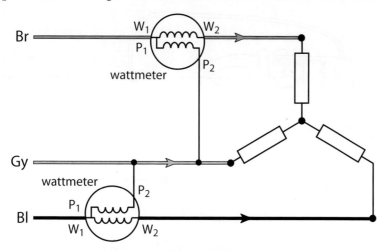

Figure 3.33: Wattmeter connected to load

In the two-wattmeter method, the total power is found by adding the two values together. At unity power factor the instruments will read the same and be half of the total load. For other power factors the instrument readings will be different, the difference in the reading could then be used to calculate the power factor.

Measuring power in an unbalanced three-phase circuit – three-wattmeter method
Here the total power will be the sum total of the readings on the three-wattmeters.

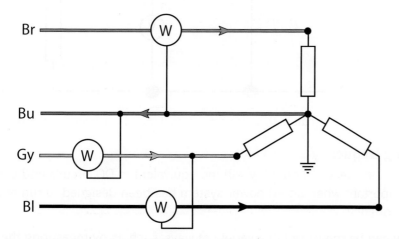

Figure 3.34: Three-phase circuit

This allows the power to be measured in a situation where the load is unbalanced, such as the three-phase supply to a large building where it is impossible to balance the load completely.

Measuring power factor
To measure power factor, there are a number of purpose-made instruments available. All of these meters include both voltage and current measurement in circuits. Most designs are based on the clamp meter idea where the meter clamps around the current-carrying conductor. However, additional leads are then required to connect the meter across the supply. Many meters are also combined with the ability to measure all aspects of power, i.e. kW, kVA and kVAr.

Figure 3.35 illustrates the connections of a power factor measuring instrument.

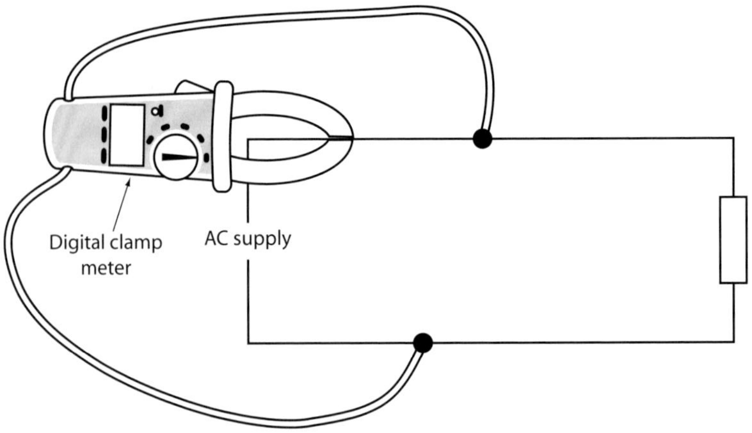

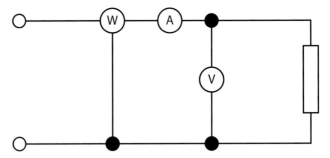

Digital clamp meter   AC supply

Figure 3.35: Circuit diagram with digital clamp meter

There is also an alternative method. The calculation to establish power factor is to divide true power by the apparent power (VA). As we know that a wattmeter will give us the true power, by adding an ammeter and a voltmeter to our circuit we can establish the apparent power (VA) and therefore establish the power factor. Figure 3.36 shows this arrangement.

Figure 3.36: Circuit with wattmeter, ammeter and voltmeter connected

Measuring frequency

Frequency is an electrical quantity with no equivalent in DC circuits and can become important when an AC power system has been designed to run at a specific frequency.

Frequency can be measured in a variety of ways, such as by measuring the shaft speed of the generator that produced the alternating current or by using a Cathode Ray Oscilloscope.

However, one very popular method is to use a vibrating reed frequency meter as shown in Figure 3.37. These work very much like a tuning fork that is used to tune a piano, in that any object that possesses elasticity has a frequency that it likes to vibrate at. If you can remember those tuning forks, the longer ones vibrate at lower notes when struck than the shorter ones, which have a higher note when struck.

Figure 3.37: Vibrating reed frequency meter

If you placed a row of such tuning forks side by side fixed to a common base material, the base could be vibrated at the frequency of the supply by means of an electromagnet. The fork that likes to vibrate at the frequency needed will therefore start to 'rattle' about, and it is the end of those forks that we can see in such a meter.

Measuring impedance

Impedance (Z) is generally defined as the total opposition a device or circuit offers to the flow of an alternating current (AC) at a given frequency, and is represented as a complex quantity which is graphically shown on a vector plane. An impedance vector consists of resistance (R) and an 'imaginary' part, reactance (X), which as we discussed earlier, takes two forms: inductive (X_L) and capacitive (X_C).

To find the impedance, we therefore need to measure at least two values because impedance is a complex quantity and many modern impedance measuring instruments measure the real and the imaginary parts of an impedance vector before converting them into the desired parameter.

Measurement ranges and accuracy for a variety of impedance parameters are then determined from those specified for impedance measurement. However, automated instruments allow you to make a measurement by simply connecting the component, circuit, or material to the instrument.

Quite often these meters are referred to as LRC meters because of the circuit components involved.

Summary

1. A load has a resistance of 23 ohms and is connected to the mains, if the mains is 230 V what current is the load drawing?

2. In a parallel circuit is the voltage the same through each branch?

3. A load has a power rating of 3 KW, and is connected to a mains voltage of 230 V, what current is the load drawing?

5. Fundamental principles which underpin the relationship between magnetism and electricity

We can really go no further with circuit theory until we have looked more closely at the magnetic behaviour of materials and the way this affects the interaction between electrical currents and magnetic fields.

Magnetic effects of electrical currents

The word magnetic originated with the ancient Greeks, who found natural rocks possessing this characteristic.

Magnetic rocks such as magnetite, an iron ore, occur naturally. The Chinese observed the effects of magnetism as early as 2600 BC when they saw that stones like magnetite, when freely suspended, had a tendency to assume a north and south direction. Because magnetic stones aligned themselves north–south, they were referred to as lodestones or leading stones.

Magnetism is hard to define – we all know what its effects are: the attraction or repulsion of a material by another material, but why does this happen? And why do we only see it in some materials, notably metals and particularly iron? The physics behind this is too complex to cover here, but it is useful to remember that magnetism is a fundamental force (like gravity) and it arises due to the movement of electrical charge. Magnetism is seen whenever electrically charged particles are in motion.

Materials that are attracted by a magnet, such as iron, steel, nickel and cobalt, have the ability to become magnetised. These are called magnetic materials.

For the purpose of this book, we are only interested in two types of magnet:

- the permanent magnet
- the electromagnet (temporary magnet).

The permanent magnet

A permanent magnet is a material that when inserted into a strong magnetic field will exhibit a magnetic field of its own, and continue to exhibit a magnetic field once it has been removed from the original field.

This remaining field would allow the magnet to exert force (the ability to attract or repel) on other magnetic materials. This magnetic field is continuous without losing strength, as long as the material is not subjected to a change in environment (temperature, de-magnetising field, etc.).

The ability to continue exhibiting a field while withstanding different environments helps to define the capabilities and types of applications in which a magnet can be successfully used.

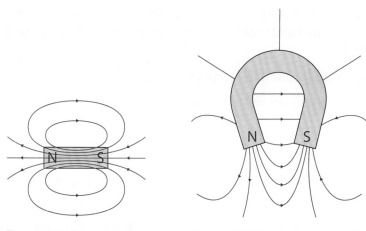

Figure 3.38: Bar magnet   Figure 3.39: Horseshoe magnet

Magnetic fields in permanent magnets come from two atomic causes: the spin and orbital motions of electrons. Therefore, the magnetic characteristics of a material can change when alloyed with other elements.

For example, a non-magnetic material such as aluminium can become magnetic in materials such as alnico or manganese-aluminium-carbon.

When a ferromagnetic material (a material containing iron) is magnetised in one direction, it will not relax back to zero magnetisation when the imposed magnetising field is removed. The amount of magnetisation it retains is called its remanence and it can only be driven back to zero by a field in the opposite direction; the amount of reverse driving field required to de-magnetise it is called its coercivity.

We have probably all experienced at some time the effect of a permanent magnet (although we cannot see the magnetic field with the naked eye), even if it is just to leave a message on the fridge door.

The magnetic field looks like a series of closed loops that start at one end (pole) of the magnet, arrive at the other and then pass through the magnet to the original start point.

At school you probably did the famous experiment where you took a magnet, placed it on a piece of paper and then sprinkled iron filings over it?

If you did, you would see that it looks like Figure 3.40, with the attraction of the magnet causing the filings to line up on the lines of magnetic flux (the direction of the field).

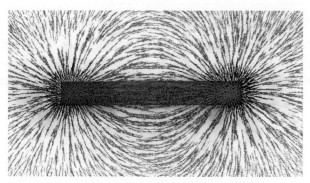

Figure 3.40: Iron filings around a bar magnet

If we were to add a small compass to the experiment, we would find that the lines run externally from the North pole of the magnet to the South and that they have the following properties:

- They will never cross, but may become distorted.

- They will always try to return to their original shape.

- They will always form a closed loop.

- Outside the magnet they run north to south.

- The higher the number of lines of magnetic flux, the stronger the magnet.

If we could count the lines, we could establish the magnetic flux (which we measure in webers), and we would find that the more lines that there were, the stronger the magnet would be. In other words the bigger the magnet the bigger the flux produced.

The strength of the magnetic field at any point is calculated by counting the number of lines that we have at that point and this is then called the flux density (measuring webers/square metre, which are given the unit title of a tesla).

We define the tesla as follows: If one weber of magnetic flux was spread evenly over a cross-sectional area of one square metre, then we have a flux density of one tesla. In other words the flux density depends upon the amount of magnetic flux lines and the area to which they are applied.

We use the following formula to express this:

$$\text{Flux density B (tesla)} = \frac{\text{magnetic flux}}{\text{CSA}} = \frac{\Phi}{A} \text{ (webers/m}^2\text{)}$$

Here is an example to help you understand what is going on.

Example

The field pole of a motor has an area of 5 cm² and carries a flux of 80 µWb. What will be the flux density?

Using the formula:

$$\text{Flux density B (tesla)} = \frac{\text{magnetic flux}}{\text{CSA}} = \frac{\Phi}{A} \text{ (webers/m}^2\text{)}$$

We need to make allowance for the area being given in cm² and the flux in mWb.

Therefore:

$$\text{Flux density B (tesla)} = \frac{\text{magnetic flux}}{\text{CSA}} = \frac{80 \times 10^{-6}\,\text{Wb}}{5 \times 10^{-4}\,\text{m}^2} = \textbf{0.16 T}$$

The electromagnet

An electromagnet is a type of magnet created where there is an electric current flowing through a conductor, which in turn produces a magnetic field around the conductor. This magnetic field is proportional to the current being carried, meaning that the larger the current flow, the greater the magnetic field strength.

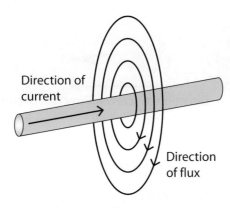

Figure 3.41: Lines of magnetic force set up around a conductor

An electromagnet is defined as being a temporary magnet because the magnetic field can only exist while there is a current flowing.

If we have a typically shaped conductor such as a wire, then, as shown in Figure 3.41, the magnetic field looks like concentric circles and these are along the whole length of the conductor. However, the direction of the field depends on the direction of the current.

Maxwell's right-hand rule and the screw rule

We traditionally work out the direction of the magnetic field by using either Maxwell's right-hand rule or the 'screw rule'.

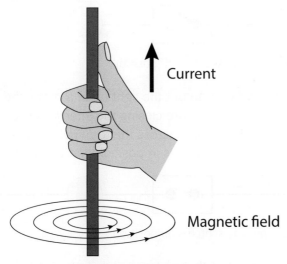

Figure 3.42: Maxwell's right-hand rule

In the screw rule we think of a normal right-hand threaded screw, where the movement of the tip represents the direction of the current through a straight conductor and the direction of rotation of the screw represents the corresponding direction of rotation of the magnetic field.

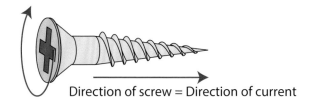

Direction of screw = Direction of current

Figure 3.43: The screw rule

Rotation of screw = rotation of magnetic field

Direction of screw = direction of current

Let's have a quick look at how we can use the magnetic effect in our industry.

The relay

A relay is an electromechanical switch used in many types of electronic device to switch voltages and electronic signals.

The most common electromechanical switch is the simple one-way wall switch used to control the lights in your home, as this type of switch requires a human to perform the 'switching' between on and off. Relays operate differently as they require no human interaction in order for the switching to occur. However, considering the one-way switch helps to explain how a relay works.

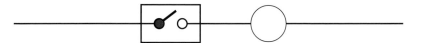

Figure 3.44: One-way switch – off position

In the one-way circuit, if we want to put the light on in a room, the switch is operated by your finger. When we do this, we are closing the internal switch contact and the contact is mechanically held in place across the terminals. Consequently when we take our finger off the switch, it remains in position and the light stays on.

Figure 3.45: One-way switch – on position

However let's say we don't want that sort of switch, but want to control the light by using a relay, which as an example, will see its coil being operated as part of a timer controlled circuit. The concept is similar if you think of a relay as being an assembly that contains a one-way switch and a coil. We'll draw the switch contact in a slightly different way this time, but the idea is exactly the same, i.e. electricity will pass from one terminal to the other when the contact is closed.

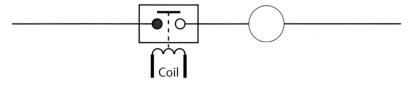

Figure 3.46: One-way switch and coil – off position

If the timer was now to energise the coil, the resulting magnetic field would pull the contact across the two terminals, thus closing the circuit and the light would come on. This time, instead of the switch contact being held in place mechanically, it is being held in place by the magnetic field produced by the coil in the relay. It will only remain this way while the coil is energised.

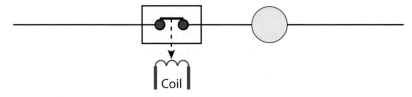

Figure 3.47: When the coil is energised, the switch is on

We describe this type of relay as having 'normally open' contacts. This means that in its normal position with no supply to the coil, the contact is open and no electricity can pass through the relay.

It is possible to have a relay where the exact opposite function takes place, i.e. when the coil is energised the contact is pulled away from the terminals. In such a relay the supply would normally be passing through the closed contact and therefore operating the coil will break the circuit. We say that such a relay has 'normally closed' contacts.

A relay is therefore an electromechanical switch that uses an electromagnet to create a magnetic field which opens or closes one or many sets of contacts.

Applications of the relay

Relays can be used to:

- control a high voltage circuit with a low voltage signal, as in some types of modem
- control a high current circuit with a low current signal, as in all the lights in the hall of a leisure centre being controlled from a 5 A switch in reception
- control a mains powered device from a low voltage switch
- switch a current between different circuits or turn a circuit on or off.

Figure 3.48: A relay

When choosing a relay there are several things to consider:

- **Coil voltage** – this indicates how much voltage (230 V, 24 V) and what kind (AC or DC) must be applied to energise the coil. Therefore, make sure that the coil voltage matches the supply fed into it.

- **Contact ratings** – this indicates how heavy a load the relay can control (e.g. 0.5 A or 10 A).

- **Contact arrangement** – there are many kinds of switches, so there are many kinds of relays. The contact geometry indicates how many poles there are, and how they open and close.

For example, a changeover relay has one moving contact and two fixed contacts. One of these is normally closed when the relay is switched off, and the other is normally open. Energising the coil will cause the normally open contact to close and the normally closed contact to open.

Force between current-carrying conductors

So far we have looked at the force on an object inside a magnetic field produced by a permanent magnet or electromagnet. But what happens when we place a current-carrying conductor (a wire that has a current flowing through it) inside a magnetic field or next to another current-carrying conductor?

We already know that a magnetic field, in the form of concentric circles, will be produced by a current-carrying conductor. If we took two such conductors and placed them side by side, we would see a force exists between them due to the magnetic flux and the direction of this force will be dictated by the direction of the current.

For example, in Figure 3.49 the direction of current in both conductors is different and therefore the direction of the flux in between the conductors is the same. This means that the largest concentration of flux is between the two conductors and a lesser amount on the outside of them and therefore the resultant force will try to push them apart.

The reverse is true, in that if the direction of current in both conductors was the same, then the direction of the flux in between the conductors will be in opposite directions. This cancels flux levels out and leaves more flux on the outside of the two conductors and therefore the resultant force will try to push them together.

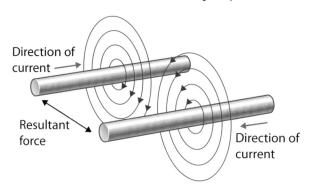

Figure 3.49: Force between current-carrying conductors

Force on a current-carrying conductor in a magnetic field

In the section on the permanent magnet, we said that lines of flux can be distorted but will never cross, and it is this principle that we will consider in this section.

If we place a current-carrying conductor between two magnetic poles we can look at the field caused only by the conductor. As shown in Figure 3.50, you will see that the current is going away from you, therefore the field is clockwise. This is the screw rule we mentioned earlier.

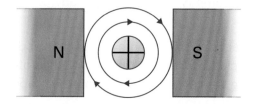

Figure 3.50: Current-carrying conductor between two magnetic poles

This time in Figure 3.51 we will look at the same arrangement, but only looking at the field caused by the two magnetic poles.

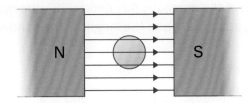

Figure 3.51: Field caused by two magnetic poles

Now bearing in mind that lines of flux cannot cross, Figure 3.52 is what the result would be if we actually had a current-carrying conductor in a magnetic field.

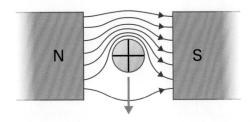

Figure 3.52: Current-carrying conductor in a magnetic field

In Figure 3.52 we can see that the main field now becomes distorted and, that as the two fields above the conductor are in the same direction, the amount of flux is high and therefore the force will move the conductor downwards. The reverse would be true if the two fields were in opposition.

The direction in which a current-carrying conductor tends to move when it is placed in a magnetic field can be determined by Fleming's left-hand (motor) rule.

This rule states that if the first finger, the second finger and the thumb of the left hand are held at right angles to each other as shown below, then with the first finger pointing in the direction of the Field (N to S), and the second finger pointing in the direction of the current in the conductor, then the thumb will indicate the direction in which the conductor tends to move.

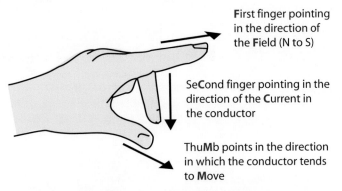

First finger pointing in the direction of the **F**ield (N to S)

Se**C**ond finger pointing in the direction of the **C**urrent in the conductor

Thu**M**b points in the direction in which the conductor tends to **M**ove

Figure 3.53: Fleming's left-hand rule

Calculating the force on a conductor

The force that moves the current-carrying conductor placed in a magnetic field depends on the strength of the magnetic flux density (B), the magnitude of the current flowing in the conductor (I), and the length of the conductor in the magnetic field (ℓ).

The following equation expresses this relationship: Force (F) = B × I × ℓ

Where B is in tesla, ℓ is in metres, I is in amperes and F is in newtons.

Here are two examples.

Example 1

A conductor 15 m in length lies at right angles to a magnetic field of 5 tesla. Calculate the force on the conductor when:

(a) 15 A flows in the coil

(b) 25 A flows in the coil

(c) 50 A flows in the coil.

Answer: Using the formula F = B × I × ℓ:

(a) F = 5 × 15 × 15 = 1125 N

(b) F = 5 × 25 × 15 = 1875 N

(c) F = 5 × 50 × 15 = 3750 N.

Example 2

A conductor 0.25 m long situated in, and at right angles to, a magnetic field experiences a force of 5 N when a current through it is 50 A. Calculate the flux density.

Answer: Transpose the formula F = B × I × ℓ for (B):

$$B = \frac{F}{I \times \ell}$$

Substitute the known values into the equation:

$$B = \frac{5}{0.25 \times 50} = \textbf{0.4 T}$$

The solenoid

A solenoid is a long hollow cylinder around which we wind a uniform coil of wire. When a current is sent through the wire, a magnetic field is created inside the cylinder.

A solenoid (Figure 3.54) usually has a length that is several times its diameter and the wire is closely wound around the outside of a long cylinder in the form of a helix with a small pitch. The magnetic field created inside the cylinder is quite uniform, especially far from the ends of the solenoid and the flux density is increased by winding on to an iron core instead of a hollow cylinder.

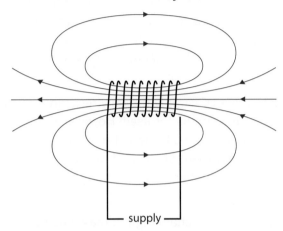

Figure 3.54: Construction of a solenoid

Essentially, the magnetic field produced by a solenoid is similar to that of a bar magnet. If an iron rod were then placed partly inside a solenoid and the current turned on, the rod will be drawn into the solenoid by the resulting magnetic field.

We can use this motion to move a lever or operate a latch to open a door and it is most commonly seen in use inside a doorbell.

As shown in Figure 3.55, we can use a switch to energise the solenoid, the magnetic field will draw the iron rod in and therefore produce a mechanical action at a remote location, e.g. the doorbell. When the supply is not present the iron rod is returned to its original position under spring pressure.

However, instead of having a current-carrying conductor placed in a magnetic field which causes it to move, what if we took a conductor with **no** current flowing in it and instead moved the conductor through the magnetic field?

Instead of having the current causing a motion, we will now have the motion causing a current and in this case the magnetic field is responsible for the flow of an electric current. We call this electromagnetic induction.

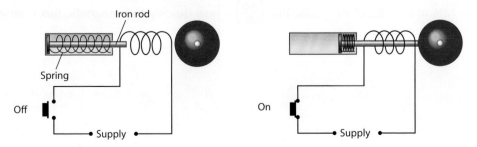

Figure 3.55: Operation of a switch in the off and on positions on a solenoid in a doorbell

Electromagnetic induction

Stated simply, if a conductor is moved through a magnetic field, then, provided there is a closed circuit, a current will flow through it.

We know that we need a 'force' to drive electrons along a conductor, and we can say that an e.m.f. must be producing the current. In this situation we are causing an e.m.f. This is known as the induced e.m.f. and it will have the same direction as the flowing current.

If we were to pass an electric current through a conductor this would generate a uniform magnetic field around the conductor and at right angles to the conductor. The strength of this magnetic field is directly proportional to the current flowing in the conductor and the strength of this magnetic field can be further increased by coiling the conductor to form a solenoid.

If the coil were connected to a DC supply the only resistance to the current flow would be the resistance of the conductor itself. However, if the coil is connected to an AC supply the situation must be looked at differently. Bear in mind that any change in the magnetic environment of a coil of wire will cause a voltage (e.m.f.) to be 'induced' in the coil and no matter how the change is produced, the voltage will be generated.

The change could be produced by changing the magnetic field strength, moving a magnet toward or away from the coil, moving the coil into or out of the magnetic field, rotating the coil relative to the magnet, etc.

Alternating current creates the effect of a continuously changing magnetic field inside the coil, and this induces an e.m.f. in the coil that acts in opposition to the supply voltage and is therefore referred to as the back e.m.f.

Thinking of the solenoid we have just been talking about, you may have realised that an e.m.f is induced only when we have a changing situation. So what could change in the solenoid set-up?

Well, the following could change:

- the material composition of the core (air, iron or steel)
- the diameter of the coil
- the material composition of the coil.
- the number of turns in the coil (N)
- the rate of change of current flowing in the coil $\left(\frac{\Delta I}{\Delta t}\right)$ – how quickly the current alternates in the coil
- the rate of change of magnetic flux $\left(\frac{\Delta \Phi}{\Delta t}\right)$ – how quickly the magnetic flux changes.

> **JTL tip**   JTL
>
> ΔI means the change in I so
> $\frac{\Delta I}{\Delta t}$
> is the rate of change of I with time t.

In the 19th century a scientist named Michael Faraday spent a lot of time looking at magnetic induction. He devised a law that tells how much e.m.f. is induced when a conductor is moving in a magnetic field. We will have a look at this and try to make it as simple as possible.

Faraday found that, for a conductor, the induced e.m.f. is given by:

$$\text{e.m.f.} = -\left(\frac{\Delta\Phi}{\Delta t}\right)$$

So we can find the induced e.m.f. by knowing the rate of change of flux. This is simply the same as how quickly the conductor cuts the lines of flux.

So, for a coil of N turns:

$$\text{e.m.f.} = -N\left(\frac{\Delta\Phi}{\Delta t}\right)$$

So we can find the induced e.m.f. by knowing the number of turns and rate of change of flux and

$$\text{e.m.f.} = -L\left(\frac{\Delta I}{\Delta t}\right)$$

So we can find the induced e.m.f. by knowing the inductance and rate of change of current.

These equations are true for both self and mutual inductance.

Note: In all these equations there is a negative (−) sign. This is because any induced e.m.f. will always be in opposition to the changes that created it.

When a number of inductors need to be connected together to form an equivalent inductance they follow the same rules as for resistors, therefore:

- to increase inductance, connect inductors in series.

- to decrease inductance and increase the current rating, connect inductors in parallel.

It takes time to build up to maximum current; however, this is important when connected to an AC supply because the rate of change of current with time can be calculated and adjusted so that a smoothing effect can be produced in the AC. If the coil is suddenly switched off, the magnetic field collapses and a high voltage is induced across the circuit. This effect is used for starting fluorescent tube circuits.

The DC generator

We know that when a current is present in a conductor, a magnetic field is set up around that conductor that is always in a clockwise direction in relation to the direction of the current flow.

We also know that when a conductor is moved at right angles through a magnetic field, a current is induced into the conductor, the direction of the induced current being dependent on the direction of movement of the conductor. The strength of the induced current is determined by the speed at which the conductor moves.

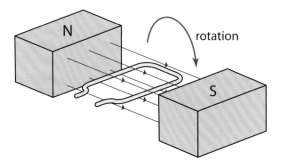

Figure 3.56: A DC generator

If we were to take this arrangement and form the conductor into a loop and then connect it to some device that would spin the wire loop within the permanent magnetic field, then it would look something like Figure 3.57.

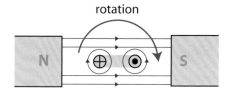

Figure 3.57: Wire loop within a permanent magnetic field

In this position, it could be said that the loop is lying in between the lines of magnetism (magnetic flux) and therefore we say that it is not 'cutting' any lines of flux (as shown in Figure 3.57).

However, as we slowly start to rotate the loop, it will start to pass through the lines of flux. When this happens, we can say that we are now cutting through the lines of flux and it is by this action that we start to induce an e.m.f.

The maximum number of lines that are being cut through will occur when the loop has moved through 90° and the maximum induced e.m.f. in this direction will therefore also occur at this point. Keep rotating the loop and the number will once again reduce to zero as we cut through less lines of flux until we are again lying between the lines of flux.

Figure 3.58 shows this and how if we connect a load via the use of a commutator and fixed carbon brushes, a current will flow around the circuit and the load would work. In other words we have created a DC generator, sometimes called a dynamo.

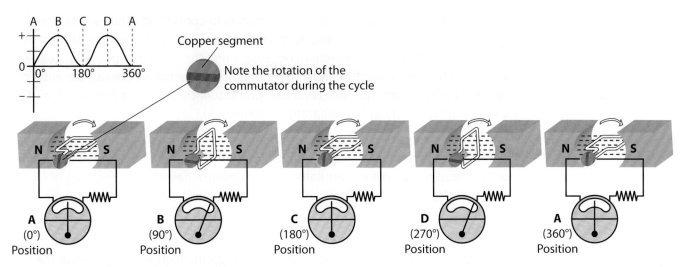

Figure 3.58: Voltage output for one complete revolution

This type of generator produces a voltage/current that alternates in magnitude but flows in one direction only: in other words it has no negative parts in its cycle and we have a direct current (DC). Because the generator only has one loop, it provides a pulsating DC output (as shown by the wave form in Figure 3.58). However, in general use, a number of coils are used to produce a more stable output.

In the loop assembly, the armature, revolves between two stationary field poles, the current in the armature moves in one direction during one half of each revolution and in the other direction during the other half. To produce a steady flow of direct current from such a device, it is therefore necessary to provide a means of reversing the current flow outside the generator once during each revolution.

As shown in Figure 3.59, in older machines this reversal is accomplished by means of the previously mentioned commutator. The commutator is a split metal ring mounted on the shaft of the armature, where the two halves of the ring are insulated from each other and serve as the terminals of the armature coil.

Fixed carbon brushes are then held against the commutator as it revolves, connecting the coil electrically to external wires and devices.

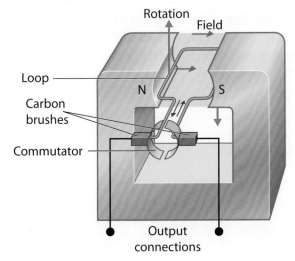

Figure 3.59: Use of a commutator

As the armature (our loop) turns, each brush is in contact alternately with the halves of the commutator, changing position at the moment when the current in the armature coil reverses its direction, because when the coil turns past the 'dead spot' where the brushes meet the gap in the ring, the connections between the ends of the coil and external terminals are reversed. Consequently there is a flow of DC in the outside circuit to which the generator is connected.

Modern DC generators use drum armatures that usually consist of a large number of windings set in longitudinal slits in the armature core and connected to appropriate segments of a multiple commutator. In an armature having only one loop of wire, the current produced will rise and fall depending on the part of the magnetic field through which the loop is moving.

A commutator of many segments used with a drum armature always connects the external circuit to one loop of wire moving through the high-intensity area of the field, and as a result the current delivered by the armature windings is virtually constant.

Summary

1. What are the two main types of magnets?
2. What are the two main components that make up the assembly of a relay?
3. The current flow when looking at a DC generator will go in which direction?

What is alternating current?

Alternating current (**AC**) is a flow of electrons, which rises to a maximum value in one direction and then falls back to zero before repeating the process in the opposite direction. In other words, the electrons within the conductor do not drift (flow) in one direction, but actually move backwards and forwards.

The journey taken, i.e. starting at zero, flowing in both directions and then returning to zero, is called a cycle. The number of cycles that occur every second is said to be the frequency and this is measured in **hertz** (Hz).

The AC generator

Sometimes referred to as an alternator, the operating principle of the AC generator is much the same as that of the DC version described on page 266. However, instead of the ends of our rotating loop terminating via carbon brushes at the commutator, they are instead terminated via brushes at slip rings as shown in Figure 3.60.

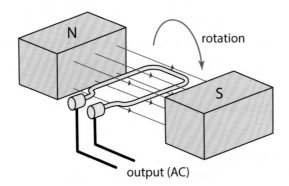

Figure 3.60: Ends of the loop are connected via slip rings

With our loop revolving between two stationary field poles, the maximum number of lines that are cut through will occur when the loop has moved through 90° and the maximum induced e.m.f. in this direction will therefore occur at this point.

Keep rotating the loop and the e.m.f. will reduce to zero as we are again lying between the lines of flux. The loop has now completed what is known as the positive half cycle.

Repeat the process and an e.m.f. will be induced in the opposite direction (the negative half cycle) until the loop returns to its original starting position.

If we were to plot this full 360° revolution (cycle) of the loop as a graph, we would see the e.m.f. induced in the loop as what is known as a sine wave (Figure 3.61).

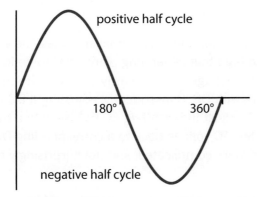

Figure 3.61: Sine wave

As we can see, the sine wave shows the e.m.f. rising from zero as we start to cut through more lines of flux, to its maximum after 90° of rotation. This is known as the peak value. However, after completing 180° (half a rotation or cycle), the e.m.f. passes through zero and then changes direction.

The opposite directions of the induced e.m.f. will still drive a current through a conductor, but that current will alternate as the loop rotates through the magnetic field. The current will be flowing in the same direction as the induced e.m.f. and consequently the current will rise and fall in the same way as the induced e.m.f. When this happens, we say that they are in phase with each other.

To access this AC output, the ends of the loop are connected via slip rings as shown above, and because the two brushes contact two continuous rings, the two external terminals are always connected to the same ends of the coil, hence sinusoidal output.

We say that such a device is called an AC generator and is producing an alternating current (AC), where the number of complete revolutions (cycles) that occur each second is known as the frequency, measured in hertz (Hz) and given the symbol f. The frequency of the supply in this country is 50 Hz.

Sine waves and AC motors

This will be covered in depth later in this chapter on pages 379–412.

Alternating current or direct current?

In the late 1880s there was conflict over the use of alternating current as advocated by George Westinghouse and Nikola Tesla, versus the Thomas Edison promotion of direct current for electric power distribution.

Originally Edison's DC was used as the main method of transmitting electricity, but as technology developed, AC became the preferred choice for two main reasons.

Reason 1

Operating at 100 volts and therefore using smaller cables, the voltage drop in Edison's system was so high that generating plants had to be located within about a mile of the user. Higher voltages cannot easily be used with the DC system as transformers don't work with DC. Consequently, adjusting a DC voltage means having to convert the DC to AC, adjust the resulting AC voltage with a transformer and then convert the adjusted AC voltage back to a corresponding DC voltage. Clearly, adjusting DC voltage is more complicated, and not surprisingly more expensive, than adjusting AC voltages.

In Tesla's alternating current system, a transformer could be used between a high voltage distribution system and the customer loads. Large loads, such as industrial motors could therefore be served by the same distribution network that fed lighting, by using a transformer with a suitable secondary voltage and the transformers made it easy to adjust AC to a higher or lower voltage very efficiently. This was useful, because to transmit at high voltage reduces current and power loss and therefore allows smaller cable sizes and a reduction in costs.

Reason 2

Good AC motors (and generators) are easier and cheaper to build than good DC ones, as although motors are available for either AC or DC, the structure and characteristics of AC and DC motors are quite different.

With AC it is easy to produce a magnetic field which rotates rapidly in space and any electric conductor placed within the rotating magnetic field rotates in the same direction as the field. Consequently, a metal armature rotates with the rotating magnetic field with little slippage and, through a shaft attached to the armature, can deliver mechanical power to a mechanical load such as a fan or a water pump. Called an AC induction motor, it is a reasonably simple means of converting electric power to mechanical power.

However, DC motors rely on a complex mechanical system of brushes and commutator switches. The mechanical complexity of DC motors, consequently, not only makes them more expensive to manufacture than AC motors, but also more expensive to maintain.

Summary

1. Describe what is meant by alternating current.
2. What are the two main reasons AC would be used over DC for transmitting electricity?
3. What is the frequency of supply in this country?

6. Types, applications and limitations of electronic components in electrotechnical systems and equipment

There are many electrical items that rely upon electronic components within their operation. Typical examples would include fire alarms, security alarms, telephones, dimmer switches, motor control as well as heating/boiler controls. This chapter will look at some of the electronic components being used in such equipment.

Resistors

There are two basic types of resistor: fixed and variable. The resistance value of a fixed resistor cannot be changed by mechanical means (though its normal value can be affected by temperature or other effects). Variable resistors have some means of adjustment (usually a spindle or slider). The method of construction, specifications and features of both fixed and variable resistor types vary, depending on what they are to be used for.

Fixed resistors

At its simplest, making a resistor consists of taking some material of a known resistivity, then making the dimensions (the CSA and the length) of a piece of that material so that the resistance between the two points at which leads will be attached (for connecting into a circuit) is the value you require.

Most of the very earliest resistors were made by taking a length of resistance wire (wire made from a metal with a relatively high resistivity, such as brass) and winding this on to a support rod of insulating material. The resistance value of the resulting resistor depended on the length of the wire used and its cross-sectional area.

This method is still used today, though it has been somewhat refined. For example, the resistance wire is usually covered with some form of enamel glazing or ceramic material to protect it from the atmosphere and mechanical damage. The external and internal view of a typical wire wound resistor is shown in Figure 3.62.

Figure 3.62: Wire wound resister

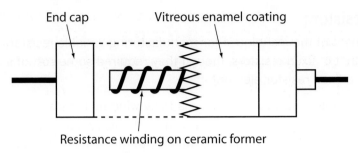

Figure 3.63: Typical wire wound resistor

Most wire wound resistors can operate at fairly high temperatures without suffering damage, so they are useful in applications where some power may be dissipated. They are, however, relatively difficult to mass-produce, which makes them expensive.

Techniques for making resistors from materials other than wire have now been developed for low power applications.

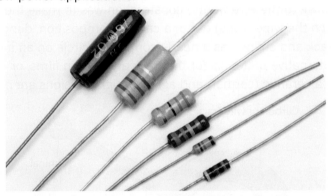

Figure 3.64: Metal oxide and carbon-composition resistors

Resistor manufacture advanced considerably when techniques were developed for coating an insulating rod (usually ceramic or glass) with a thin film of resistive material (see Figure 3.65). The resistive materials in common use today are carbon and metal oxides. Metal end caps fitted with leads are pushed over the ends of the coated rod and the whole assembly is coated with several layers of very tough varnish or similar material to protect the film from the atmosphere and from knocks during handling. These resistors can be mass-produced with great precision at very low cost.

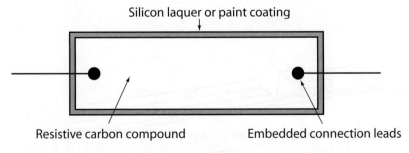

Figure 3.65: Resistor construction

Variable resistors

The development of the techniques for manufacturing variable resistors followed fairly closely that of fixed resistors, though they required some sort of sliding contact together with a fixed resistor element.

Wire wound variable resistors are often made by winding resistance wire onto a flat strip of insulating material, which is then wrapped into a nearly complete circle. A sliding contact arm is made to run in contact with the turns of wire as they wrap over the edge of the wire strip as in Figure 3.66 below. Straight versions are also possible. A straight former is used and the wiper travels in a straight line along it as shown in Figure 3.67.

While wire wound resistors are ideal for certain applications, there are many others where their size, cost and other disadvantages make them unattractive, and as a consequence alternative types have been developed.

The early alternative to the wire wound construction was to make the resistive element (on which the wiper rubs) out of a carbon composition, deposited or moulded as a track and shaped as a nearly completed circle on an insulating support plate. Alternative materials for the track are carbon films, or metal alloys of a metal oxide and a ceramic (cermet) and again straight versions are possible.

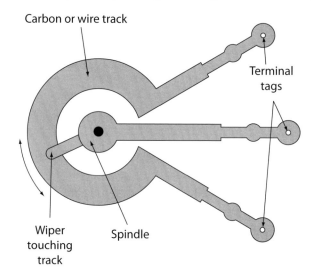

Figure 3.66: Layout of internal track of rotary variable

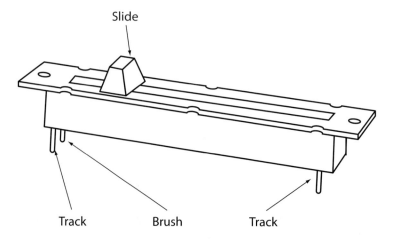

Figure 3.67: Linear variable resistor resistor

In theory, there's no reason why you couldn't have resistors in every imaginable resistance value; from zero to, say, tens or hundreds of megohms. In reality, however, such an enormous range would be totally impractical to manufacture and store and, from the point of view of the circuit designer, it's not usually necessary.

So, rather than an overwhelming number of individual resistance values, what manufacturers do is make a limited range of preferred resistance values. In electronics, we use the preferred value closest to the actual value we need.

Preferred values

E6 series 20% Tol	E12 series 10% Tol	E24 series 5% Tol
10	10	10
		11
	12	12
		13
15	15	15
		16
	18	18
		20
22	22	22
		24
	27	27
		30
33	33	33
		36
	39	39
		43
47	47	47
		51
	56	56
		62
68	68	68
		75
	82	82
		91

Table 3.11: Table of preferred values

A resistor with a preferred value of $1000\,\Omega$ and a 10% tolerance can have any value between $900\,\Omega$ and $1100\,\Omega$. The next largest preferred value, which would give the maximum possible range of resistance values without too much overlap, is $1200\,\Omega$. This can have a value between $1080\,\Omega$ and $1320\,\Omega$.

Together, these two preferred value resistors cover all possible resistance values between $900\,\Omega$ and $1320\,\Omega$. The next preferred values would be $1460\,\Omega$, $1785\,\Omega$ etc.

Resistance markings

There is obviously the need for the resistor manufacturer to provide some sort of markings on each resistor so that it can be identified.

The user should be able to tell, by looking at the resistor, what its nominal resistance value is and its tolerance. Various methods of marking this information on each resistor have been used and sometimes a resistor code will use numbers and letters rather than colours.

Where physical size permits, putting the actual value on the resistor in figures and letters has an obvious advantage in terms of easy interpretation. However, again because of size restrictions, we don't use the actual words and instead use a code system. This code is necessary because when using small text on a small object, certain symbols and the decimal point become very hard to see. This code system is also commonly used to represent resistance values on circuit diagrams for the same reason.

In reality resistance values are generally given in either Ω, kΩ or MΩ using numbers from 1–999 as a prefix (e.g. 10 Ω, 567 kΩ).

In the code system we replace Ω, kΩ and MΩ and represent them instead by using the following letters:

- Ω = R
- kΩ = K
- MΩ = M

These letters are now inserted wherever the decimal point would have been in the value. So for example a resistor of value 10 Ω resistor would now be shown as 10 R, and a resistor of value 567 kΩ resistor would become 567 K.

In theory, there's no reason why you couldn't have resistors in every imaginable resistance value; from zero to, say, tens or hundreds of megohms. In reality, however, such an enormous range would be totally impractical to manufacture and store, and from the point of view of the circuit designer it's not usually necessary.

So, rather than an overwhelming number of individual resistance values, what manufacturers do is make a limited range of preferred resistance values. In electronics, we use the preferred value closest to the actual value we need.

Table 3.12 gives some more examples of this code system. Table 3.13 shows the letters that are then commonly used to represent the tolerance values. These letters are added at the end of the resistor marking so that, for example, a resistor of value 2.7 MΩ with a tolerance of ±10% would be shown as 2M7K.

0.1 Ω	is coded	R10
0.22 Ω	is coded	R22
1.0 Ω	is coded	1R0
3.3 Ω	is coded	3R3
15 Ω	is coded	15R
390 Ω	is coded	390R
1.8 Ω	is coded	1R8
47 Ω	is coded	47R
820 kΩ	is coded	820K
2.7 MΩ	is coded	2M7

Table 3.12 Examples of resistance value codes

F	=	± 1%
G	=	± 2%
J	=	± 5%
K	=	± 10%
M	=	± 20%
N	=	± 30%

Table 3.13 Codes for common tolerance values

Resistor coding

Standard colour code

Many resistors are so small that it is impractical to print their value on them. Instead, they are marked with a code that uses bands of colour. Located at one end of the component, it is these bands that identify the resistor's value and tolerance.

Most general resistors have four bands of colour, but high-precision resistors are often marked with a five-colour band system. No matter which system is being used, the value of the colours is the same.

JTL tip

Before you read a resistor, turn it so that the end with bands is on the left-hand side. Now you read the bands from left to right (as shown in Figures 3.68 to 3.71).

Band colour	Value
Black	0
Brown	1
Red	2
Orange	3
Yellow	4
Green	5
Blue	6
Violet	7
Grey	8
White	9
Gold	0.1
Silver	0.01

Figure 3.68: Resistor colour code

Band colour	±%
Brown	1
Red	2
Gold	5
Silver	10
None	20

Figure 3.69: Tolerance colour code

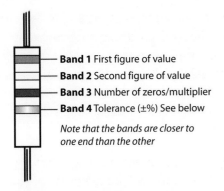

- **Band 1** First figure of value
- **Band 2** Second figure of value
- **Band 3** Number of zeros/multiplier
- **Band 4** Tolerance (±%) See below

Note that the bands are closer to one end than the other

Figure 3.70: What the bands mean

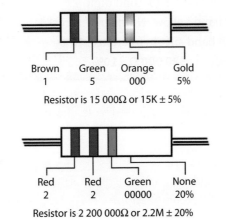

Brown	Green	Orange	Gold
1	5	000	5%

Resistor is 15 000Ω or 15K ± 5%

Red	Red	Green	None
2	2	00000	20%

Resistor is 2 200 000Ω or 2.2M ± 20%

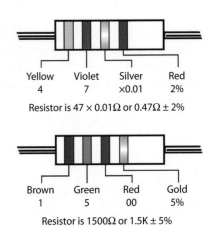

Yellow	Violet	Silver	Red
4	7	×0.01	2%

Resistor is 47 × 0.01Ω or 0.47Ω ± 2%

Brown	Green	Red	Gold
1	5	00	5%

Resistor is 1500Ω or 1.5K ± 5%

Figure 3.71: Examples of colour coding

Example 1

A resistor is colour-coded red, yellow, orange, gold. Determine the value of the resistor.
- First band red (First digit) 2
- Second band yellow (Second digit) 4
- Third band orange (Number of zeros) 3
- Fourth band gold (Tolerance) 5%
- The value is **24 000 Ω ±5%**

Example 2

A resistor is colour-coded yellow, yellow, blue, silver. Determine the value of the resistor.
- First band yellow (First digit) 4
- Second band yellow (Second digit) 4
- Third band blue (Number of zeros) 6
- Fourth band silver (Tolerance) 10%
- The value is **44 000 000 Ω ±10%**

Example 3

A resistor is colour-coded violet, orange, brown, gold. Determine the value of the resistor.
- First band violet (First digit) 7
- Second band orange (Second digit) 3
- Third band brown (Number of zeros) 1
- Fourth band gold (Tolerance) 5%
- The value is **730 Ω ± 5%**

Example 4

A resistor is colour-coded green, red, yellow, silver. Determine the value of the resistor.
- First band green (First digit) 5
- Second band red (Second digit) 2
- Third band yellow (Number of zeros) 4
- Fourth band silver (Tolerance) 10%
- The value is **520 000 Ω ±10%**

Testing resistors

Resistors must be removed from a circuit before testing, otherwise readings will be false. To measure the resistance, the leads of a suitable ohmmeter should be connected to each resistor connection lead and a reading obtained which should be close to the preferred value and within the tolerance stated.

Resistors as current limiters

A resistor is often provided in a circuit to limit, restrict or reduce the current flowing in the circuit to some level that better suits the ratings of some other component in the circuit. For example, consider the problem of operating a solenoid valve from a 36 V DC supply, given the information that the energising current of the coil fitted to the valve is 100 mA and its resistance is 240 Ω.

Note that the coil, being a wound component, is actually an inductor. However, we are concerned here with the steady DC current through the coil and not the variation in coil current at the instant the supply is connected, so we can ignore the effects of its inductance and consider only the effects of its resistance.

If the solenoid valve were connected directly across the 36 V supply, as shown in Figure 3.72, then from Ohm's Law the steady current through its coil would be:

$$I = \frac{V}{R}$$

$$= \frac{36}{240}$$

$$= 0.15 \text{ A or } 150 \text{ mA}$$

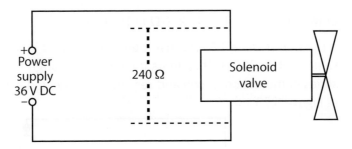

Figure 3.72: Solenoid valve connected across 36 V supply

As the coil was designed to produce an adequate magnetic 'pull' when energised at 100 mA, any increase in the energising current is unnecessary and may in fact be highly undesirable due to the resulting increase in the power, which would be dissipated (as heat) within the coils.

Note: The power dissipated in the coil of the solenoid valve, when energised at the recommended current of 100 mA is:

$P = I^2 \times R$

$= 0.1^2\,A \times 240\,\Omega = 2.4$ watts

Now if the current were to be 0.15 A on the 36 V supply it would be:

$P = V \times I$

$= 36 \times 0.15$

$= 5.4$ watts

Thus connecting the coil directly across a 36 V supply would result in the power dissipation in it being more than doubled. If the valve is required to be energised for more than very brief periods of time, the coil could be damaged by overheating.

Some extra resistance must therefore be introduced into the circuit so that the current through the coil is limited to 100 mA even though the supply is 36 V.

For a current of 100 mA to flow from a 36 V supply, the total resistance R_t connected across the 36 V must, from Ohm's Law, be:

$R_t = \frac{36}{0.1} = 360\,\Omega$

of which there is already 240 Ω in the coil.

A resistor of value 120 Ω must therefore be fitted in series with the coil to bring the value of R_t to 360 Ω. This limits the current through the coil to 100 mA when the series combination of coil and resistor is connected across the 36 V supply as shown in Figure 3.73.

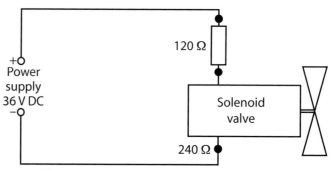

Figure 3.73: Series combination of coil and resistor connected across 36 V supply

Resistors for voltage control

Within a circuit it is often necessary to have different voltages at different stages and we can achieve this by using resistors.

For example, if we physically opened up a resistor and connected its ends across a supply, we would find that, if we then measured the voltage at different points along the resistor, the values would vary along its length. In doing so, we are effectively imitating the 'tapping' technique that we will discuss in the transformers section of this book.

However, reality will stop us from doing this as resistors are sealed components. But we can create the same tapping effect by combining two resistors in series as shown in Figure 3.74, and then our tapping becomes a connection point made between the two resistors.

If we look at Figure 3.74, we can see that the series combination of resistors R_1 and R_2 is connected across a supply that is provided by two rails. One is shown as V+ (the positive supply rail or in other words our input) and the other as 0V (or common rail of the circuit).

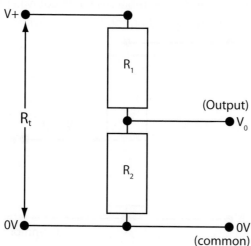

Figure 3.74: Series circuit for voltage control

The total resistance of our network (R_t) will be:

$R_t = R_1 + R_2$

We know, using Ohm's Law, that $V = I \times R$ and the same current flows through both resistors. Therefore for this network, we can see that $V+ = I \times R_t$ and the voltage dropped across resistor R_2 will be:

$V_0 = I \times R_2$

We now have two expressions, one for V+ and one for V_0. We can find out what fraction V_0 is of V+ by putting V_0 over V+ on the left-hand side of an equation and then putting what we said each one is equal to in the corresponding positions on the right-hand side. This gives us the following formula:

$$\frac{V_0}{V+} = \frac{I \times R_2}{I \times R_t}$$

As current is common on the right hand side of our formula, they cancel each other out. This leaves us with:

$$\frac{V_0}{V+} = \frac{R_2}{R_t}$$

To establish what V_0 (our output voltage) actually is, we can transpose again, which would give us:

$$V_0 = \frac{R_2 V+}{R_t}$$

Finally, we can replace R_t by what it is actually equal to, and this will give us the means of establishing the value of the individual resistors needed to give a desired output voltage (V_0). By transposition, our final formula now becomes:

$$V_0 = \frac{R_2}{R_1 + R_2} \times V$$

This equation is normally referred to as the potential divider rule.

In reality R_1 and R_2 could each be a combination (series or parallel) of many resistors.

However, as long as each combination is replaced by its equivalent resistance so that the simplified circuit looks like Figure 3.75, then the potential divider rule can be applied.

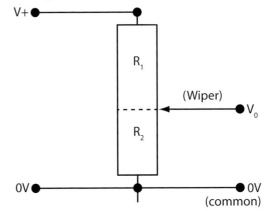

Figure 3.75: Circuit diagram for voltage applied across potentiometer

The potential divider circuit is very useful where the full voltage available is not required at some point in a circuit and, as we have seen, by a suitable choice of resistors in the potential divider, the desired fraction of the input voltage can be produced.

In applications where the fraction produced needs to be varied from time to time, the two resistors are replaced by a variable resistor (also known as a potentiometer, which is often abbreviated to the word 'pot'), which would be connected as shown in Figure 3.75.

$$V_0 = \frac{R_2}{R_1 + R_2} \times V+$$

The output V_0 will be dependent upon the position of the arrow. The output V_0 can be anything from V+ to 0V.

The potentiometer has a resistor manufactured in the form of a track, the ends of which effectively form our V+ and 0V connections. Our output voltage (V_0) is achieved by means of a movable contact that can touch the track anywhere on its length and this is called the wiper. We have therefore effectively created a variable tapping point.

To compare this with our potential divider, we can say that the part of the track above the wiper can be regarded as R_1 and that part below the wiper as R_2. The fraction of the input voltage appearing at the output can therefore be calculated for any setting of the wiper position by using our potential divider equation:

$$V_0 = \frac{R_2}{R_1 + R_2} \times V+$$

Obviously, when the wiper is at the top of the track, R_1 becomes zero and the equation would give the result that V_0 is equal to V+. Equally, with the wiper right at the bottom of the track, R_2 now becomes zero and therefore V_0 also becomes zero, which is not too surprising as the wiper is now more or less directly connected to the 0V rail.

This sort of circuit finds practical application in a wide variety of control functions such as volume or tone controls on audio equipment, brightness and contrast controls on televisions and shift controls on oscilloscopes.

Power ratings

Resistors often have to carry comparatively large values of current so they must be capable of doing this without overheating and causing damage. As the current has to be related to the voltage, it is the power rating of the resistor that needs to be identified.

The power rating of a resistor is thus really a convenient way of stating the maximum temperature at which the resistor is designed to operate without damage to itself. In general the more power a resistor is designed to be capable of dissipating, the larger physically the resistor is; the resulting larger surface area aids heat dissipation.

Resistors with high power ratings may even be jacketed in a metal casing provided with cooling ribs and designed to be bolted flat to a metal surface – all to improve the radiation and conduction of heat away from the resistance element.

Power is calculated by:

$P = V \times I$

Instead of V we can substitute $I \times R$ for V and $\frac{V}{R}$ for I. We can then use the following equations to calculate power:

$P = I^2 \times R$

Or:

$P = \frac{V^2}{R}$

What would the power rating of the 50 Ω resistor in Figure 3.76 be?

$P = V \times I$ $= 4 \times 0.08$ $= 0.32$ watts

$P = I^2 \times R$ $= 0.08^2 \times 50$ $= 0.32$ watts

$P = \frac{V^2}{R}$ $= \frac{4 \times 4}{50}$ $= 0.32$ watts

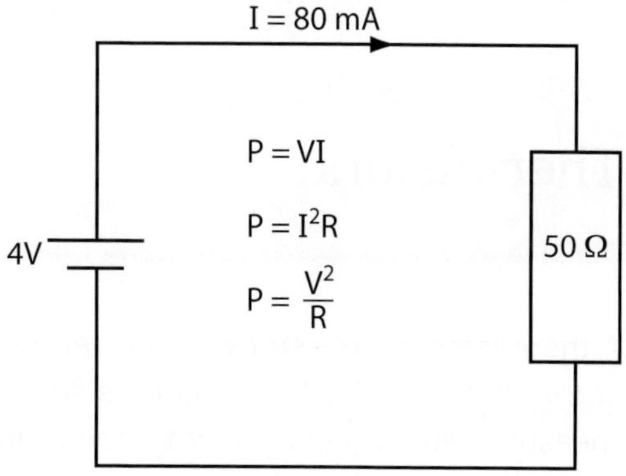

Figure 3.76: Typical power ratings for resistors

Normally only one calculation is required. Typical power ratings for resistors are shown in Table 3.14.

Carbon resistors	0 to 0.5 watts
Ceramic resistors	0 to 6 watts
Wire wound resistors	0 to 25 watts

Table 3.14: Typical power ratings for resistors

Manufacturers also always quote a maximum voltage rating for their resistors on their data sheets. The maximum voltage rating is basically a statement about the electrical insulation properties of those parts of the resistor, which are supposed to be insulators (e.g. the ceramic or glass rod which supports the resistance element or the surface coating over the resistance element).

If the maximum voltage rating is exceeded there is a danger that a flashover may occur from one end of the resistor to the other. This flashover usually has disastrous results. If it occurs down the outside of the resistor it can destroy not only the protective coating but, on film resistors, the resistor film as well.

If it occurs down the inside of the resistor the ceramic or glass rod is frequently cracked (if not shattered) and, of course, this mechanical damage to the support for the resistance element results in the element itself being damaged as well.

Light-dependent resistors

These resistors are sensitive to light. They consist of a clear window with a cadmium sulphide film under it. When light shines onto the film its resistance varies, with the resistance reducing as the light increases.

Figure 3.77: Light-dependent resistor

These resistors are commonly found in street lighting. You may sometimes observe street lights switching on during a thunderstorm in the daytime. This is because the sunlight is obscured by the dark thunderclouds, thus increasing the resistance, which in turn controls the light 'on' circuit.

Thermistors

Figure 3.78: Thermistors

A thermistor is a resistor which is temperature sensitive. The general appearance is shown in Figure 3.78. They can be supplied in various shapes and are used for the measurement and control of temperature up to their maximum useful temperature limit of about 300°C. They are very sensitive and because of their small construction they are useful for measuring temperatures in inaccessible places.

Thermistors are used for measuring the temperature of the motor's field or stator windings and sensing overloads. The thermistor can be wired into the control circuit so that it automatically cuts the supply to the motor when the motor windings overheat, thus preventing damage to the windings.

Thermistors can have a temperature coefficient that may be positive (PTC) or negative (NTC).

- A PTC thermistor is made from barium titanate and its resistance of the thermistor increases as the surrounding temperature increases.

- An NTC thermistor is made from oxides of nickel, manganese, copper and cobalt and its resistance decreases as the temperature increases.

The rated resistance of a thermistor may be identified by a standard colour code or by a single body colour used only for thermistors. Typical values are shown in Table 3.15.

Colour	Resistance
Red	3000 Ω
Orange	5000 Ω
Yellow	10 000 Ω
Green	30 000 Ω
Violet	100 000 Ω

Table 3.15: Colour coding for rated resistance of thermistor

Thermocouples

Thermocouples are two different metals bonded together and each has a lead. When the bonded metals are heated a voltage appears across the two leads. The hotter the metals become, the larger the voltage (mV). An example of their use is for measuring the temperature of furnaces within the steel industry.

Figure 3.79: Thermocouples

Capacitors

We use components known as capacitors to introduce capacitance into a circuit. Capacitance always exists in circuits – though, as you'll see when we have discussed the subject in more detail, capacitance exists between conductors whereas resistance exists in conductors.

Basic principles

A capacitor is basically two metallic surfaces usually referred to as plates, separated by an insulator commonly known as the **dielectric**. The plates are usually, though not necessarily, metal and the dielectric is any insulating material. Air, glass, ceramic, mica, paper, oils and waxes are some of the many materials commonly used. The common symbols used for capacitors are identified in Figure 3.80.

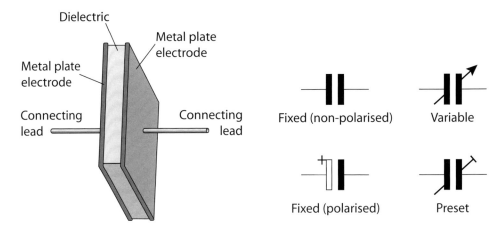

Figure 3.80: Basic construction of a capacitor and circuit symbols

These two plates are not in contact with each other and so they do not form a circuit in the same way that conductors with resistors do. However, the capacitor stores a small amount of electric charge and it can be thought of as a small rechargeable battery, which can be quickly recharged.

The capacitance of any capacitor depends on three factors:

1. The working area of the plates, i.e. the area of the conducting surfaces facing each other.

    We can think of the degree of crowding of excess electrons near the surface of one plate of a capacitor (and the corresponding sparseness of electrons near the surface of the other) as being directly related to the potential difference (p.d.) applied across the capacitor, for example connecting it directly across a battery. If we increase the area of the plates, then more electrons can flow onto one of the plates before the same degree of crowding is reached. The battery voltage determines this level of crowdedness. There is of course a similar increased loss of electrons from the other plate. The working area of the plates is directly proportional to the capacitance. If we double the area of the plates we double the capacitance of the capacitor.

Key term

Dielectric – an electrical insulator that can be polarised by an applied electric field

Safety

Never pick a capacitor up by the terminals as it may still be charged and you will receive a shock. Always ensure the capacitor has been discharged before handling. Some capacitors have a discharge resistor connected in the circuit for this reason.

2. The thickness of the dielectric between the plates.

    As mentioned earlier, the capacitance effect depends on the forces of repulsion or attraction caused by an electron surplus or shortage on the plates on either side of the dielectric. The further apart the plates are, the weaker these factors become. As a result, the degree of crowding of electrons on one plate (and the shortage of electrons on the other) produced by a given p.d across the capacitor decreases.

3. The nature of the dielectric or spacing material used.

    This fundamental principle of capacitors and the time constant of capacitor resistor circuits will be looked at later under the heading of electrostatics.

Capacitor types

There are two major types of capacitor, fixed and variable, both of which are used in a wide range of electronic devices. Fixed capacitors can be further subdivided into electrolytic and non-electrolytic types and together they represent the majority of the market.

All capacitors possess some resistance and inductance because of the nature of their construction. These undesirable properties result in limitations, which often determine their applications.

Fixed capacitors

Electrolytic capacitors

These capacitors have a much higher capacitance, volume for volume, than any other type. This is achieved by making the plate separation extremely small by using a very thin dielectric (insulator). The dielectric is often mica or paper.

They are constructed on the Swiss roll principle as are the paper dielectric capacitors used for power factor correction in electrical installation circuits, for example, fluorescent lighting circuits.

The main disadvantage of an electrolytic capacitor is that it is polarised and must be connected to the correct polarity in a circuit, otherwise a short circuit and destruction of the capacitor will result.

Figure 3.81 illustrates a newer type of electrolytic capacitor using tantalum and tantalum oxide to give a further capacitance/size advantage. It looks like a raindrop with two leads protruding from the bottom. The polarity and values may be marked on the capacitor or the colour code can be used (see Figure 3.88 on page 291).

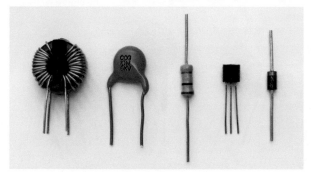

Figure 3.81: Tantalum capacitor

Safety

In any application the capacitor to be used should meet or preferably exceed the capacitor voltage rating. The voltage rating is often called 'the working voltage' and refers to DC voltage values. When applied to AC circuits the peak voltage value must be used as a comparison to the DC working voltage of a capacitor.

Non-electrolytic capacitors

There are many different types of non-electrolytic capacitor. However, only mica, ceramic and polyester are of any significance. Older types using glass and vitreous enamel are expected to disappear over the next few years and even mica will be replaced by film types.

Mica

Mica is a naturally occurring dielectric and has a very high resistance; this gives excellent stability and allows the capacitors to be accurate within a value of ±1 per cent of the marked value. Since costs usually increase with increased accuracy, they tend to be more expensive than plastic film capacitors. They are used where high stability is required, for example in tuned circuits and filters required in radio transmission. Figure 3.82 illustrates a typical mica capacitor.

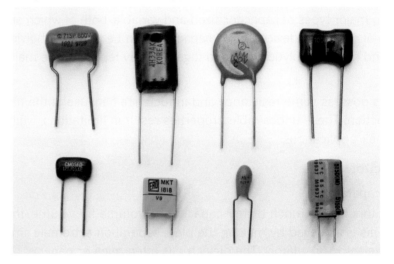

Figure 3.82: Mica capacitor

Ceramic capacitors

These consist of small rectangular pieces of ceramic with metal electrodes on opposite surfaces. Figure 3.83 illustrates a typical ceramic capacitor. These capacitors are mainly used in high-frequency circuits subjected to wide temperature variations. They have high stability and low Equivalent Series Resistance (ESR) loss, which is the sum loss caused by the dielectric and the metallic element of the capacitor. This is useful as ceramic capacitors with high losses can drain, and therefore waste, power.

Figure 3.83: Ceramic capacitor

Polyester capacitors

These are an example of a plastic film capacitor. Polypropylene, polycarbonate and polystyrene capacitors are other types of plastic film capacitors. They are widely used in the electronics industry due to their good reliability and relative low cost but are not suitable for high-frequency circuits. Figure 3.84 illustrates a typical polyester capacitor; however, they can also be a tubular shape (see Figure 3.85).

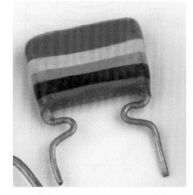

Figure 3.84: Polyester capacitor

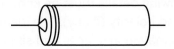

Figure 3.85: Tubular capacitor

Variable capacitors

Variable capacitors generally have air or a vacuum as the dielectric, although ceramics are sometimes used. The two main sub-groups are tuning and trimmer capacitors.

Tuning capacitors

These are so called because they are used in radio tuning circuits and consist of two sets of parallel metal plates, one isolated from the mounting frame by ceramic supports while the other is fixed to a shaft which allows one set to be rotated into or out of the first set. The rows of plates interlock like fingers, but do not quite touch each other.

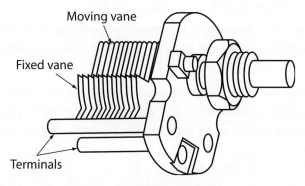

Figure 3.86: A typical variable capacitor of the tuning type

Trimmer capacitors

These are constructed of flat metal leaves separated by a plastic film; these can be screwed towards each other. They have a smaller range of variation than tuning capacitors, and so are only used where a slight change in value is needed.

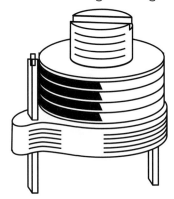

Figure 3.87: A typical capacitor used as a trimmer

Capacitor coding

To identify a capacitor the following details must be known: the capacitance, working voltage, type of construction and polarity (if any). The identification of capacitors is not easy because of the wide variation in shapes and sizes. In the majority of cases the capacitance will be printed on the body of the capacitor, which often gives a positive identification that the component is a capacitor.

The capacitance value is the farad (symbol F); this was named after the English scientist Michael Faraday. However, for practical purposes the farad is much too large and in electrical installation work and electronics we use fractions of a farad as follows:

- 1 microfarad = $1\,\mu F = 1 \times 10^{-6}\,F$

- 1 nanofarad = $1\,nF = 1 \times 10^{-9}\,F$

- 1 picofarad = $1\,pF = 1 \times 10^{-12}\,F$

The power factor correction capacitor found in fluorescent luminaires would have a value typically of $8\,\mu F$ at a working voltage of 400 V. One microfarad is one million times greater than one picofarad.

The working voltage of a capacitor is the maximum voltage that can be applied between the plates of the capacitor without breaking down the dielectric insulating material.

It was quite common for capacitors to be marked with colour codes but today relatively few capacitors are colour coded. At one time nearly all plastic foil type capacitors were colour coded, as in Figure 3.88, but this method of marking is rarely encountered. However, it is a useful skill to know and be able to use the colour-coding method as shown in Table 3.16.

This method is based on the standard four-band resistor colour coding. The first three bands indicate the value in normal resistor fashion, but the value is in picofarads. To convert this into a value in nanofarads it is merely necessary to divide by 1000. Divide the marked value by 1 000 000 if a value in microfarads is required. The fourth band indicates the tolerance, but the colour coding is different from the resistor equivalent. The fifth band shows the maximum working voltage of the component. Details of this colour coding are shown in Figure 3.88 and Table 3.16.

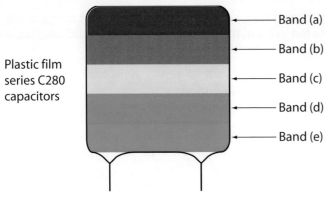

Plastic film series C280 capacitors

— Band (a)
— Band (b)
— Band (c)
— Band (d)
— Band (e)

Figure 3.88: Capacitor colour bands

Standard capacitor colour coding

Colour	1st digit	2nd digit	3rd digit	Tol. band	Max. voltage
Black		0	None	20%	
Brown	1	1	1		100 V
Red	2	2	2		250 V
Orange	3	3	3		
Yellow	4	4	4		400 V
Green	5	5	5	5%	
Blue	6	6	6		630 V
Violet	7	7	7		
Grey	8	8	8		
White	9	9	9	10%	

Table 3.16: Standard capacitor colour coding

Bands are then read from top to bottom. Digit 1 gives the first number of the component value; the second digit gives the second number. The third band gives the number of zeros to be added after the first two numbers and the fourth band indicates the capacitor tolerance, which is normally black 20%, white 10% and green 5%.

Example 1

A plastic film capacitor is colour-coded from top to bottom brown, red, yellow, black, red. Determine the value of the capacitor, its tolerance and working voltage.

- band (a) – brown = 1
- band (b) – red = 2
- band (c) – yellow = 4 multiply by 10 000
- band (d) – black = 20% tolerance
- band (e) – red = 250 volts.

The capacitor has a value of 120 000 pF or 0.12 μF with a tolerance of 20% and a maximum working voltage of 250 volts.

Example 2

A plastic film capacitor is colour-coded from top to bottom orange, orange, yellow, green, yellow. Determine the value of the capacitor, its tolerance and working voltage.

- band (a) – orange = 3
- band (b) – orange = 3
- band (c) – yellow = 4 multiply by 10 000
- band (d) – green = 5%
- band (e) – yellow = 400 volts.

The capacitor has a value of 330 000 pF or 0.33 μF with a tolerance of 5% and a maximum working voltage of 400 volts.

Example 3

A plastic film capacitor is colour-coded from top to bottom violet, blue, orange, black, and brown. Determine the value of the capacitor, its tolerance and working voltage.

- band (a) – violet = 7
- band (b) – blue = 6
- band (c) – orange = 3 multiply by 1000
- band (d) – black = 20%
- band (e) – brown = 100 volts.

The capacitor has a value of 76 000 pF or 0.076 μF with a tolerance of 20% and a maximum working voltage of 100 volts.

Often the value of a capacitor is simply written on its body, possibly together with the tolerance and/or its maximum operating voltage. The tolerance rating may be omitted, and it is generally higher for capacitors than resistors. Most modern resistors have tolerances of 5% or better, but for capacitors the tolerance rating is generally 10% or 20%. The tolerance figure is more likely to be marked on a close tolerance capacitor than a normal 10% or 20% type.

The most popular form of value marking on modern capacitors is for the value to be written on the components in some slightly cryptic form. Small ceramic capacitors generally have the value marked in much the same way that the value is written on a circuit diagram.

Where the value includes a decimal point, it is standard practice to use the prefix for the multiplication factor in place of the decimal point. This is the same practice as is used for resistors.

The abbreviation μ means microfarad; n means nanofarad; p means picofarad. Therefore:

- 3.5 pF capacitor would be abbreviated to 3 p5
- 12 pF capacitor would be abbreviated to 12 p
- 300 pF capacitor would be abbreviated to 300 p or n 30
- 4500 pF capacitor would be abbreviated to 4 n5
- 1000 pF = 1 nF = 0.001 μF

Polarity

Once the size, type and DC voltage rating of a capacitor have been determined it now remains to ensure that its polarity is known. Some capacitors are constructed in such a way that if the component is operated with the wrong polarity its properties as a capacitor will be destroyed, especially electrolytic capacitors. Polarity may be indicated by a + or – as appropriate. Electrolytic capacitors that are contained within metal cans will have the can casing as the negative connection. If there are no markings a slight indentation in the case will indicate the positive end.

Tantalum capacitors have a spot on one side as shown in Figure 3.90.

When this spot is facing you the right-hand lead will indicate the positive connection.

Electrostatics and calculations with capacitors

The charge stored on a capacitor is dependent on three main factors: the area of the facing plates; the distance between the plates; and the nature of the dielectric. The charge stored by a capacitor is measured in coulombs (Q) and is related to the value of capacitance and the voltage applied to the capacitor:

Charge (coulombs) = Capacitance (farads) × Voltage (volts)

$Q = C \times V$

The formula for energy stored in a capacitor can be calculated by using the formula:

$W = \frac{1}{2}CV^2$

Capacitors in combination

Capacitors, like resistors, may be joined together in various combinations of series or parallel connections. Figures 3.91 and 3.92 illustrate the equivalent capacitance C_t of a number of capacitors. C_t can be found by applying similar formulae as for resistors. However, these formulae are the opposite way round to series and parallel resistors.

Figure 3.89: Capacitor showing polarity

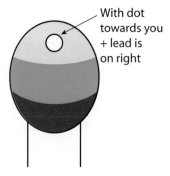

Figure 3.90: Tantalum capacitor

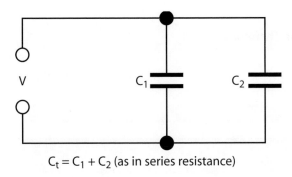

$C_t = C_1 + C_2$ (as in series resistance)

Figure 3.91: Capacitors connected in parallel

or

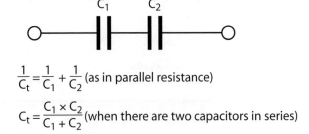

$\frac{1}{C_t} = \frac{1}{C_1} + \frac{1}{C_2}$ (as in parallel resistance)

$C_t = \frac{C_1 \times C_2}{C_1 + C_2}$ (when there are two capacitors in series)

Figure 3.92: Capacitors connected in series

Example 1

Capacitors of $10\,\mu F$ and $40\,\mu F$ are connected in series and then in parallel. Calculate the effective capacitance for each connection.

Series:

$$\frac{1}{C_t} = \frac{1}{C_1} + \frac{1}{C_2}$$

$$\frac{1}{C_t} = \frac{1}{10\mu F} + \frac{1}{40\mu F}$$

$$\frac{1}{C_t} = \frac{4\mu F + 1\mu F}{40\mu F}$$

$$\frac{1}{C_t} = \frac{5\mu F}{40\mu F}$$

Therefore:

$$\frac{C_t}{1} = \frac{40\mu F}{5\mu F}$$

$$C_t = \mathbf{8\mu F}$$

Parallel:

$$C_t = C_1 + C_2$$

$$C_t = 10\mu F + 40\mu F$$

$$C_t = 50\mu F$$

Example 2

Three capacitors of $30\,\mu F$, $20\,\mu F$ and $15\,\mu F$ are connected in series across a $400\,V$ DC supply. Calculate the total capacitance and the charge on each capacitor.

$$\frac{1}{C_t} = \frac{1}{C_1} + \frac{1}{C_2} + \frac{1}{C_3}$$

$$= \frac{1}{30\mu F} + \frac{1}{20\mu F} + \frac{1}{15\mu F}$$

$$= \frac{9\mu F}{60\mu F}$$

Therefore $C_t = 6.66\mu F$

Q, the charge, is common to each capacitor. Therefore:

$$Q = C \times V$$

$$Q = 6.66 \times 10^{-6} \times 400$$

$$Q = \mathbf{2.664\,mC}$$

Example 3

Three capacitors of $30\,\mu F$, $20\,\mu F$ and $15\,\mu F$ are connected in parallel across a $400\,V$ DC supply. Calculate the total capacitance, the total charge and the charge on each capacitor.

$$C_t = C_1 + C_2 + C_3$$

$$C_t = 30 + 20 + 15$$

$$C_t = 65\,\mu F$$

Total charge $Q = C \times V$

$Q_t = C_1 \times V$	$Q_1 = C_1 \times V$	$Q_2 = C_2 \times V$	$Q_3 = C_3 \times V$
$Q_t = 65 \times 10^{-6} \times 400$	$Q_1 = 30 \times 10^{-6} \times 400$	$Q_2 = 20 \times 10^{-6} \times 400$	$Q_3 = 15 \times 10^{-6} \times 400$
$Q_t = \mathbf{26\,mC}$	$Q_1 = \mathbf{12\,mC}$	$Q_2 = \mathbf{8\,mC}$	$Q_3 = \mathbf{6\,mC}$

Charging and discharging capacitors

Figure 3.93 shows a typical charge and discharge circuit for an uncharged capacitor (C) connected via a three-position switch (S1) to a 6 V supply (V_S), with a voltmeter (V) connected across the capacitor.

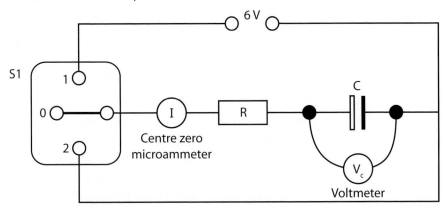

Figure 3.93: A typical charge and discharge circuit

The charging phase

With the switch in position (0), we can see that the circuit is open; no voltage exists across the capacitor (V_c as measured by the voltmeter) and therefore no electrostatic field can exist between the plates.

If we now close switch S1 to position (1), the capacitor will be connected to the supply; current will flow through the resistor (R) and both positive and negative charges will be deposited on the capacitor plates. This results in an increasing potential difference (V_C) being created that will rise exponentially from zero to a maximum value that will be the same value as the supply, in this case 6 V.

Once the voltage at the terminals of the capacitor (V_C) is equal to the supply voltage of 6 V (V_S), then no further current can flow and the capacitor can be said to be charged.

We can look at this in another way. From Ohm's Law we know that the supply voltage (V_S) is equal to the sum of the p.d.s across each individual component (V = V1 + V2 etc.).

We can therefore use Ohm's Law to find the charging current, where the voltage across the resistor (V_R) will be ($V_S - V_C$).

Charing current $(I) = \dfrac{(V_S - V_C)}{R}$

When we first switch to position (1), V_C is zero and therefore from Ohm's Law, our initial charging current will be:

$(I) = \dfrac{V_S}{R}$

We also said that V_C increases exponentially as a charge starts to build up on the capacitor. In turn this will reduce the voltage across the resistor ($V_R = V_S - V_C$) and therefore reduce the charging current. This means that the rate of charging becomes progressively slower as V_C increases.

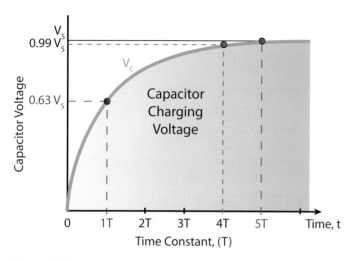

Figure 3.94

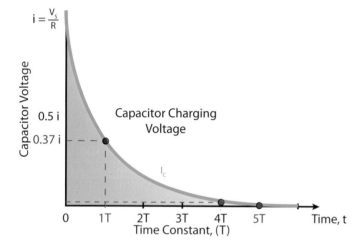

Figure 3.95

As we have discussed, the charging and discharging of a capacitor is never instantaneous. The time taken for the capacitor to charge/discharge to within a certain percentage of its maximum supply value is the time constant and is taken as the product of the circuit resistance and the capacitance. Therefore:

Time constant (T) = Resistance (Ω) × Capacitance (μF)

In other words: T = RC

As the capacitor charges, the potential difference across its plates increases with the actual time taken for the charge on the capacitor to reach 63% of its maximum possible voltage (V_s). This is known as the time constant or 1RC.

In theory our capacitor (C) never fully charges to the supply voltage (V_s). In the first time constant, (C) charges to 63% of V_s and in the second time constant (C) charges to 86% of V_s. This is also 63% of the remaining voltage difference between V_s and V_c.

This continues indefinitely, with V_c always approaching, but never quite reaching, the full value of V_s.

However, at the end of five time constants (5T or 5RC), V_c will reach 99% of the value of V_s and to all intents and purposes the capacitor is deemed to be fully charged. We can show these relationships in Figures 3.94 and 3.95.

The discharging phase

To discharge the capacitor, we simply move the switch (S1) to position (2) where it will discharge through the resistor, again falling exponentially over five time constants and again not fully discharging, but instead reaching a value just above zero.

Summary

1. What are the two main types of resistors?
2. What does each colour-coded band on a resistor mean?
3. What is the difference between a resistor and a thermistor?
4. A capacitor is colour-coded (from top to bottom) red, blue, violet, white and yellow. What is the value of the capacitor, its tolerance and maximum working voltage?

Semiconductor devices

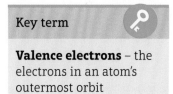

The crystal radio that can be constructed from modern electronic game sets depends on the detector action produced by a 'cat's whisker' and a crystal (a cat's whisker was a piece of wire, the point of which was pressed firmly into contact with a suitably mounted piece of natural crystal).

This crystal detector was in fact a diode. It is the use of diodes, semiconductors and semiconductor devices that we will investigate in this section.

Semiconductor basics

Try to think of a semiconductor as being a material that has an electrical quality somewhere between a conductor and an insulator, in that it is neither a good conductor nor a good insulator. Typically, we use semiconducting materials such as silicon or germanium, where the atoms of these materials are arranged in a 'lattice' structure. The lattice has atoms at regular distances from each other, with each atom 'linked' or 'bonded' to the four atoms surrounding it. Each atom then has four **valence electrons**.

Key term

Valence electrons – the electrons in an atom's outermost orbit

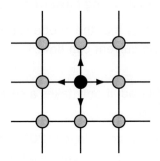

Figure 3.96: Lattice structure of semiconducting material

However, we have a problem in that, with atoms of pure silicon or germanium, no conduction is possible because we have no free electrons. To allow conduction to take place we add an impurity to the material via a process known as **doping**. When we dope the material we can add two types of impurity:

*   pentavalent – e.g. arsenic which contains five valence electrons

*   trivalent – e.g. aluminium that contains three valence electrons.

As we can see by the number of valence electrons in each, adding a pentavalent (five) material introduces an extra electron to the semiconductor and adding a trivalent (three) material to the semiconductor 'removes' an electron (also known as creating a hole).

When we have an extra electron, we have a surplus of negative charge and call this type of material 'n-type'. When we have 'removed' an electron we have a surplus of positive charge and call this material 'p-type'. It is the use of these two materials that will allow us to introduce the component responsible for rectification, the diode.

The p–n junction

A semiconductor diode is basically created when we bring together an 'n-type' material and a 'p-type' material to form a p–n junction. The two materials form a barrier where they meet which we call the depletion layer. In this barrier, the coming together of unlike charges causes a small internal p.d. to exist.

We now need to connect a battery across the ends of the two materials, where we call the end of the p-type material the anode and the end of the n-type material the cathode.

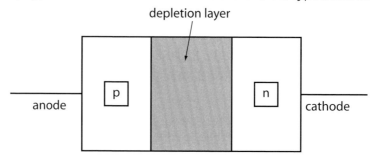

Figure 3.97: p–n junction

If the anode is positive and the battery voltage is big enough, it will overcome the effect of the internal p.d. and push charges (both positive and negative) over the junction. In other words, the junction has a low enough resistance for current to flow. This type of connection is known as being forward biased.

Reverse the battery connections so that the anode is now negative and the junction becomes high resistance and no current can flow. This type of connection is known as being reverse biased.

When the junction is forward biased, it only takes a small voltage (0.7 V for silicon) to overcome the internal barrier p.d.

When reversed biased, it takes a large voltage (1200 V for silicon) to overcome the barrier and thus destroy the diode, effectively allowing current to flow in both directions. As a general summary of its actions, we can therefore say that a diode allows current to flow through it in one direction only.

We normally use the symbol in Figure 3.99 to represent a diode. In this symbol, the direction of the arrow can be taken to represent the direction of current flow.

Figure 3.98: Diodes   Figure 3.99: Symbol representing a diode

Zener diode

We have just established that a conventional diode will not allow current flow if reverse biased and below its reverse breakdown voltage. We also said that when forward biased (in the direction of the arrow), the diode exhibits a voltage drop of roughly 0.6 V for a typical silicon diode. If we were to exceed the breakdown voltage, the internal barrier of the diode would be destroyed, thus allowing current flow in both directions. However, this normally results in the total destruction of the device.

Zener diodes are p–n junction devices that are specifically designed to operate in the reverse breakdown region without completely destroying the device. The breakdown voltage of a zener diode V_z (known as the zener voltage, named after the American physicist Clarence Zener who first discovered the effect) is set by carefully controlling the doping level during manufacture. The breakdown voltage can be controlled quite accurately in the doping process and tolerances to within 0.05% are available, although the most widely used tolerances are 5% and 10%.

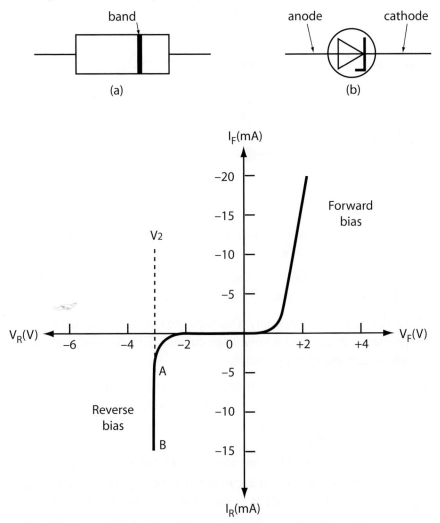

Figure 3.100: Zener diode characteristic

Therefore, a reverse biased zener diode will exhibit a controlled breakdown, allow current to flow and thus keep the voltage across the zener diode at the predetermined zener voltage. Because of this characteristic, the zener diode is commonly used as a form of voltage limiting/regulation when connected in parallel across a load.

When connected so that it is reverse biased in parallel with a variable voltage source, a zener diode acts as a short circuit when the voltage reaches the diode's reverse breakdown voltage and therefore limits the voltage to a known value.

A zener diode used in this way is known as a shunt voltage regulator (shunt meaning connected in parallel and voltage regulator being a class of circuit that produces a fixed voltage).

For a low current power supply, a simple voltage regulator could be made with a resistor (to limit the operating current) and a reverse biased zener diode as shown in Figure 3.101. Here, V_s is the supply voltage, remembering that V_z is our zener breakdown voltage.

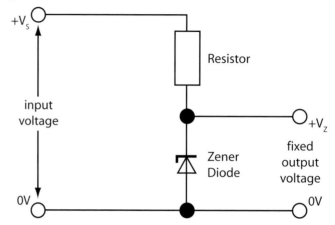

Figure 3.101: A simple voltage regulator made with a resistor and a reverse biased zener diode

As a summary, we can therefore say that a zener's properties are as follows:

- When forward biased (although not normally used for a zener) the behaviour is like an ordinary semiconductor diode.

- When reverse biased, at voltages below V_z the device essentially doesn't conduct, and it behaves just like an ordinary diode.

- When reverse biased, any attempt to apply a voltage greater than V_z causes the device to be prepared to conduct a very large current. This has the effect of limiting the voltage we can apply to around V_z.

As with any characteristic curve, the voltage at any given current, or the current at any given voltage, can be found from the curve of a zener diode (see Figure 3.100).

Light emitting diodes (LEDs)

The light emitting diode is a p–n junction especially manufactured from a semi-conducting material, which emits light when a current of about 10 mA flows through the junction. No light is emitted if the diode is reverse biased and if the voltage exceeds 5 volts then the diode may be damaged. If the voltage exceeds 2 volts then a series connected resistor may be required.

Figure 3.102 illustrates the general appearance of a LED.

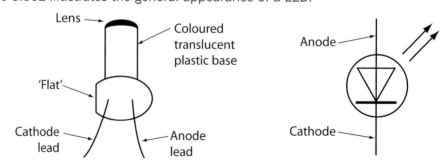

Figure 3.102: Light emitting diode

Photo cell and light-dependent resistor

The photo cell shown in Figure 3.103 changes light (also infrared and ultraviolet radiation) into electrical signals and is useful in burglar and fire alarms as well as in counting and automatic control systems. Photoconductive cells or light-dependent resistors make use of the semiconductors in which resistance decreases as the intensity of light falling on them increases. The effect is due to the energy of the light setting free electrons from donor atoms in the semiconductor, making it more conductive. The main use of this type of device is for outside lights along the streets, roads and motorways. There are also smaller versions for domestic use within homes and businesses.

Photodiode

A photodiode is a p–n junction designed to be responsive to optical input. As a result, they are provided with either a window or optical fibre connection that allows light to fall on the sensitive part of the device.

Photodiodes can be used in either zero bias or reverse bias. When zero biased, light falling on the diode causes a voltage to develop across the device, leading to a current in the forward bias direction. This is called the photovoltaic effect and is the principle of operation of the solar cell, a solar cell being a large number of photodiodes. The use of the solar cell can then be seen in providing power to equipment such as calculators, solar panels and satellites orbiting the earth.

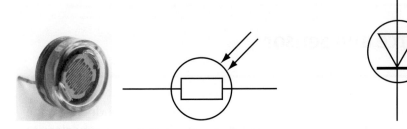

Figure 3.103: Photo cell and its circuit symbol   Figure 3.104: Circuit symbol for photodiode

When reverse biased, diodes usually have extremely high resistance. This resistance is reduced when light of an appropriate frequency shines on the junction. When light falls on the junction, the energy from the light breaks down bonds in the 'lattice' structure of the semiconductor material, thus producing electrons and allowing current to flow. Circuits based on this effect are more sensitive to light than ones based on the photovoltaic effect. Consequently, the photodiode is used as a fast counter or in light meters to measure light intensity.

Opto-coupler

The opto-coupler, also known as an opto-isolator, consists of an LED combined with a photodiode or phototransistor in the same package, as shown in Figure 3.105 and 3.106.

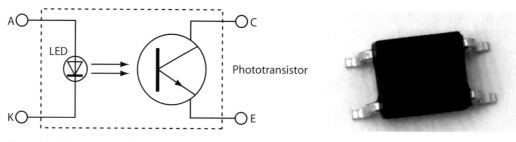

Figure 3.105: Opto-coupler circuit

Figure 3.106: Opto-coupler package

The opto-coupler package allows the transfer of signals, analogue or digital, from one circuit to another in cases where the second circuit cannot be connected electrically to the first, for example, due to different voltages.

In operation, current from the source signal passes through the input LED which emits infra-red light levels that are proportional to the signal. This light lands on the base of the photo-transistor, causing it to switch 'on'. When the current flowing through the LED is interrupted, the infra-red light disappears, causing the photo-transistor to cease conducting. The photo-transistor can therefore be used to switch current in an output circuit.

Infrared source and sensor

An infrared beam of light is projected from an LED which is a semiconductor made from gallium arsenide crystal. The light emitted is not visible light, but very close to the white light spectrum. Figure 3.107 shows various housings for both the source output and the sensors within the security alarms industry.

Infrared beams have a receiver, which reacts to the beam in differing ways depending upon its use. Infrared sources/receivers are used for alarm detection and as remote control signals for many applications. The passive infrared (PIR) detector is housed in only one enclosure and uses ceramic infrared detectors. The device does not have a projector but detects the infrared heat radiated from the human body.

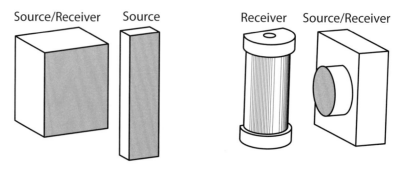

Figure 3.107: Housings for infrared source output and sensors for security alarms

Fibre optic link

The simplified block diagram in Figure 3.108 shows a system of communication, which can be several thousand kilometres in length. On the far left we input information such as speech or visual pictures as electrical signals. They are then pulse code modulated in the coder and changed into equivalent digital light signals by the optical transmitter via a miniature laser or LED at the end of the fibre optic cable.

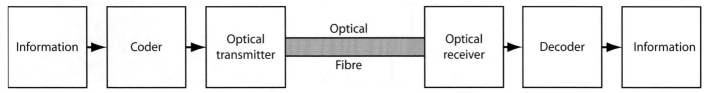

Figure 3.108: Simplified block diagram of fibre optic link

The light is transmitted down the cable to the optical receiver which uses a photodiode or phototransistor which converts the incoming signals back to electrical signals before they are decoded back into legible information.

The advantages of this type of link over a conventional communication system are:

- high information carrying capacity
- free from the noise of electrical interference
- greater distance can be covered, as there is no volt drop
- the cable is lighter, smaller and easier to handle than copper
- crosstalk between adjacent channels is negligible
- it offers greater security to the user.

The fibre optic cable

The fibre optic cable (see Figure 3.109) has a glass core of higher refractive index than the glass cladding around it. This maintains the light beam within the core by total internal reflection at the point where the core and the cladding touch.

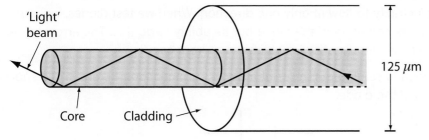

Figure 3.109: Fibre optic cable

This is similar to the insulation of the single core cable preventing the current leaking from the conductor. The beam of light bounces off the outer surface of the core in a zigzag formation along its length.

There are two main types of cable: multimode and singlemode (monomode).

Multimode

The wider core of the multimode fibre (Figure 3.110) allows the infrared to travel by different reflected paths or modes. Paths that cross the core more often are longer and take more time to travel along the fibre. This can sometimes cause errors and loss of information.

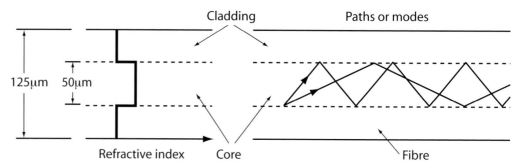

Figure 3.110: Multimode fibre optic cable

Singlemode

The core of the singlemode fibre (Figure 3.111) is about one tenth of the multimode and only straight through transmission is possible.

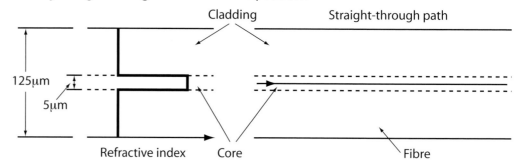

Figure 3.111: Singlemode fibre optic cable

Diode testing

Diodes allow electricity to flow in only one direction. When we test diodes, we are testing not only the condition of the diode but its ability to do this. The arrow in the circuit symbol shows the direction in which the current can flow.

We therefore need to remind ourselves of a diode's connections. Figure 3.112 shows the connections of the diode.

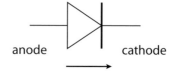

Figure 3.112: Diode connections

We can therefore say that:

- a good diode will show an extremely high resistance with reverse bias and a very low resistance with forward bias
- a defective open diode will show an extremely high resistance for both forward and reverse bias
- a defective shorted or resistive diode will show zero or a low resistance for both forward and reverse bias.

A defective open diode is the most common type of failure.

It is also important to remember that the test method used will depend upon the type of multimeter available, i.e. whether it is an analogue or digital meter.

Using an analogue multimeter

The following list explains the key points you should remember when using an analogue multimeter to carry out tests of diodes.

- Set the multimeter to a low value resistance scale such as ×10.

- **An important point** – when on the resistance settings only, most analogue meters reverse the polarity of the leads, so black become positive.

- Therefore connect the black (+) positive lead to the anode and the red (–) negative lead to the cathode. The diode should conduct and the meter will display a low resistance (the needle will be heading towards zero).

- Reverse the connections so that black (+) positive is connected to the cathode.

- The diode should not conduct this way so the meter will show a high resistance (the needle will be heading towards infinity).

Using a digital multimeter

Digital multimeters have a special setting for testing a diode, usually indicated by the diode symbol.

When connected to this diode setting the meter provides an internal voltage sufficient to forward bias and reverse bias a diode.

- Connect the red (+) positive lead to the anode and the black (–) negative lead to the cathode.

- If the diode is good, expect a reading of between approximately 0.5 V and 0.9 V, with 0.7 V being typical for forward bias.

- Reverse the connections.

- The diode should not conduct this way, so if the diode is working properly, expect a voltage reading based on the meter's internal voltage source. The value indicates that the diode has an extremely high reverse resistance with essentially all of the internal voltage therefore appearing across it.

Using a digital multimeter on Ohms function

If the multimeter does not have a special diode setting then the diode can be checked using a low resistance scale, much as with the analogue meter. However, there will be no need to reverse the lead polarity. Red should be positive this time!

For a forward bias check of a good diode, expect a low resistance reading and for the reverse bias check of a good diode expect an extremely high value or a reading of 'OL' as the reverse resistance is too high for the meter to measure. The actual resistance of forward biased diode is typically much less than $100\,\Omega$.

Rectification

Rectification is the conversion of an AC supply into a DC supply. Despite the common use of AC systems in our day-to-day work as an electrician, there are many applications (e.g. electronic circuits and equipment) that require a DC supply. The following section looks at the different forms this can take.

Half-wave rectification

A diode will only allow current to flow in one direction and it does this when the anode is more positive than the cathode. In the case of an AC circuit, this means that only the positive half cycles are allowed 'through' the diode and, as a result, we end up with a signal that resembles a series of 'pulses'. This tends to be unsuitable for most applications, but can be used in situations such as battery charging. A transformer is also commonly used at the supply side to ensure that the output voltage is to the required level. The waveform for this form of rectification would look as in Figure 3.113.

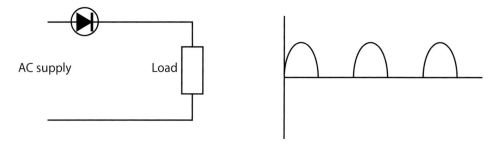

Figure 3.113: Half-wave rectification

Full-wave rectification

We have seen that half-wave rectification occurs when one diode allows the positive half cycles to pass through it. However, we can connect two diodes together to give a more even supply. We call this type of circuit **biphase**. In this method, we connect the anodes of the diodes to the opposite ends of the secondary winding of a centre-tapped transformer. As the anode voltages will be 180° out of phase with each other, one diode will effectively rectify the positive half cycle and one will rectify the negative half cycle. The output current will still appear to be a series of pulses, but they will be much closer together, with the waveform shown in Figure 3.114.

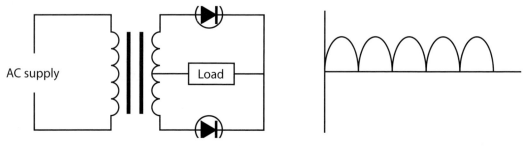

Figure 3.114: Full-wave rectification

The full-wave bridge rectifier

This method of rectification doesn't have to rely on the use of a centre-tapped transformer, but the output waveform will be the same as that of the biphase circuit previously described. In this system, we use four diodes, connected in such a way that at any instant in time two of the four will be conducting. The connections would be as in Figure 3.115, where we have shown two drawings to represent the route through the network for each half cycle.

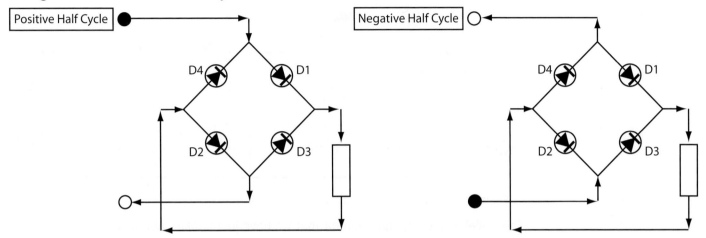

Figure 3.115: Full-wave bridge rectifier

The circuits that we have looked at so far convert AC into a supply which, although never going negative, is still not a true DC supply. This brings us to the next stage of the story – smoothing.

Smoothing

We have seen that the waveform produced by our circuits so far could best be described as having the appearance of a rough sea. The output current is not at a constant value, but constantly changing. This, as we have said before, is acceptable for battery charging, but useless for electronic circuits where a smooth supply voltage is required.

To make it useful for electronic circuits, we need to smooth out the waveform by creating a situation that is sometimes referred to as ripple-free and in essence there are three ways to achieve this, namely capacitor smoothing, choke smoothing and filter circuits.

Capacitor smoothing

If we connect a capacitor in parallel across the load, then the capacitor will charge up when the rectifier allows a flow of current and discharge when the rectifier voltage is less than the capacitor. However, the most effective smoothing comes under no-load conditions. The heavier the load current, the heavier the ripple. This means that the capacitor is only useful as a smoothing device for small output currents.

Choke smoothing

If we connect an inductor in series with our load, then the changing current through the inductor will induce an e.m.f. in opposition to the current that produced it. This means that the e.m.f. will try to maintain a steady current. Unlike the capacitor, this means that the heavier the ripple (rate of change of current) the more that ripple will be smoothed. This effectively means that the choke is more useful in heavy current circuits.

Filter circuits

This is the name given to a circuit that removes the ripple and is basically a combination of the two previous methods. The most effective of these is the capacitor input filter, shown in Figure 3.116.

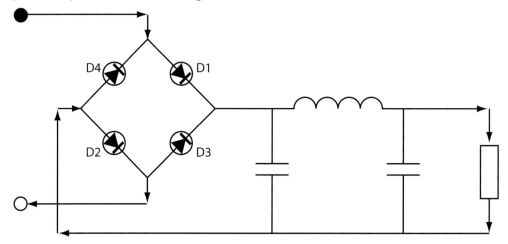

Figure 3.116: Capacitor input filter

The waveform for the filter circuit that we have just spoken about is shown in Figure 3.117, where the dotted line indicates the waveform before smoothing.

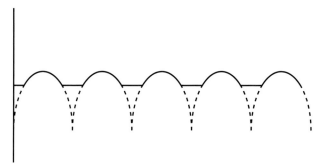

Figure 3.117: Waveform for capacitor input filter

Three-phase rectifier circuits

Whereas Figure 3.117 indicates that a reasonably smooth waveform can be obtained from a single-phase system, we can get a much smoother wave from the three-phase supply mains. To do so we use six diodes connected as a three-phase bridge circuit (see Figure 3.118). These types of rectifier are used to provide high-powered DC supplies.

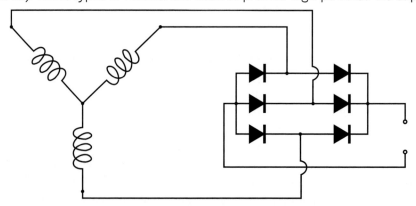

Figure 3.118: Six diodes connected as a three-phase bridge circuit

Thyristors, diacs and triacs

Thyristors

Figure 3.119: Thyristor

Sometimes referred to as a 'silicon controlled rectifier' (SCR), the thyristor is a four-layer semiconducting device, with each layer consisting of an alternating n or p type material as shown in Figure 3.120.

The main terminals (the anode and cathode) are across the full four layers, while the control terminal (the gate) is attached to one of the middle layers. The circuit symbol for a thyristor is shown in Figure 3.121.

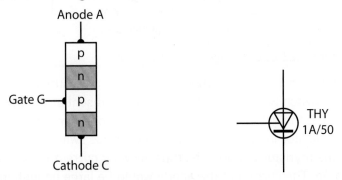

Figure 3.120: Construction of a thyristor   Figure 3.121: Thyristor circuit symbol

Effectively acting as a high speed switch, thyristors are available that can switch large amounts of power (as high as MW) and can therefore be seen in use within high voltage direct current (HVDC) systems. These can be used to interconnect two AC regions of a power-distribution grid, albeit the equipment needed to convert between AC and DC can add considerable cost. That said, above a certain distance (about 35 miles for undersea cables and 500 miles for overhead cables), the lower cost of the HVDC electrical conductors can outweigh the cost of the electronics required.

Principle of operation

A thyristor acts like a semiconductor version of a mechanical switch, having two states; in other words it is either 'on' or 'off' with nothing in between. This is how they gained their name from the Greek word thyra (which means door), the inference being something that is either open or closed.

The thyristor is very similar to a diode, with the exception that it has an extra terminal (the gate) which is used to activate it. Effectively in its normal or 'forward biased' state, the thyristor acts as an open-circuit between anode and cathode, thus preventing current flow through the device. This is known as the 'forward blocking' state.

However, the thyristor can allow current to flow through it by the application of a control (gate) current to the gate terminal. It is this concept that allows a small signal at the gate to control the switching of a higher power load. In this respect the thyristor is performing in a similar way to a relay (pages 258–259).

Once activated, a thyristor doesn't require a control (gate) current to continue operating and will therefore continue to conduct until either the supply voltage is turned off, reversed or when a minimum 'holding' current is no longer maintained between the anode and cathode.

These concepts are shown in Figure 3.122.

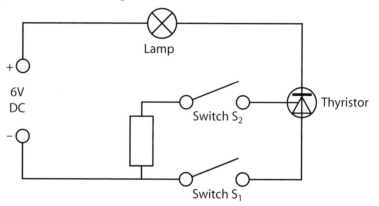

Figure 3.122: Circuit diagram of a thyristor

In Figure 3.122, switch S_1 acts as a master isolator and no supply is present at the thyristor. Closing switch S_1 will allow a supply to be present at the thyristor, but there is no signal at the gate terminal as switch S_2 is open and therefore no current will flow to the indicator lamp. However, if we now close switch S_2, the gate will be energised and the thyristor will operate, thus allowing current to flow through it to the indicator lamp. The current at the anode would be large enough in this situation to allow the thyristor to continue operating, even if we opened switch S_2.

The control of AC power can also be achieved with the thyristor by allowing current to be supplied to the load during part of each half cycle. If a gate pulse is applied automatically at a certain time during each positive half cycle of the input, then the thyristor will conduct during that period until it falls to zero for the negative half cycle.

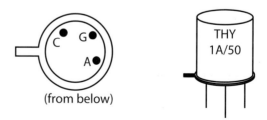

Figure 3.123: Typical small value thyristor

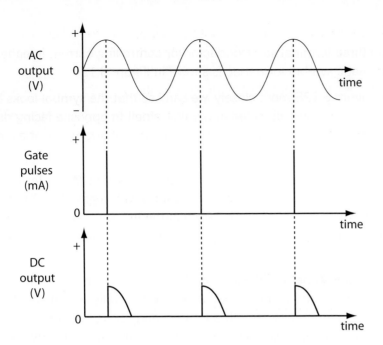

Figure 3.124: Supply of current to load during part of each half cycle

You will see from Figure 3.124 that the gate pulse (mA) occurs at the peak of the AC input (V). During negative half cycles the thyristor is reverse biased and will not conduct and will not conduct again until half way through the next positive half cycle. Current actually flows for only a quarter of the cycle, but by changing the timing of the gate pulses, this can be decreased further or increased. The power supplied to the load can be varied from zero to half wave rectified DC.

Thyristor testing

To test thyristors a simple circuit needs to be constructed as shown in Figure 3.125. When switch B only is closed the lamp will not light, but when switch A is closed the lamp lights to full brilliance. The lamp will remain illuminated even when switch A is opened. This shows that the thyristor is operating correctly. Once a voltage has been applied to the gate the thyristor becomes forward conducting like a diode and the gate loses control.

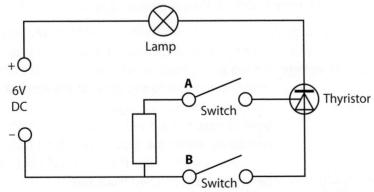

Figure 3.125: Circuit for testing thyristor

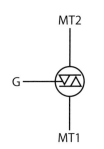

Figure 3.126: Triac symbol

The triac

The triac is a three terminal semiconductor for controlling current in either direction and the schematic symbol for a triac is shown in Figure 3.126.

If we look at Figure 3.126 more closely, we can see that the symbol looks like two thyristors that have been connected in parallel, albeit in opposite facing directions and with only one gate terminal. We refer to this type of arrangement as an inverse parallel connection.

The main power terminals on a triac are designated as MT1 (Main Terminal 1) and MT2. When the voltage on terminal MT2 is positive with regard to MT1, if we were to apply a positive voltage to the gate terminal the left thyristor would conduct. When the voltage is reversed and a negative voltage is applied to the gate, the right thyristor would conduct.

As with the thyristor generally, a minimum holding current must be maintained in order to keep a triac conducting. A triac therefore generally operates in the same way as the thyristor, but operating in both a forward and reverse direction. It is therefore sometimes referred to as a bidirectional thyristor, in that it can conduct electricity in both directions. One disadvantage of this is that triacs can require a fairly high current pulse to turn them on.

Figure 3.127: Diac symbol

The diac

Before consideration is given to practical triac applications and circuits, it is necessary to examine the diac. This device is often used in triac triggering circuits because it, along with a resistor-capacitor network, produces an ideal pulse-style waveform. It does this without any sophisticated additional circuitry, due to its electrical characteristics. Also it provides a degree of protection against spurious triggering from electrical noise (voltage spikes).

The symbol is shown in Figure 3.127. The device operates like two breakdown (zener) diodes connected in series, back to back. It acts as an open switch until the applied voltage reaches about 32–35 volts, at which point it will conduct.

Lamp dimmer circuit

Figure 3.128 shows a typical 230 V GLS lamp dimmer circuit.

The GLS lamp has a tungsten filament, which allows it to operate at about 2500°C and is wired in series with the triac. The variable resistor is part of a trigger network providing a variable voltage into the gate circuit, which contains a diac connected in series. Increasing the value of the resistor increases the time taken for the capacitor to reach its charge level to pass current into the diac circuit. Reducing the resistance allows the triac to switch on faster in each half cycle. By this adjustment the light output of the lamp can be controlled from zero to full brightness.

The capacitor is connected in series with the variable resistor. This combination is designed to produce a variable phase shift into the gate circuit of the diac. When the p.d. across the capacitor rises, enough current flows into the diac to switch on the triac.

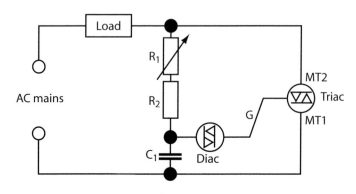

Figure 3.128: GLS lamp dimmer circuit

The diac is a triggering device having a relatively high switch on voltage (32–35 volts) and acts as an open switch until the capacitor p.d. reaches the required voltage level.

The triac is a two-directional thyristor, which is triggered on both halves of each cycle. This allows it to conduct current in either direction of the AC supply. Its gate is in series with the diac, allowing it to receive positive and negative pulses.

A relatively high resistive value resistor R_2 (100 Ω) is placed in series with a capacitor to reduce false triggering of the triac by mains voltage interference. The capacitor is of a low value (0.1 mF). This combination is known as the **snubber circuit**.

Working life

You are asked to look at a problem at a small private residential care home. When you arrive the warden explains that there is a problem with the nurse call system. It has very recently been installed but, as the electrical contractor that fitted it has gone into receivership, no one is quite sure of its operation. Additionally, they require another 'patient call' button to be installed in a further bedroom. The warden has a circuit diagram of the system, which is shown below.

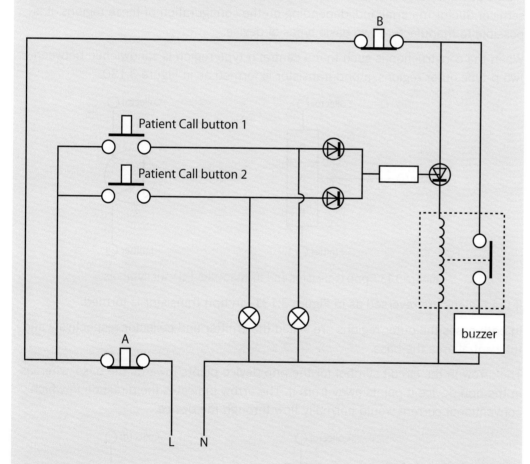

All components, with the exception of the patient call buttons, are located inside the nurse call panel, which is located at the nurses' station. Looking at the diagram, identify the components and prepare a written report for the warden, explaining in writing how the system operates. Then, produce a revised circuit diagram to show how an additional patient could be added to the system. (Please assume that the values and ratings of any components for this exercise will be acceptable.) Your new drawing and report will be held by the warden for future reference.

Transistors

Figure 3.129: Transistor

The term 'transistor' is derived from the two words 'transfer-resistor'. This is because in a transistor approximately the same current is transferred from a low to a high resistance region. The term 'bipolar' means both electrons and holes are involved in the action of this type of transistor.

What is usually referred to as simply a transistor, but is more accurately described as a bipolar transistor, is a semiconductor device, which has two p–n junctions. It is capable of producing current amplification and, with an added load resistor, both a load and voltage power gain can be achieved.

Transistor basics

A bipolar transistor consists of three separate regions or areas of doped semiconductor material and, depending on the configuration of these regions, it is possible to manufacture two basic types of device.

When the construction is such that a central n-type region is sandwiched between two p-type outer regions, a pnp transistor is formed as in Figure 3.130.

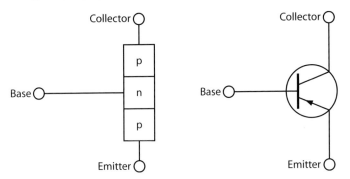

Figure 3.130: pnp transistor and its associated circuit symbols

If the regions are reversed as in Figure 3.131, an npn transistor is formed.

In both cases the outer regions are called the emitter and collector respectively and the central area the base.

The arrow in the circuit symbol for the pnp device points towards the base, whereas in the npn device it points away from it. The arrow indicates the direction in which conventional current would normally flow through the device.

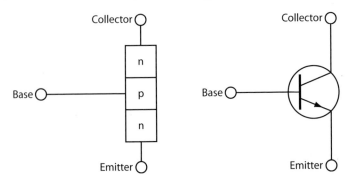

Figure 3.131: npn transistor and its associated circuit symbols

Electron flow is of course in the opposite direction as explained on pages 227–230. Note that in these idealised diagrams, the collector and emitter regions are shown to be the same size. This is not so in practice; the collector region is made physically larger since it normally has to dissipate the greater power during operation. Further, the base region is physically very thin, typically only a fraction of a micron (a micron is one millionth of a metre).

Hard-wire connections are made to the three regions internally; wires are then brought out through the casing to provide an external means of connection to each region. Either silicon or germanium semiconductor materials may be used in the fabrication of the transistor but silicon is preferred for reasons of temperature stability.

Transistor operation

For transistors to operate three conditions must be met:

1. The base must be very thin.

2. Majority carriers in the base must be very few.

3. The base-emitter junction must be forward biased and the base-collector junction reverse biased.

Electrons from the emitter enter the base and diffuse through it. Due to the shape of the base most electrons reach the base-collector junction and are swept into the collector by the strong positive potential. A few electrons stay in the base long enough to meet the indigenous holes present and recombination takes place.

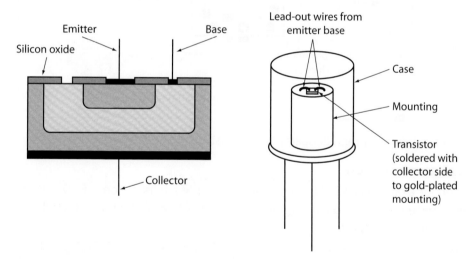

Figure 3.132: Transistor operation

To maintain the forward bias on the base-emitter junction, holes enter the base from the base bias battery. It is this base current which maintains the base-emitter forward bias and therefore controls the size of the emitter current entering the base. The greater the forward bias on the base-emitter junction, the greater the number of emitter current carriers entering the base.

The collector current is always a fixed proportion of the emitter current set by the thinness of the base and the amount of doping. Holes from the emitter enter the base and diffuse through it – see Figure 3.133. Due to the shape of the base most holes reach the base-collector junction and are swept into the collector by the strong negative potential.

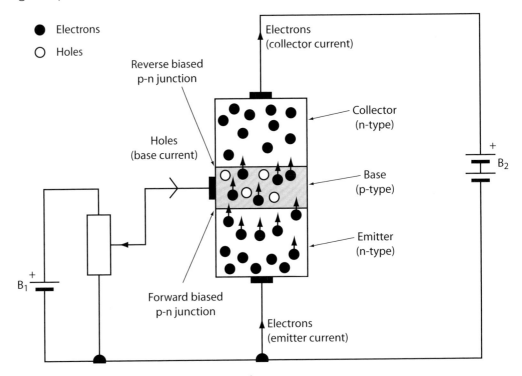

Figure 3.133: Circuit diagram for operation of transistor

Current amplification

Consider, for example, as in Figure 3.134, that a base bias of some 630 mV has caused a base current of 0.5 mA to flow but more importantly has initiated a collector current of 50 mA.

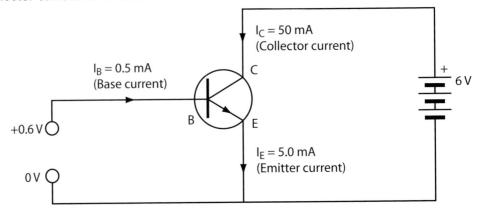

Figure 3.134: Current flow in transistor

Although these currents may seem insignificant, it's the comparison between the base and collector currents which is of interest. This relationship between I_B and I_C is termed the 'static value of the short-circuit forward current transfer' – we normally just call it the gain of the transistor, and it is simply a measure of how much amplification we would get. The symbol that we use for this is h_{FE}. This is the ratio between the continuous output current (collector current) and the continuous input current (base current). Thus when I_B is 0.5 mA and I_C is 50 mA the ratio is:

$$h_{FE} = \frac{I_C}{I_B}$$
$$= \frac{50 \, \text{mA}}{0.5 \, \text{mA}}$$

i.e. approximately equal to 100.

It can therefore be said that a small base current initiated by the controlling forward base-bias voltage produces a significantly higher value of collector current to flow dependent on the value of h_{FE} for the transistor. Thus current amplification has been achieved.

Voltage amplification

Mention was previously made of the derivation of the word 'transistor' and quoted the device as transferring current from a low resistive circuit to approximately the same current in a high resistive circuit. This is an npn transistor so the low resistive reference is the emitter circuit and the high resistive reference, the collector circuit, the current in both being almost identical.

The reason the emitter circuit is classed as having a low resistance is because it contains the forward biased (pn) base-emitter junction. Conversely, the collector circuit contains the reverse biased (np) base-collector junction, which is of course in the order of tens of thousands of ohms (it varies with I_C). In order to produce a voltage output from the collector, a load resistor (R_B) is added to the collector circuit as indicated in the circuit diagram in Figure 3.135.

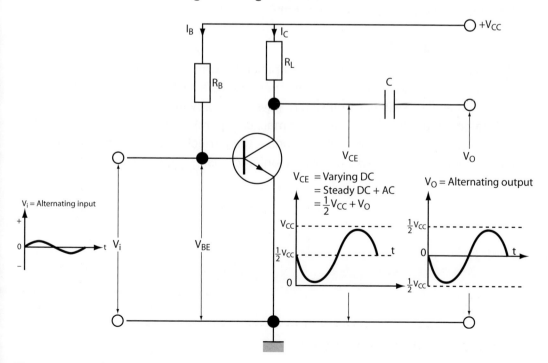

Figure 3.135: Voltage amplification

This shows the simplest circuit for a voltage amplifier. To see how voltage amplification occurs we have to consider that there is no input across V_i, which is called the quiescent (quiet) state. For transistor action to take place the base emitter junction V_{BE} must be forward biased (and has to remain so when V_i goes positive and negative due to the AC signal input).

By introducing resistor R_B between collector and base, a small current I_B will flow from V_{CC} through R_B into the base and down to 0 V via the emitter, thus keeping the transistor running (ticking over).

Component resistor values R_B and R_L are chosen so that the steady base current I_B makes the quiescent collector-emitter voltage V_{CE} about half the power supply voltage V_{CC}. This allows V_O to replicate the input signal V_i at an amplified voltage with a 180° phase shift. When an AC signal is applied to the input V_i and goes positive it increases V_{BE} slightly to around 0.61 V. When V_i swings negative, V_{BE} drops slightly to 0.59 V. As a result a small alternating current is superimposed on the quiescent base current I_B, which in effect is a varying DC current.

The collector emitter voltage (V_{CE}) is a varying DC voltage, or an alternating voltage superimposed on a normal steady DC voltage. The capacitor C is there to block the DC voltage, but allow the alternating voltage to pass on to the next stage. So in summing up, a bipolar transistor will act as a voltage amplifier if:

- it has a suitable collector load R_L

- it is biased so that the quiescent value V_{CE} is around half the value of V_{CC}, which is known as the class A condition

- the transistor and load together bring about voltage amplification

- the output is 180° out of phase with the input signal as Figure 3.135 indicates

- the emitter is common to the input, output and power supply circuits and is usually taken as the reference point for all voltages, i.e. 0 V. It is called 'common', 'ground' or 'earth' if connected to earth.

Transistor as a switch

We have looked at the transistor as an amplifier of current and voltage. If we connect the transistor as in Figure 3.136, we can operate it as a switch. Compared with other electrically operated switches, transistors have many advantages, whether in discrete or integrated circuit (IC) form. They are small, cheap, reliable, have no moving parts and can switch millions of times per second – the perfect switch that has infinite resistance when 'off', no resistance when 'on' and changes instantaneously from one state to another, using up no power.

Figure 3.136 shows the basic circuit for an npn common emitter as in previous diagrams with a load resistor R_L connected in series with the supply (V_{CC}) and the collector.

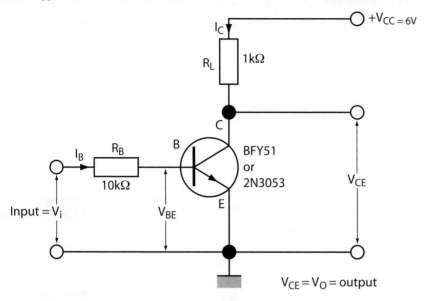

Figure 3.136: Circuit diagram for transistor used as a switch

R_B prevents excessive base currents, which would seriously damage the transistor when forward biased. With no input across V_I, the transistor is basically turned off. This means then that there will be no current (I_C) through R_L, therefore there will be no volt drop across R_L so the $+V_{CC}$ voltage (6 V) will appear across the output V_{CE}.

If we now connect a supply of between 2 to 6V across V_i input, the transistor will switch on, current will flow through the collector load resistor R_L and down to common, making the output V_{CE} around 0 V. From this we can state that:

- when the input V_i = 0 V, the output V_{CE} = 6 V

- when the input V_i = between 2 to 6V, the output V_{CE} = 0 V.

From this we can see that the transistor is either High (6 V) or Low (0 V), or we can confirm, like a switch that it is either 'On' (6V) or 'Off' (0 V).

This circuit can be used in alarms and switch relays for all types of processes and is the basic stage for programmable logic control (plc) which uses logic gates with either one or zero to represent what the output is from a possible input.

In Figure 3.137 are identified basic logic gate circuits with their inputs/outputs, 'truth table' and symbols.

There is also an Exclusive NOR which gives an output as indicated in Figure 3.138.

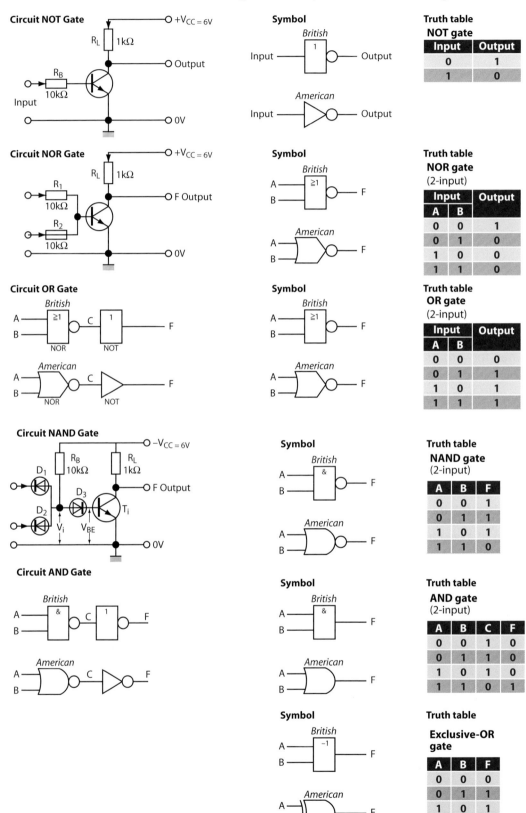

Figure 3.137: Basic logic gate circuits

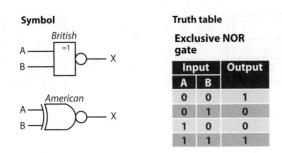

| Symbol | Truth table |

Symbol

British

A ———[=1]o— X

B ———

American

A ———)Do— X

B ———

Truth table

Exclusive NOR gate

Input		Output
A	**B**	
0	0	1
0	1	0
1	0	0
1	1	1

Figure 3.138: Exclusive NOR gate

Testing transistors

As all transistors consist of either an npn or a pnp construction the testing of them is similar to diodes. Special meters with three terminals for testing transistors are available and many testing instruments have this facility. However, an ohmmeter can be used for testing a transistor to check if it is conducting correctly. The following results should be obtained from a transistor assuming that the red lead of an ohmmeter is positive.

Note: This is not always the case. With some older analogue meters, the battery connections internally are the opposite way round, so it is always good to check both ways across base and emitter as shown in Figures 3.139 and 3.140.

A good npn transistor will give the following readings:

- Red to base and black to collector or emitter will give a low resistance.

- However, if the connections are reversed it will result in a high resistance reading.

- Connections of any polarity between the collector and emitter will also give a high reading.

A good pnp transistor will give the following readings:

- Black to base and red to collector or the emitter will give a low resistance reading.

- However, if the connections are reversed a high resistance reading will be observed.

- Connections of either polarity between the collector and emitter will give a high resistance reading.

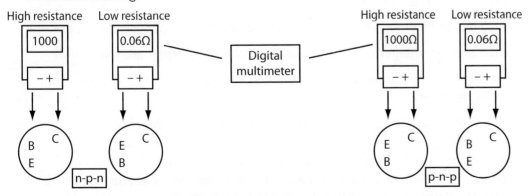

Figure 3.139: Testing transistors with digital multimeter

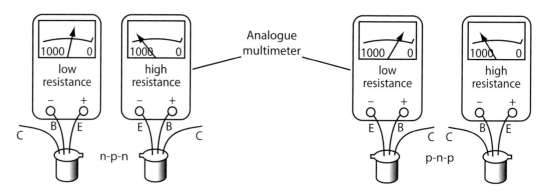

Figure 3.140: Testing transistors with analogue multimeter

Field effect transistors (FETs)

Field effect transistor devices first appeared as separate (or discrete) transistors, but now the field effect concept is employed in the fabrication of large-scale integration arrays such as semiconductor memories, microprocessors, calculators and digital watches.

There are two types of field effect transistor: the junction gate field effect transistor, which is usually abbreviated to JUGFET, JFET or FET, and the metal oxide semiconductor field effect transistor known as the MOSFET. They differ significantly from the bipolar transistor in their characteristics, operation and construction.

The main advantages of an FET over a bipolar transistor are:

- Its operation depends on the flow of majority current carriers only. It is, therefore, often described as a unipolar transistor.

- It is simpler to fabricate and occupies less space in integrated form.

- Its input resistance is extremely high, typically above 10 MΩ especially for MOSFET devices. In practice, this is why voltage measuring devices such as oscilloscopes and digital voltmeters employ the FET in their input circuitry, so that the voltage being measured is not altered by the connection of the instrument.

- Electrical noise is the production of random minute voltages caused by the movement of current carriers through the transistor structure. Since the FET does not employ minority carriers, it therefore has the advantage of producing much lower noise levels compared with the bipolar transistor.

- Also due to its unipolar nature it is more stable during changes of temperature.

The main disadvantages of an FET over its bipolar counterpart are the following.

- Its very high input impedance renders it susceptible to internal damage from static electricity.

- Its voltage gain for a given bandwidth is lower. Although this may be a disadvantage at low frequencies (below 10 MHz), at high frequencies the low noise amplification that an FET achieves is highly desirable. This facet of FET operation, though, is usually only exploited in radio and TV applications, where very small high frequency signals need to be amplified.

- The FET cannot switch from its fully on to its fully off condition as fast as a bipolar transistor. It is for this reason that digital logic circuits employing MOSFET technology are slower than bipolar equivalents, although even faster switching speeds are being achieved as FET production technology continues to advance.

Figure 3.141 illustrates the basic construction of the FET, which consists of a channel of n-type semiconductor material with two connections, source (S) and drain (D). A third connection is made at the gate (G), which is made of p-type material to control the n-channel current. The symbol is shown in Figure 3.142.

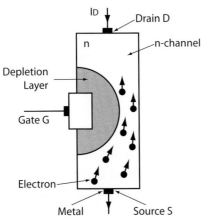

Figure 3.141: Basic construction of field effect transistor (FET)

Figure 3.142: Field effect transistor (FET) symbol

In theory, the drain connection is made positive with respect to the source, and electrons are attracted towards the D terminal. If the gate is made negative there will be reverse bias between G and S, which will limit the number of electrons passing from S to D.

The gate and source are connected to a variable voltage supply, such as a potentiometer, and increasing or lowering the voltage makes G more or less negative, which in turn reduces or increases the drain current.

Component positional reference

As electronic diagrams become more complex a system called the component positional reference system is used. This system uses a simple grid reference to identify holes on a board on which components are installed. This is done by counting along the columns at the top of the board starting from the left and numbering them as you count. Then starting from the left and counting down rows, each row is given a letter in turn from the alphabet starting from A. For example the position reference point 7:J would be 7 holes from the left and 10 holes down.

Inverters

Earlier we looked at the conversion of AC to DC by the process of rectification. The opposite process, namely converting DC into AC is called inversion and a device called an inverter is used to do so.

We know them as inverters because of their origin. Early devices were actually mechanical devices that used an AC motor connected to a generator to produce DC and were known as converters. By running the converter in reverse, DC could be applied to the field and commutator windings to turn the machine, thus producing AC and leading to them being called an 'inverted rotary converter'.

Nowadays, the inverter uses electronic components such as thyristors and mosfets to switch the DC to create pulses of AC. As we saw earlier in this unit, alternating current produces a sine wave that is smooth with continuous curves from positive to negative and back again, and the modern power inverter creates an approximation of a sine wave that meets all equipment needs and is commonly referred to as a pure sine wave inverter.

Solid-state inverters have no moving parts and can be found from switching power supplies in computers to large high-voltage direct current systems (HVDC) that transport large amounts of power. More commonly, inverters are used to supply AC from a DC source such as solar panels or batteries.

Equally, in terms of emergency supplies, an 'uninterruptible power supply' (UPS) will use batteries and an inverter to supply AC to equipment when there has been a mains failure. Additionally, as has also been mentioned earlier in this unit, variable-frequency drives control the operating speed of an AC motor by controlling the frequency and voltage of the power supplied to the motor via an inverter.

Integrated circuits

Integrated circuits are complete electronic circuits within a plastic case (known as the black box). The chip contains all the components required, which may include diodes, resistors, capacitors, transistors etc.

There are several categories, which include analogue, digital and memories. The basic layout is shown in Figure 3.143, which is an operational amplifier (**dual in-line IC**).

The plastic case has a notch at the end and, if you look at the back of the case with the notch at the top, Pin 1 is always the first one on the left hand side, sometimes noted with a small dot. The other pin numbers follow down the left hand side, 2, 3 and 4 and then back up the right hand side from the bottom right to the top 5, 6, 7 and 8. This is an 8-pin chip but you can get some chips with 32 pins or more.

Key term

Dual in-line IC – the type of IC with the pins lined up down each side

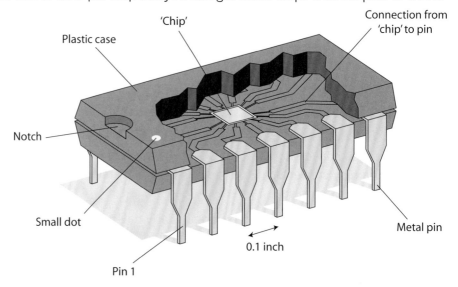

Figure 3.143: Operational amplifier

Summary

1. What three conditions must be met for a Transistor to operate?
2. What device often used in triac triggering circuits, along with a resistor capacitor network is able to produce an ideal pulse-style waveform?

Operating principles of components and devices

Now that we have a basic understanding of electronic components, let's look at some of the ways in which they are incorporated into systems and devices that we use every day.

Security and fire alarms

All of these electronic systems share the same concept:

- a unit senses danger and emits an output (1)

- this output is fed to a processing unit (2)

- the processing unit makes a decision and sends another output to a signalling device (3).

In the case of (1) above, we could be talking about a number of series-connected, normally-closed switches wired to protect a door or window, so that if the door is opened it breaks the circuit and sends a signal to a processing unit (2). This would be the control panel and via an internal relay and transistor it would in turn send a signal to (3), the alarm sounder.

In the case of a fire alarm system, the unit in (1) could be a break glass contact or a smoke detector.

Telephones

Households and individuals are gradually moving from landlines to mobile phones. The average smartphone is a technological wonder, but when it comes to making a call, it does share some basic concepts with the old landline namely:

- it has an earpiece (a speaker) and a mouthpiece (a microphone)

- the speaker converts electrical signals into the sound that you hear and the microphone is a bit like a speaker in reverse – it picks up your voice, takes the varying pressure waves in the air and converts them into varying electrical signals

- it has a switch that connects/disconnects your phone from the network.

Other components in your smartphone include:

- an LCD or LED display screen
- the chip that contains the processors etc. (known as 'system on a chip')
- light sensors for the camera and screen brightness
- proximity sensors to lock the screen when placing the phone to your ear
- photo diodes that capture infrared rays
- network couplers, zener diodes and resistors.

When we make a call, the numbers we press send a corresponding number of pulses to the network to create a 'circuit' based on digital circuit switching. In order to connect one phone to another, the numbers are sent out as a radio wave via the phone's aerial until it reaches the nearest network mast. The mast receives the signal and passes it on to its base station, which effectively coordinates what happens inside each local part of the mobile network (which is called a cell). From the base station, the calls are routed onward to their destination.

Dimmer switches

Using a combination of resistor, capacitor, diac and triac, we discussed an example of a lamp dimmer circuit earlier in this unit.

You can find the full description and diagram on page 312.

Heating controls

Most properties will have central heating. These systems include a boiler, pump, radiators and controls such as electronic programmable thermostats.

Some systems use a digital thermostat, an automatic switch whose operation will be based around an NTC thermistor (negative temperature coefficient – its resistance decreases as temperature rises) or semi-conducting device such as a resistance thermometer. The thermostat uses the resistance in the thermistor to calculate the temperature of the air in the room. If the temperature is too high, the thermostat sends a signal to a relay or triac in the programmer to turn the boiler off. If it's too cold, it sends a signal to turn the boiler on. You can see and do this via the LCD screen.

Electronic motor control

Every electric motor will have some sort of controller. In its simplest form, it could be a switch that connects the motor directly to the power source (e.g. an electric drill or fan).

However, by using controllers containing silicon controlled rectifiers (SCRs), diodes and transistors at the complex end, we can save energy using variable speed drives such as a variable frequency drive (VFD), which in essence control the speed of an induction or synchronous motor by adjusting the input frequency and voltage supplied to the motor.

Wireless control systems

In these systems, we use a part of the electromagnetic spectrum energy in the form of radio waves to transmit information. It's normally referred to as radio frequency (RF).

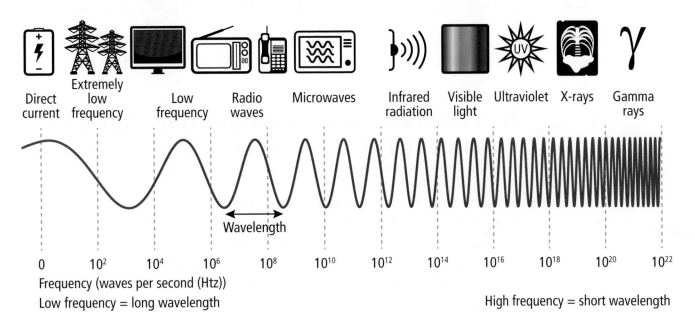

Figure 3.144 Electromagnetic spectrum used to transmit information

Here are some of the applications of wireless control systems that are currently in use:

* audio/video (AV) control systems

* building management systems (BMS)

* long range pump controls

* security alarm systems

* fire alarm systems

* car parking and city traffic controls

* street lighting.

It is essential to have wireless networking standards in order to avoid every system trying to do its own thing or being unable to talk to other systems. We do not yet have universal standardisation, but some popular protocols are C-Bus, Zigbee, KNX and Telensa.

Let's look ahead to the future. The Internet of Things (IoT) is the system of interconnected computing devices, mechanical and digital machines, objects, animals or people that are provided with unique identifiers and the ability to transfer data over a network. This relationship or interaction can be human-to-human, human-to-device, or device-to-device without human-to-human or human-to-computer intervention.

Simply put, this is the concept of connecting any device with an appropriate on/off switch to the internet. Analysts are currently predicting that by 2020 there will be over 26 billion connected devices!

7. Electrical supply systems

The basic method of generating electricity by turning a loop of wire between the poles of a magnet is still the basis of electricity generation in our power stations today.

How electricity is generated and transmitted for domestic and industrial/commercial consumption

There are several methods of generating electricity. A Van De Graaf generator for example can be used to generate static electricity and in a small number of power stations, nuclear reaction can be converted directly into electricity. However, in the main, electricity is generated using electromagnetic induction, in which mechanical energy is used to rotate the shaft of an AC generator.

But how do we get the generator to rotate?

In general, the shaft of a three-phase AC generator is turned by using steam turbines, and most electricity in the UK is produced by this method.

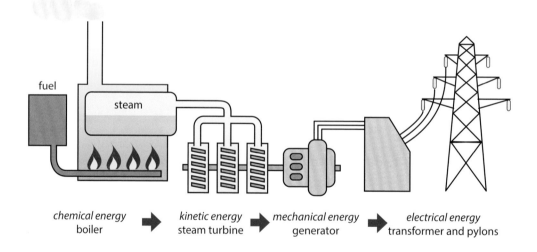

Figure 3.145: The basic components of electricity generation systems

As we can see from Figure 3.145, water is heated by a fuel until it becomes high pressure steam. At this point the steam is forced onto the vanes of a steam turbine, which in turn rotates the generator. A variety of energy sources can be used to heat the water in the first place and the more common ones are coal, gas, oil and nuclear power.

We do have other methods of getting the generator to rotate, some being more eco-friendly than others. Such other options include hydro (where running water turns the generator), wind and tidal power.

Features and characteristics of transmission and distribution

Power station generator output is transformed upwards before transmission. Electricity is then transmitted at very high voltage (400 kV or 275 kV for the super grid) in order to reduce the power losses that occur in the power lines, as transmission at low voltage would necessitate the installation of very large cables and switchgear indeed.

At this point, the electricity is fed into the National Grid system (132 kV for the national grid), which is a network of nearly 5000 miles of overhead and underground power lines that link power stations together and are interconnected throughout the country.

The concept of the National Grid is that, should a fault develop in any one of the contributing power stations or transmission lines, then electricity can be requested from another station on the system to maintain supplies.

Electricity is transmitted around the grid, mainly via steel-cored aluminium conductors, which are suspended from steel pylons. We do this for three main reasons.

- The cost of installing cables underground is excessive.
- Air is a very cheap and readily available insulator.
- Air also acts as a coolant for the heat being generated in the conductors.

Electricity is then 'taken' from the National Grid via a series of appropriately located sub-stations that sequentially transform the grid supply down as follows:

- 66 kV and 33 kV for secondary transmission to heavy industry
- 11 kV for high-voltage distribution to lighter industry
- 415/400 V to commercial consumer supplies
- 240/230 V to domestic consumer supplies.

At the 11 kV stage we distribute electricity to a series of local sub-stations. It is their job to then take the 11 kV supply, transform it down to 400 V and then distribute this via a network of underground radial circuits to customers. In rural areas this distribution is usually with overhead lines.

It is also at this point that we see the introduction of the neutral conductor, which is normally done by connecting the secondary winding of the transformer in star and then connecting the star point to earth via an earth electrode beneath the sub-station.

Final distribution to the customer

The connection is then from the local sub-station to the customer. The connection within the customer's premises is called the main intake position.

There are many different sizes of installation, but generally speaking we will find certain items at every main intake position. These items, which belong to the supply company, are:

- a sealed overcurrent device that protects the supply company's cable
- an energy metering system to determine the customer's electricity usage.

It is after this point that we say we have reached the consumer's installation. The consumer's installation must be controlled by a main switch located as close as possible to the supply company equipment and be capable of isolating all live conductors. In the average domestic installation this device is combined with the means of distributing and protecting the final circuits in what we know as the consumer unit.

> # Generating electricity from other sources

In the ever-increasing search for 'green' technology and a need for energy conservation, a variety of environmentally friendly technologies and alternative sources of electricity have been developed.

Under the headings of micro-generation (small scale as used in individual households) and macro generation (large scale commercial), some of them are as follows.

Solar photovoltaic

These systems work by converting solar radiation into electricity that can be used immediately, stored or even sold back to the electricity provider (with a grid-connected system). Correctly installed systems, even in the UK, could allow efficiently managed domestic properties to generate about half of their own electricity.

Virtually all photovoltaic devices are some type of photodiode, and in most photovoltaic applications the radiation is sunlight. This is why the devices are known as solar photovoltaic.

A photodiode is a p-n junction that responds to light. If we take a zero-biased p-n junction, sunlight falling on the material causes a voltage to develop across the device, leading to a current in the forward-biased direction. This is the 'photovoltaic effect'. Assemble many photodiodes together and you have a solar cell. Solar cells are commonly assembled into panels (solar panels) to produce DC electricity from sunlight.

In a grid-connected system, power generated is first used within the property to reduce electricity consumption then any surplus is exported to the grid. Various schemes and tariffs are available through electricity suppliers to give credits or payments for both generated and exported power. A standard power inverter then takes the DC from the photovoltaic system and converts it to AC for use in the property.

However, you can't just plug any inverter into the UK grid. Try thinking of the problems faced by a car trying to join a busy motorway from a slip road (such as the right speed, right direction) and you have a good starting point.

The problem is that electricity in the two systems may not be 'in phase': the electricity from your inverter may be cycling up when the grid is cycling down. A 'grid-tied inverter' monitors the power from the grid and makes sure the power coming from the inverter stays in sync with the phase of the electricity from the grid.

The grid-tied inverter also differs from the stand-alone variety in that the control circuit has to be able to operate in the presence of the existing grid voltage and force the grid to accept power, instead of providing it. Because the grid is essentially a very low-impedance voltage source, the inverter must be able to act as a current source, only allowing the desired amount of current to be sent into the grid. This process requires close control of the inverter output voltage.

Generally, the inverter will control its bulk DC input voltage and use this to determine the output power level. The power level signal is then used to determine the output power, and the inverter output will be adjusted upward until this amount of power is delivered to the grid.

Because of the extra work involved in monitoring and conditioning the output power to match the power from the grid, a grid-tied inverter is more expensive than a more simple power inverter that cannot tie into the grid. Figure 3.146 shows a simple solar photovoltaic system.

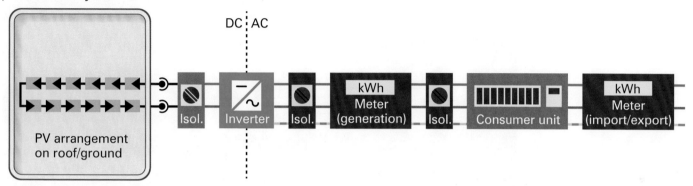

Figure 3.146: A simple power inverter system

Advantages

- Sunlight is free and solar power is pollution-free during use.

- PV installations can operate for many years, with little maintenance or intervention after their initial set-up.

- Solar electricity generation is economically superior where grid connection or fuel transport is difficult, costly or impossible.

- When grid connected, solar electric generation replaces some or all of the highest cost.

- Grid connected solar electricity can be used locally thus reducing transmission and distribution losses.

Disadvantages

- Photovoltaics are costly to install.

- While the modules are often guaranteed for about 20 years, the personal investment in a domestic system can be lost if the owner moves.

- You need enough space (roof or ground) for solar panels and the panels need a clear view of the southern sky. For houses, solar panels are usually located on the roof; solar panels can also be located on the ground. For maximum efficiency, it is best for the solar panels to be built to turn to face the sun throughout the day.

- Solar panels work most efficiently in parts of the world that get a lot of sun. The more sun, the more electricity. Less sun and cloudy days doesn't mean that you won't produce solar electricity, but you need a bigger array of panels to produce the same amount.

JTL tip JTL

Isolators are required in several locations in the installation. Remember also that PV installations are unusual in that they can be live from both sides – as soon as the sun shines on a PV array it will start to produce power.

Wind energy generation

These systems rely on wind to turn a shaft linked to a generator, which in turn produces electricity. There are two common types of wind turbine used in homes in the UK:

- mast-mounted (2.5 kW to 6 kW)
- roof-mounted (1kW to 2 kW).

Figure 3.147: Wind power is one of many alternative power sources which may increase over the next few years

The greater the wind speed, the greater the power produced. As wind speed increases with height, large rotating blades are normally seen at the top of a tall supporting mast or tower. As wind speed and direction vary, this may not be the best option for domestic properties unless they are in remote locations. As with solar PV, any surplus electricity can be exported back to the grid.

In the UK, large-scale developments, known as **wind farms**, are becoming more popular, both on shore and off shore. The UK is the windiest country in Europe – so much so that we could power our country several times over using this free fuel. A modern 2.5 MW turbine located at a reasonable site will probably generate 6.5 million units of electricity each year, and that is enough to meet the annual needs of over 1400 households.

Advantages

- It is a plentiful energy source.
- It is a renewable energy that doesn't release any harmful carbon dioxide or other pollutants.
- The equipment is reasonably low maintenance and wind is free, so once you've paid for the initial installation your electricity costs will be reduced.
- It is useful in remote locations away from the grid.
- You can store electricity in batteries and use it when there is no wind.
- You can sell surplus electricity back to the grid.

Key term

Wind farm – a large number of wind turbines gathered in one location; there are currently on-shore and off-shore wind farms in the UK

Disadvantages

- You rely on wind to turn the turbine.

- Wind speed is variable.

- Small domestic turbines really need an exposed location without nearby obstacles that cause turbulence and affect air speed.

- Unlike solar PV, planning permission is required.

Micro (small scale) hydro generation

Although you may not realise it, people in the UK have used this concept for hundreds of years. Micro hydro generation is the process of using running water to turn something, on a small scale. Years ago, water was used to turn wheels in a mill, which in turn was used to grind flour. Today the system uses running or falling water to turn a turbine to produce electricity.

Useful power may be produced from even a small stream. For houses with no mains connection but with access to a micro hydro site, a good hydro system can generate a steady, more reliable electricity supply than any of the other renewable technologies.

Turbine technology is now available that can use quite small spring-fed streams for power, as long as the fall is sufficient.

Advantages

- It is environmentally friendly.

- No fuel deliveries are required.

- It is very good in rural areas.

- It is very low maintenance.

Disadvantages

- Total system costs can be high initially (£20 000), but often less than the cost of a grid connection.

- It requires sufficient flow of water.

Air and ground source heat pumps

Simply put, a ground source heat pump works by absorbing heat from the ground and raising its temperature. It is normally for use in the home. An air source heat pump does the same from the air.

The two types of pump work in the same way. The operating principles for the ground source version described are below and shown in Figure 3.148.

- Brine circulates in a closed loop known as the collector coil, which is buried in the ground and absorbs the heat energy from the ground.

- Inside the heat pump, the collector coil is wound around a heat exchanger (the evaporator). The lukewarm brine in the collector coil begins to warm the ice-cold refrigerant in the heat exchanger. This refrigerant has a very low boiling point, and the brine in the collector causes its temperature to rise by a few degrees. This is enough to cause it to boil and evaporate. Think of a boiling kettle which, as it boils, turns liquid into vapour.

With the air source heat pump, the operating principle is exactly the same except that it absorbs heat from the air (even very cold air has heat within it). By contrast, the ground source system makes use of the fact that, throughout the world, only a few metres under the ground surface, the temperature remains at a fairly constant 12°C, even in winter.

Key term

Carbon footprint – the total amount of greenhouse gases produced by an organisation, event, product or person

- The evaporated refrigerant now moves into a compressor. Compression raises pressure, causing the refrigerant to rise in temperature (to about 50°C). It then passes into another heat exchanger (the condenser) and condenses. Think of the kettle again; the boiling steam vapour condenses back to liquid.

- Another closed loop (the distribution system out to the radiators) is wound around the condenser, causing the generated heat in the condenser to transfer from it to the closed loop feeding the radiators. From there it is sent out hot to the radiators, cools as it is passes through them and returns to be heated again by the condenser.

- The condensing refrigerant circulates from the heat exchanger and into an expansion valve that lowers the pressure, and the refrigerant becomes cold once again. The process then begins again when the circulating refrigerant meets the warm brine in the collector coil.

Advantages

- It has a low **carbon footprint**.

- No fuel deliveries are required.

- It can provide space heating and hot water.

- It can lower fuel bills, especially when measured against electric heating.

- It is often classed as a 'fit and forget' technology, as it needs so little maintenance.

Disadvantages

- It has high set-up costs.

- Ground source heat pumps produce a lower temperature heat than traditional boilers. It's essential that your home is insulated and well draught-proofed for the heating system to be effective. It could also make the system cheaper and smaller.

- Air source heat pumps tend to produce lower temperatures than ground source ones.

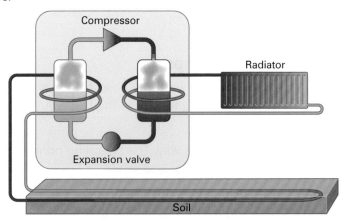

Figure 3.148: A ground source heat pump

Micro combined heat and power (Micro-CHP) unit

Although not strictly a renewable energy system, this system does have an energy-saving aspect to it. Sometimes called co-generation, micro-CHP involves having a domestic boiler that contains a condensing boiler to heat the home and provide hot water, but also includes something called a Stirling engine to generate electricity.

Invented by Scotsman Dr. Robert Stirling in 1816, these engines generate motion from heat without combustion. However, as you only generate electricity when the boiler is generating heat – and they only generate approximately 1.5 kW of electricity – the idea is to reduce your electricity bills, rather than replace your electricity supply.

Figure 3.149: A micro combined heat and power (Micro-CHP) unit

Grey water recycling

Grey water is waste water generated by activities in the home such as bathing, laundry and dish washing. Up to half of the water used in a house can end up as grey water.

Grey water does not include waste water from toilets, but with water reserves dwindling, it would seem sensible to put grey water to better use wherever possible.

As grey water is less contaminated than other waste water, common recycling sees it treated and then used for flushing toilets or for watering gardens. Some toilets now include a sink built into them to feed grey water straight to them without the need for additional pipework.

Advantages
- It can bring a reduction in water consumption without changing consumer behaviour.
- It is easy to install and maintenance free.
- It removes the need for complex water treatment.
- If properly designed, a grey water system can lower sewage costs.
- It can reduce ground water usage for irrigation.
- Less water will enter a city's sewage systems. This saves building new, or extending old, treatment plants.

Disadvantages
The main disadvantage is that the water is not suitable for drinking.

Rainwater harvesting

Rainwater harvesting is simply the gathering and storage of rainwater. Once stored, it can be used for any normal use of water, including drinking. Collecting rainwater can make an important contribution to drinking water. In some situations, rainwater may be the only available, or economical, water source.

Most rainwater systems are simple and inexpensive to build, as they will use the existing guttering and downpipes on a house. Water then flows via a filter to an underwater storage tank.

Water can be of such good quality that it may not need any form of treatment before being of drinking standard (potable). Even when the rainwater is not going to be used for drinking, it is fine for flushing, washing and gardening – processes that make up half the water used in the average home.

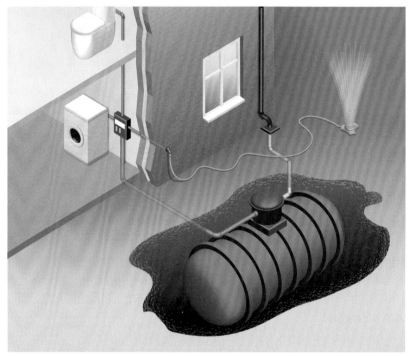

Figure 3.150: Rainwater harvesting system

Some commercial and domestic projects have also seen the introduction of rainwater harvesting systems as part of a fire protection system for the building, where the stored water can be used to feed the sprinkler system.

Advantages

- It is generally free (although some countries do charge).

- Large volumes of water are kept out of the storm-water management system, helping to reduce flooding risks.

- It is low maintenance.

Disadvantages

Treatment is often required to make the water reach a drinkable standard.

Biomass heating

Biomass is biological material (derived from living or recently living organisms) that can be converted into electricity or clean-burning fuels in an environmentally friendly and sustainable manner. It is accepted as a renewable replacement for fossil fuels as it can be replaced at the same rate as it used. The essential difference between biomass and fossil fuels is one of timescale.

Fossil fuels such as coal, oil and gas originally came from biological material, but that material absorbed CO_2 from the atmosphere many millions of years ago. Using these materials as fuel involves burning them, a process which leads to the carbon oxidising into carbon dioxide and the hydrogen becoming water (vapour). Unless these combustion products are captured and stored, they are usually released back into the atmosphere, resulting in increased concentrations in the atmosphere.

Biomass, on the other hand, takes carbon out of the atmosphere while it is growing, and returns it as it is burned. If it is managed on a sustainable basis, biomass is harvested as part of a constantly replenished crop. This maintains a closed carbon cycle, with no net increase in atmospheric CO_2 levels – hence it is called 'carbon neutral'.

Biomass energy is derived from five distinct energy sources:

- virgin wood from forestry or wood processing

- energy crops (high-yield crops grown specifically for energy applications)

- agricultural residues (residues from agriculture, harvesting or processing)

- food waste from food and drink manufacture, preparation and processing and consumer waste

- industrial waste and co-products from manufacturing and industrial processes.

Wood energy is derived both from direct use of wood as a fuel to provide heat (for example, in domestic wood-burning stoves) or in some cases as a replacement for fossil fuel in a power station. Crops such as corn and sugar cane can be fermented to produce ethanol, which can be used as transportation fuel or as an additive to petrol.

Biodiesel, another transportation fuel, can be produced from leftover food products like vegetable oils and animal fats. Biomass alcohol fuel, or ethanol, is derived primarily from sugarcane and corn and can be used directly as a fuel or as an additive to petrol.

Advantages

- Biomass production is carbon neutral – it produces no more carbon dioxide than it absorbs.

- The materials used to fuel biomass energy are otherwise sent to landfill, so it's an excellent green use for waste.

- Biomass energy could realistically produce up to 80 per cent of a home's energy needs.

Disadvantages

- Although biomass energy (like most alternative fuels) is more cost-effective than fossil fuels, there are both initial set-up costs and ongoing running costs.

- Storage space is required, and that requires ventilation and a dry environment.

Solar water heating

Solar water-heating systems use heat from the sun to work alongside a conventional water heater. They collect heat from the sun's radiation via a flat plate system or an evacuated glass-tube system before being stored in a hot-water cylinder. The system is normally not pressurised and often uses 'drain back' technology: the pipework slopes between items and so doesn't have water inside it once it is used, meaning there is no need for insulation.

When a solar water-heating and hot-water central heating system are used in conjunction, solar heat will either be concentrated inside a pre-heating tank that feeds into the tank heated by the central heating, or the solar heat exchanger will replace the lower heating element. The upper element will remain in place to provide for any heating that solar cannot provide.

However, we all normally use our central heating at night and in winter when solar gain is lower. Solar water heating for washing and bathing can often be a better application than central heating because supply and demand is better matched.

Advantages

- It is environmentally friendly.

- No fuel deliveries are needed.

- It is low maintenance.

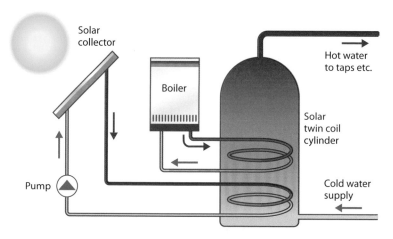

Figure 3.151: Solar water heating system

Disadvantages

The main disadvantage is that the system has a relatively high set-up cost.

Voltage management

Voltage in Europe was harmonised to be 230 V ± 10%, so many installations may experience supply voltages in excess of 240 V.

BS 7671 specifies a maximum value of voltage drop of 3% for lighting and 5% for all other uses, where the supply is directly from a public distribution system. On such installations, electrical equipment is running at a voltage much higher than the optimum voltage needed, resulting in excessive losses (optimum voltage will depend on the type of equipment). Voltage management is intended to reduce the voltage to this optimum level to reduce losses.

Before using this system, assess the implications. Supply voltages vary and the type of equipment used may have a bearing on the decision to use it. Installing a voltage regulator can help to ensure the voltage is maintained at the desired level and properly balanced to improve equipment efficiency and reliability.

Cells and batteries

A cell is a device that produces electricity from a chemical reaction. A battery is generally perceived as two or more connected cells. However, in normal day-to-day conversation, we tend to call a single cell device a battery as well. A cell and a battery can be the same thing.

It is generally accepted that the world's first 'battery' was invented by Alessandro Volta around 1800. The principle he used remains the same today. Volta used two dissimilar metal plates separated by an electrolyte.

Such a cell consists of a negative electrode called the cathode, a positive electrode called the anode and an electrolyte that causes a chemical reaction, which in turn produces an e.m.f.

When the cell is connected to any external load, in this case a lamp, the negative electrode supplies a current of electrons that flow through the lamp before returning to the cathode. When the external load is removed, the chemical reaction stops.

A primary cell (battery) is a cell whose chemicals produce an e.m.f. until they run out. A secondary cell (battery) is a cell that can be recharged and can therefore be used many times.

There are many different types of battery, mostly categorised by the chemicals used in them. Perhaps the most commonly seen are the cylindrical batteries, such as the AA or AAA that we use in portable equipment.

The construction of such a battery is shown in Figure 3.153, but you can see that the basic concept has not changed.

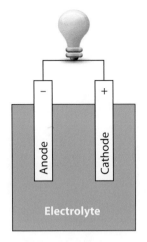

Figure 3.152: The basic structure of a battery

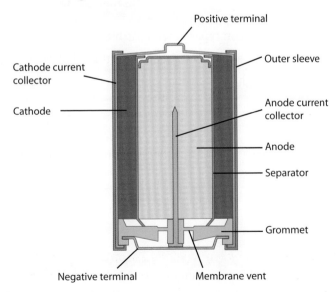

Figure 3.153: Construction of a cylindrical battery

Geothermal generation

Geothermally generated electricity was first produced in Italy in 1904 and geothermal power plants have three different methods of operation:

1. Steam is taken directly from fractures in the ground and used to drive a turbine.

2. Hot water (in excess of 200°C) is taken from the ground, allowed to boil as it rises to the surface and then steam is separated and used to turn the turbine.

3. Extracted hot water flows through heat exchangers, where it boils a fluid that in turn spins the turbine.

Geothermal power is considered to be sustainable because the heat extraction is small compared with the Earth's heat content. Also, much like the ground source heat pump, the condensed steam and remaining geothermal fluid from all three types of plants are injected back into the hot rock to collect more heat.

Countries such as Iceland and the Philippines generate about 20% of their electricity in this way.

Wave generated electricity

Waves are generated by wind passing over the surface of the sea. The height and frequency of the waves is then governed by wind speed, the time the wind has been blowing and the pattern of the sea floor.

Still very much an emerging technology, wave power devices are generally categorised by the method used to capture and convert the energy of the waves.

Some do this by using the vertical motion of buoys on the surface to create hydraulic pressure that in turn spins a generator. Others such as a 'Wave Dragon', use the principle of water from a wave being directed into the device and the falling water then turns the turbine.

Summary

1. What are the two most common types of wind turbines used in UK homes?
2. In general, the shaft of a three-phase AC generator is turned by what method?
3. What voltage is used for high-voltage distribution to lighter industry?

Operating principles, applications and limitations of transformers

The **transformer** is one of the most widely used pieces of electrical equipment and can be found in situations such as electricity distribution, construction work and electronic equipment. Its purpose, as the name implies, is to transform something – the something in this case being the voltage, which can enter the transformer at one level (input) and leave at another (output).

When the output voltage is higher than the input voltage we say that we have a step-up transformer and when the output voltage is lower than the input, we say that we have a step-down transformer.

In this section we will be looking at the following areas:

- mutual inductance
- transformer types
- step-up and step-down transformers.

Mutual inductance

In their operation, transformers make use of an action known as mutual inductance. Let us look at the situation in Figure 3.154. Two coils, primary and secondary, are placed side by side, but not touching each other. The primary coil has been connected to an AC supply and the secondary coil is connected to a load, such as a resistor.

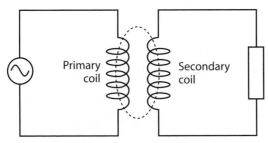

Figure 3.154: Mutual inductance

If we now allow current to flow in the primary coil, we know that current flow will create a magnetic field. Therefore, as the current in the primary coil increases up to its maximum value, it creates a changing magnetic flux and, as long as there is a changing magnetic flux, there will be an e.m.f. 'induced' into the secondary coil, which would then start flowing through the load.

This effect, where an alternating e.m.f. in one coil causes an alternating e.m.f. in another coil, is known as mutual inductance.

In transformers we are only really interested in mutual inductance, and it is the rising and falling alternating current that causes the change of magnetic flux. In other words, **we need an AC supply to allow transformers to operate correctly**.

If the two coils were now wound on an iron core, we would find that the level of magnetic flux is increased and consequently the level of mutual inductance is also increased.

Transformer types

Core-type transformers

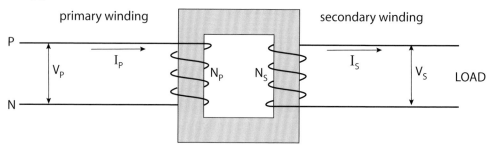

Figure 3.155: Double wound, core-type transformer

In Figure 3.155 the supply is wound on one side of the iron core (primary winding) and the output is wound on the other (secondary winding). In other words, double wound means that there is more than one winding.

The number of turns in each winding will affect the induced e.m.f., with the number of turns in the primary being referred to as (N_P), and those in the secondary referred to as (N_S). We call this the turns ratio. When voltage (V_P) is applied to the primary winding, it will cause a changing magnetic flux to circulate in the core. This changing flux will cause an e.m.f. (V_S) to be induced in the secondary winding.

Assuming that we have no losses or leakage (i.e. 100% efficient), then power input will equal power output and the ratio between the primary and secondary sides of the transformer can be expressed as follows:

$$\frac{V_P}{V_S} = \frac{N_P}{N_S} = \frac{I_S}{I_P}$$

(where I_P represents the current in the primary winding and I_S the current in the secondary winding).

As we can see from Figure 3.155, a transformer has no moving parts. Consequently, provided that the following general statements apply, it ends up being a very efficient piece of equipment.

- Transformers use laminated (layered) steel cores, not solid metal. In a solid metal core 'eddy currents' are induced which cause heating and power losses. Using laminated cores reduces these eddy currents.

- Laminated cores, where each lamination is insulated, help to reduce this effect.

- Soft iron with high magnetic properties is used for the core.

- Windings are made from insulated, low resistance conductors. This prevents short circuits occurring either within the windings, or to the core.

The losses that occur in transformers can normally be classed under the following categories.

Copper losses

Although windings should be made from low resistance conductors, the resistance of the windings will cause the currents passing through them to create a heating effect and subsequent power loss. This power loss can be calculated using the formula:

$$P_c = I^2 \times R \text{ watts}$$

Iron losses

These losses take place in the magnetic core of the transformer. They are normally caused by eddy currents (small currents which circulate inside the laminated core of the transformer) and **hysteresis**. To demonstrate let's say that you push on some material and it bends. When you stop pushing, does it return to its original shape immediately? If it doesn't the material is demonstrating hysteresis. Let's look at this in context.

Figure 3.156 shows the effect within ferromagnetic materials of hysteresis. Starting with an unmagnetised material at point A; here both field strength and flux density are zero. The field strength increases in the positive direction and the flux begins to grow along the dotted path until we reach saturation at point B. This is called the initial magnetisation curve.

If the field strength is now relaxed, instead of retracing the initial magnetisation curve, the flux falls more slowly. In fact, even when the applied field has returned to zero, there will still be a degree of flux density (known as the remanence) at point C. To force the flux to go back to zero (point D), we have to reverse the applied field. The field strength here that is necessary to drive the field back to zero is known as the coercivity. We can then continue reversing the field to get to point E, and so on. This is known as the hysteresis loop.

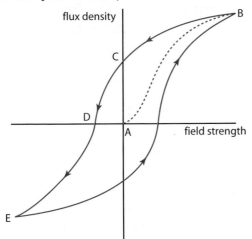

Figure 3.156: Hysteresis loop diagram

As we have already said, we can help reduce eddy currents by using a laminated core construction. We can also help to reduce hysteresis by adding silicon to the iron from which the transformer core is made.

The version of the double wound transformer that we have looked at so far makes the principle of operation easier to understand. However, this arrangement is not very efficient, as some of the magnetic flux being produced by the primary winding will not react with the secondary winding and is often referred to as 'leakage'. We can help to reduce this leakage by splitting each winding across the sides of the core (see Figure 3.157).

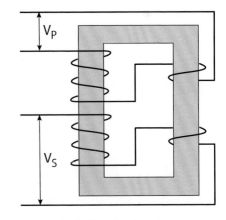

Figure 3.157: Reducing 'leakage'

Shell-type transformers

We can reduce the magnetic flux leakage a bit more, by using a shell-type transformer.

In the shell-type transformer, both windings are wound onto the central leg of the transformer and the two outer legs are then used to provide parallel paths for the magnetic flux.

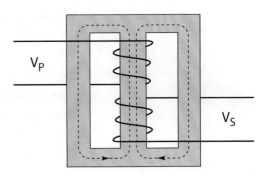

Figure 3.158: Shell-type transformer

The autotransformer

The autotransformer uses the principle of 'tapped' windings in its operation. Remember that the ratio of input voltage against output voltage will depend upon the number of primary winding turns and secondary winding turns (the turns ratio). But what if we want more than one output voltage?

Some devices are supplied with the capability of providing this, such as small transformers for calculators, musical instruments or doorbell systems. Tapped connections are the normal means by which this is achieved. A tapped winding means that we have made a connection to the winding and then brought this connection out to a terminal. Now, by connecting between the different terminals, we can control the number of turns that will appear in that winding and we can therefore provide a range of output voltages.

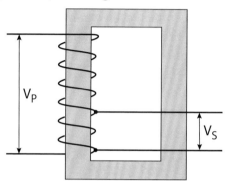

Figure 3.159: Autotransformer

An autotransformer has only one tapped winding and the position of the tapping on that winding will dictate the output voltage.

One of the advantages of the autotransformer is that, because it only has one winding, it is more economical to manufacture. However, on the down side, we have made a physical connection to the winding. Therefore, if the winding ever became broken between the two tapping points, then the transformer would not work and the input voltage would appear on the output terminals. This would then present a real hazard.

Instrument transformers

Instrument transformers are used in conjunction with measuring instruments because it would be very difficult and expensive to design normal instruments to measure the high current and voltage that we find in certain power systems. We therefore have two types of instrument transformer, both being double wound.

The current transformer

The current transformer (c.t.) normally has very few turns on its primary winding so that it does not affect the circuit to be measured, with the actual meter connected across the secondary winding.

Care must be taken when using a c.t. Never open the secondary winding while the primary is 'carrying' the main current. If this happened, a high voltage would be induced into the secondary winding. Apart from the obvious danger, the heat build-up could cause the insulation on the c.t. to break down.

Figure 3.160: Current transformer

The voltage transformer

This is very similar to our standard power transformer, in that it is used to reduce the system voltage. The primary winding is connected across the voltage that we want to measure and the meter is connected across the secondary winding.

Step-up and step-down transformers

Step-up transformers

A step-up transformer is used when it is desirable to step voltage up in value.

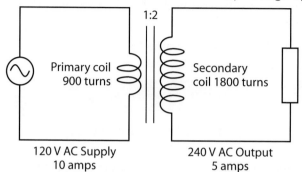

Figure 3.161: Step-up transformer

The primary coil has fewer turns than the secondary coil. We already know that the number of turns in a transformer is given as a ratio. When the primary has fewer turns than the secondary, voltage and impedance are stepped up. In the circuit shown in Figure 3.161, voltage is stepped up from 120 V AC to 240 V AC. Since impedance is also stepped up, current is stepped down from 10 A to 5 A.

Step-down transformers

A step-down transformer is used when it is desirable to step voltage down in value.

The primary coil has more turns than the secondary coil. The step-down ratio is 2:1. Since the voltage and impedance are stepped down, the current is stepped up in this case to 10 A.

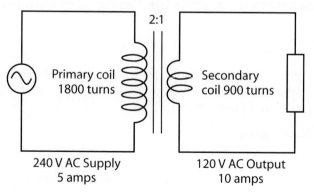

Figure 3.162: Step-down transformer

Safety isolating transformer

Another use of a transformer is to isolate the secondary output from the supply. In a bathroom, the shower socket should be supplied from a 1:1 safety isolating transformer. The output of the transformer has no connection to earth thereby ensuring that output from the transformer is totally isolated from the supply.

In areas of installations where there is an increased risk of electric shock, the voltage is reduced to less than 50 V and is supplied from a safety isolating transformer; we refer to this as **Separated Extra Low Voltage (SELV)** supply.

Transformer ratings

Transformers are rated in kVA (kilovolt-amps). This rating is used rather than watts because loads are not purely resistive. Only resistive loads are measured in watts.

The kVA rating determines the current that a transformer can deliver to its load without overheating. Given volts and amps, kVA can be calculated. Given kVA and volts, amps can be calculated.

The kVA rating of a transformer is the same for both the primary and the secondary. At this point let us try some examples.

Example 1

A transformer having a turns ratio of 2:7 is connected to a 230 V supply. Calculate the output voltage.

When we give transformer ratios, we give them in the order primary, then secondary. Therefore in this example we are saying that for every two windings on the primary winding, there are seven on the secondary. If we therefore use our formula:

$$\frac{V_P}{V_S} = \frac{N_P}{N_S}$$

We should now transpose this to get:

$$V_S = \frac{V_P \times N_S}{N_P}$$

However, we do not know the exact number of turns involved. But do we need to, if we know the ratio? Let us find out.

The ratio is 2:7, meaning for every 2 turns on the primary, there will be 7 turns on the secondary. Therefore, if we had 6 turns on the primary, this would give us 21 turns on the secondary, but the ratio of the two has not changed. For every 2 on the primary we are still getting 7 on the secondary.

This means we can just insert the ratio rather than the individual number of turns into our formula:

$$V_S = \frac{V_P \times N_S}{N_P} = \frac{230 \times 7}{2} = \textbf{805 V}$$

Now, to prove our point about ratios, let us say that we know the number of turns in the windings to be 6 in the primary and 21 in the secondary (which is still giving us a 2:7 ratio). If we now apply this to our formula we get:

$$V_S = \frac{V_P \times N_S}{N_P} = \frac{230 \times 21}{6} = \textbf{805 V}$$

The same answer.

Example 2

A single phase transformer, with 2000 primary turns and 500 secondary turns, is fed from a 230 V AC supply. Find:

(a) the secondary voltage

(b) the volts per turn.

(a) Secondary voltage

$$\frac{V_P}{V_S} = \frac{N_P}{N_S}$$

Using transposition, rearrange the formula to give:

$$V_S = \frac{V_P \times N_S}{N_P}$$

$$V_S = \frac{230 \times 500}{2000} = \frac{115\,000}{2000} = \textbf{57.5 V}$$

(b) Volts per turn

This is the relationship between the volts in a winding and the number of turns in that winding. To find volts per turn, we simply divide the voltage by the number of turns.

Therefore, in the primary:

$$\frac{V_P}{V_S} = \frac{230}{2000} = \textbf{0.115 volts per turn}$$

In the secondary:

$$\frac{V_P}{V_S} = \frac{57.5}{500} = \textbf{0.115 volts per turn}$$

Example 3

A single-phase transformer is being used to supply a trace heating system. The transformer is fed from a 230 V 50 Hz AC supply and needs to provide an output voltage of 25 V. If the secondary current is 150 A and the secondary winding has 50 turns, find:

(a) the output kVA of the transformer

(b) the number of primary turns

(c) the primary current

(d) the volts per turn.

(a) The output kVA

$$kVA = \frac{volts \times amperes}{1000} = \frac{V_S \times L_S}{1000} = \frac{25 \times 150}{1000} = \textbf{3.75 kVA}$$

(b) The number of primary turns

If: $\frac{V_P}{V_S} = \frac{N_P}{N_S}$ then by transposition

$$N_P = \frac{V_P \times N_S}{V_S} = \frac{250 \times 50}{25} = \textbf{460 turns}$$

(c) The primary current

If: $\frac{V_P}{V_S} = \frac{I_S}{I_P}$ then by transposition

$$I_P = \frac{V_P \times I_S}{V_P} = \frac{25 \times 150}{230} = \textbf{16 A}$$

(d) The volts per turn

In the primary: $\frac{V_P}{N_P} = \frac{230}{460} = \textbf{0.5 volts per turn}$

In the secondary: $\frac{V_S}{N_S} = \frac{25}{50} = \textbf{0.5 volts per turn}$

Example 4

A step-down transformer, having a ratio of 2:1, has an 800 turn primary winding and is fed from a 400 V AC supply. The output from the secondary is 200 V and this feeds a load of 20 Ω resistance. Calculate:

(a) the power in the primary winding

(b) the power in the secondary winding.

Well, we know that the formula for power is: $P = V \times I$

And we also know that we can use Ohm's Law to find the current.

Therefore, if we insert the values that we have, we can establish the current in the secondary winding:

$$I_S = \frac{V_S}{R_S} = \frac{200}{20} = \textbf{10 A}$$

Now that we know the current in the secondary winding, we can use the power formula to find the power generated in the secondary winding:

$P = V \times I = 200 \times 10 = 2000$ watts = **2 kW**

We now need to find the current in the primary winding. To do this we can use the formula:

$$\frac{V_P}{V_S} = \frac{I_S}{I_P}$$

However, we need to transpose the formula to find I_P. This would give us:

$$I_P = \frac{I_S \times V_S}{V_P}$$

Which, if we now insert the known values, gives us:

$$I_P = \frac{I_S \times V_S}{V_P} = \frac{10 \times 200}{400} = \frac{2000}{400} = \textbf{5 A}$$

Now that we know the current in the primary winding, we can again use the power formula to find the power generated in the secondary winding:

$P = V \times I = 400 \times 5 = 2000$ watts = **2 kW**

Summary

1. There are two sides to a transformer, what are these?

2. If there are less turns on the primary coil of a transformer than the secondary this would be called?

8. How different electrical properties can affect circuits, systems and equipment

Characteristics of supplies

Alternating current theory

Alternating current (**AC**) uses a flow of electrons, which rises to a maximum value in one direction and then falls back to zero before repeating the process in the opposite direction. In other words, the electrons move backwards and forwards. This journey, from starting at zero, flowing in both directions and returning to zero is called a cycle. The number of cycles per second is called the frequency and measured in **hertz** (Hz). A sine wave is used to show this.

If we look at the graph of a sine wave (Figure 3.61 on page 269), there are several values that can be measured from such an alternating waveform.

Instantaneous value

If we took a reading of induced electromotive force (e.m.f.) from the sine wave at any point in time during its cycle, this would be classed as an instantaneous value.

Average value

Using equally spaced intervals in our cycle (say every 30°) we could take a measurement of current as an instantaneous value. To find the average we would add together all the instantaneous values and then divide by the number of values used. As with the average of anything, the more values used, the greater the accuracy. For a sine wave only, we say that the average value is equal to the maximum value multiplied by 0.637. As a formula:

Average current = Maximum (peak) current × 0.637

Peak value

You will remember when the loop in an AC generator has rotated for 90° it is cutting the maximum lines of magnetic flux and therefore the greatest value of induced e.m.f. is experienced at this point. This is known as the peak value and both the positive and negative half cycles have a **peak value**.

Peak to peak value

We have said that the maximum value of induced e.m.f., irrespective of direction, is called the maximum or peak value. The voltage measured between the positive and negative peaks is known as the **peak to peak value**. The graph in Figure 3.163 shows this more clearly.

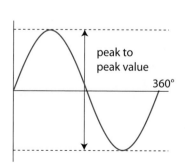

Figure 3.163: Peak to peak value

Root mean square (r.m.s.) or effective value of a waveform (voltage and current)

We have seen that in direct current (DC) circuits, the power delivered to a resistor is given by the product of the voltage across it and the current through it. However, in an AC circuit this is only true of the instantaneous power to a resistor as the current is constantly changing.

In most cases the instantaneous power is of little interest, and it is the average power delivered over time that is of most use. In order to have an easy way of measuring power, the r.m.s. method of measuring voltage and current was developed.

The r.m.s. or effective value is defined as being the AC value of an equivalent DC quantity that would deliver the same average power to the same resistor.

When current flows in a resistor, heat is produced. When it is direct current flowing in a resistor, the amount of electrical power converted into heat is expressed by the formulae:

$P = I^2 \times R$ or $P = V \times I$

However, an alternating current having a maximum (peak) value of 1 A does not maintain a constant value (see Figure 3.163). The alternating current will not produce as much heat in the resistance as will a direct current of 1 A. Consider the circuits in Figure 3.164.

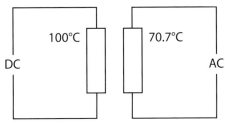

Figure 3.164: DC and AC circuits

In both the circuits in Figure 3.164, the supplies provide a maximum (peak) value of current of 1 A to a known resistor. However, the heat produced by 1 ampere of alternating current is only 70.7°C compared to the 100°C of heat that is produced by 1 ampere of direct current. We can express this using the following formula:

$$\frac{\text{Heating effect of 1 A maximum AC}}{\text{Heating effect of 1 A maximum DC}} = \frac{70.7}{100} = 0.707$$

Therefore, **the effective or r.m.s. value of an AC = 0.707 × I_{max}**

where I_{max} = the peak value of the alternating current.

We can also establish the maximum (peak) value from the r.m.s. value with the following formula:

$I_{max} = I_{r.m.s.} \times 1.414$

The rate at which heat is produced in a resistor is a convenient way of establishing an effective value of alternating current, and is known as the 'heating effect' method.

An alternating current is said to have an effective value of one ampere when it produces heat in a given resistance at the same rate as one ampere of direct current.

To see where the r.m.s. value sits alongside the peak value, look at Figure 3.165.

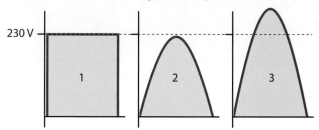

Figure 3.165: Peak value diagrams

The wave in Figure 3.165 (1) represents a 230 V DC supply, running for a set period of time, with the heating effect produced shown as the shaded area.

The wave in Figure 3.165 (2) represents an AC 50 Hz supply in which the voltage peaks at 230 V during one half-cycle, with the heating effect produced shown as the shaded area. As the wave only reaches 230 V for a small period of time, less heat is produced overall than in the DC wave.

The wave in Figure 3.165 (3) represents an increased peak value of voltage to give the same amount of shaded area as in the DC example. In this diagram 230 V has become our r.m.s. value.

Important Note: Unless stated otherwise, all values of AC voltage and current are given as r.m.s. values.

Frequency and period

Remember that the number of cycles that occur each second is referred to as the frequency of the waveform and this is measured in hertz (Hz). The frequency of the UK supply system is 50 Hz.

In the basic arrangement of the AC generator loop, if one cycle of e.m.f. was generated with one complete revolution of the loop over a period of one second, then we would say the frequency was 1 Hz. If we increased the speed of loop rotation so that it was producing five cycles every second, then we would have a frequency of 5 Hz.

We can therefore say that the frequency of the waveform is the same as the speed of the loop's rotation, measured in revolutions per second. We can express this using the following equation:

Frequency (f) = Number of revolutions (n) × Number of pole pairs

If we apply this to the simple AC generator and rotate the loop at 50 revolutions per second, then:

Frequency = 50 × 1 (there is 1 × pole pair) = 50 Hz

The amount of time taken for the waveform to complete just one full cycle is known as the periodic time (T) or period. Therefore, if 50 cycles are produced in one second, one cycle must be produced in a fiftieth of one second. This relationship is expressed using the following equations:

Frequency (f) = $\frac{1}{\text{Periodic time}}$ = $\frac{1}{T}$

Periodic time (T) = $\frac{1}{\text{Frequency}}$ = $\frac{1}{f}$

Power factor

When we are dealing with AC circuits, we often look at the way power is used in particular types of component within the circuit.

Generally, the power factor is a number less than 1.0, which is used to represent the relationship between the apparent power of a circuit and the true power of that circuit. In other words:

Power Factor (PF) $= \dfrac{\textbf{True Power (PT)}}{\textbf{Apparent Power (PA)}}$ or $\textbf{PF} = \dfrac{\textbf{PT}}{\textbf{PA}}$

The units of power factor are $\frac{\text{Watts}}{\text{Watts}}$, but actually power factor has no unit, it is simply shown as a number. It is also determined by the phase angle, which we will cover shortly.

We will be returning to this over the next few pages, so by the end of the section you will have a good understanding of power factor.

Explain the relationship between, and calculate, resistance, inductance, capacitance and impedance

Resistance (R) and phasor representation

Although the sine wave is useful, it is also difficult and time-consuming to draw. We can therefore also represent AC by the use of phasors. A **phasor** is a straight line where the length is a scaled representation of the size of the AC quantity and the direction represents the relationship between the voltage and current, this relationship being known as the phase angle.

To see briefly how we use phasors, let us look at Figure 3.166, where a tungsten filament lamp has been included as the load.

Circuits like this are said to be **resistive**, and in this type of circuit the values of e.m.f. (voltage) and current actually pass through the same instants in time together. In other words, as voltage reaches its maximum value, so does the current (see Figure 3.166).

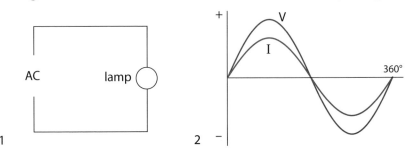

Figure 3.166: Circuit and sine wave diagrams

This happens with all resistive components connected to an AC supply and as such the voltage and current are said to be '**in phase**' with each other, or possess a zero phase angle.

The graph in Figure 3.166 shows this when represented by a sine wave. However, we could also show this by using a phasor diagram as shown in Figure 3.167.

Figure 3.167: Phasor diagram for zero phase angle

We can therefore say that a resistive component will consume power and we would carry out calculations as we would for a DC circuit (i.e. using $P = V \times I$).

We can also say that resistive equipment (filament lamps, fires, water heaters) uses this power to create heat, but such a feature in long cable runs, windings etc. would be seen as unsuitable power loss in the circuit (i.e. using $P = I^2R$).

Inductance (L)

If the load in our circuit were not a filament lamp, but a motor or transformer (i.e. something that possess windings), then we would say that the load is inductive.

With an inductive load the voltage and current become '**out of phase**' with each other. This is because the windings of the equipment set up their own induced e.m.f., which opposes the direction of the applied voltage, and thus forces the flow of electrons (current) to fall behind the force pushing them (voltage). However, over one full cycle, we would see that no power is consumed. When this happens, it is known as possessing a lagging phase angle or power factor.

As voltage and current are no longer perfectly linked, this type of circuit would be given a power factor of less than 1.0 (perfection), for example 0.8.

As we can see from Figure 3.168, the current is lagging the applied voltage by 90°. To make things easier in this exercise, we assumed that the above circuit is purely inductive. However, in reality this is not possible, as every coil is made of wire and that wire will have a resistance. (The opposition to current flow in a resistive circuit is resistance.)

The sine wave used to represent this inductive circuit would look like this:

If we represented this as a phasor diagram we end up with:

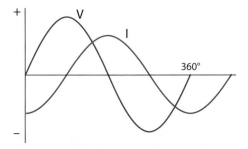

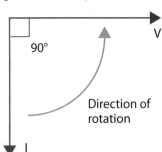

Figure 3.168: Sine wave and phasor diagrams for inductive circuit

The limiting effect to the current flow in an inductor is called the inductive reactance, which we are able to calculate with the following formula:

$X_L = 2\pi \, fL \; (\Omega)$

where:

X_L = inductive reactance (ohms – Ω)

f = supply frequency (hertz – Hz)

L = circuit inductance (henrys – H)

Let us now look at inductive and resistive circuits and see if the current is affected by a lagging phase angle.

To recap, we said that power factor is the relationship between voltage and current and that the ideal situation would seem to be the resistive circuit, where both these quantities are perfectly linked.

In the resistive circuit we know that the power in the circuit could only be the result of the voltage and the current (P = V × I). This is known as the apparent power, and possesses what we call unity power factor, to which we give the value one (1.0).

However, we now know that depending upon the equipment, the true power (actual) in the circuit must take into account the phase angle and will often be less than the apparent power, but never greater.

True power (in watts) is calculated using the cosine of the phase angle (cos Ø). The formula is:

P = VI cos Ø (remember we do not have to use the '×' sign)

When there is no phase lag, Ø = 0 and cos Ø = 1, a purely resistive circuit. To prove our previous points, let us consider the following example.

Example

If we have an inductive load, consuming 3 kW of power from a 230 V supply and with a power factor of 0.7 lagging, then the current (amount of electrons flowing) required to supply the load is:

P = V × I × cos Ø

We know that cos Ø = Power Factor. Therefore by transposition:

$$I = \frac{P}{V \times cos\ Ø}$$

Or in other words:

$$I = \frac{P}{V \times PF}$$ Therefore: $I = \frac{3000}{230 \times 0.7}$

And so:

I = 18.6 A

However, if the same size of load was purely resistive, then cos Ø = 0, thus the power factor would be 1.0, and thus:

P = V × I × PF

Therefore by transposition:

$$I = \frac{P}{V \times PF}$$ Therefore: $I = \frac{3000}{230 \times 1}$

And consequently:

I = **13 A**

In other words, the lower the power factor of a circuit, then the higher the current will need to be to supply the load's power requirement.

It therefore follows that if the power factor is low, then it will be necessary to install larger cables, switchgear etc. to be capable of handling the larger currents. There will also be the possibility of higher voltage drop due to the increased current in the supply cables.

Consequently, local electricity suppliers will often impose a financial fine on premises operating with a low power factor. Fortunately, we have a component that can help. It is called the capacitor.

Capacitance (C)

Simply put, a **capacitor** is a component that stores an electric charge if a potential difference is applied across it.

The capacitor's use is then normally based on its ability to return that energy back to the circuit. When a capacitor is connected to an AC supply, it is continuously storing the charge and then discharging as the supply moves through its positive and negative cycles. But, as with the inductor, no power is consumed.

This means that in a capacitive circuit, we have a leading phase angle or power factor. The sine wave and phasors used to represent this would look as in Figure 3.169.

As we can see from Figure 3.169, the current leads the voltage by 90°. Consequently, the capacitor is able to help because it provides a leading power factor, and therefore if we connect it in parallel across the load, it can help neutralise the effect of a lagging power factor.

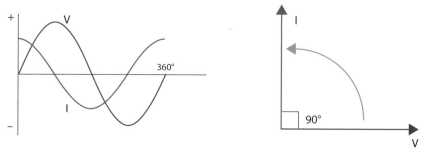

Figure 3.169: Sine wave and phasor diagrams for capacitive circuit

The opposition to the flow of AC to a capacitor is termed capacitive reactance, which, like inductive reactance, is measured in ohms and calculated using the following formula:

$$X_c = \frac{1}{2\pi fC} \, (\Omega)$$

where:

X_c = capacitive reactance (ohms – Ω)

f = supply frequency (hertz – Hz)

C = circuit **capacitance** (farads – F)

Since, in this type of circuit, we have voltage and current but no real power (in watts), the formula of P = V × I is no longer accurate. Instead, we say that the result of the voltage and current is reactive power, which is measured in reactive volt amperes (VAr).

The current to the capacitor, which does not contain resistance or consume power, is called reactive current.

Well, so far in our attempt to explain power factor, we have looked at a range of different subjects including resistance, inductance, capacitance and also talked about phasor diagrams. As if that wasn't bad enough, some circuits contain combinations of these components.

In order to work out these calculations, you will need to use trigonometry and also the following small section regarding the addition of phasors.

Phasors

When sine waves for voltage and current are drawn, the nature of the wave diagram can be based upon any chosen alternating quantity within the circuit. In other words, we can start from zero on the wave diagram with either the voltage or the current.

In electrical science we often need to add together alternating values. If they were 'in phase' with each other, then we would simply add the values together. However, when they are not in phase we cannot do this, hence the need for phasor diagrams.

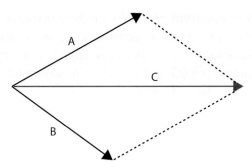

Figure 3.170: Phasor diagram

When we use phasor diagrams the chosen alternating quantity is drawn horizontally and is known as the reference.

When choosing the reference phasor, it makes sense to use a quantity that has the same value at all parts of the circuit. For example, in a series circuit the same current flows in each part of the circuit, therefore use current as the reference phasor. In a parallel circuit, the voltage is the same through each branch of the circuit and therefore we use voltage as the reference phasor.

Using the knowledge gained in the previous section, we can now measure all phase angles from this reference phasor.

Our answer (the resultant) is then found by completing a parallelogram. If we use Figure 3.170 as an example, we have been given the values of phasor A and phasor B. Therefore, the result of adding A and B together will be phasor C.

Impedance

Previously, we have been discussing components with an AC circuit. In fact, what those components are actually offering is opposition to the flow of current. By way of a summary, we could say that we now know that:

- The opposition to current in a resistive circuit is called resistance (R), is measured in ohms and the voltage and current are in phase with each other.

- The opposition to current in an inductive circuit is called inductive reactance (X_L), is measured in ohms and the current lags the voltage by 90°.

- The opposition to current in a capacitive circuit is called capacitive reactance (X_C), is measured in ohms and the current leads the voltage by 90°.

However, we also know that circuits will contain a combination of these components. When this happens we say that the total opposition to current is called the **impedance** (Z) of that circuit.

In summary:

- The power consumed by a resistor is dissipated in heat and not returned to the source. This is called the **true power**.

- The energy stored in the magnetic field of an **inductor** or the plates of a capacitor is returned to the source when the current changes direction.

- The power in an AC circuit is the sum of true power and reactive power. This is called the **apparent power**.

Key terms

Impedance – total opposition to current in a circuit

True or active power – the rate at which energy is used

Apparent power – in an AC circuit the sum of the true or active power and the reactive power

- **True power is equal to apparent power in a purely resistive circuit** because the voltage and current are in phase. Voltage and current are also in phase in a circuit containing equal values of inductive reactance and capacitive reactance. If the voltage and current are 90° out of phase, as would be the case in a purely capacitive or purely inductive circuit, the average value of true power is equal to zero. There are high positive and negative peak values of power, but when added together the result is zero.

- Apparent power is measured in volt-amps (VA) and has the formula: **P = VI**

- True power is measured in watts and has the formula: **P = VI cos Ø**

- **In a purely resistive circuit** where current and voltage are in phase, there is no angle of displacement between current and voltage. The cosine of a zero° angle is one, and so, the power factor is one. This means that all the energy that is delivered by the source is consumed by the circuit and dissipated in the form of heat.

- **In a purely reactive circuit**, voltage and current are 90° apart. The cosine of a 90° angle is zero so the power factor is zero. This means that the circuit returns all the energy it receives from the source, back to the source.

- **In a circuit where reactance and resistance are equal**, voltage and current are displaced by 45°. The cosine of a 45° angle is 0.7071, and so the power factor is 0.7071. This means that such a circuit uses approximately 70% of the energy supplied by the source and returns approximately 30% back to the source.

- We can therefore use the following formula to calculate power factor: $PF = \frac{R}{Z}$ where R = resistance and Z = total impedance.

Example

A coil of inductance 0.2 H is connected in series with a 60 Ω resistor and connected to a 100 V 50 Hz supply. What is the power factor?

Our formula states that $PF = \frac{R}{Z}$ and therefore we need to establish the circuit impedance.

To do this, we use the formula $Z = \sqrt{R^2 + X_L^2}$ but we first need to find out the inductive reactance. To do that we will use the formula $X_L = 2\pi fL$

$X_L = 2\pi fL$ means that $X_L = 2 \times 3.142 \times 50 \times 0.2$ which gives us 62.84 Ω

We can now calculate the impedance as being: $Z = \sqrt{60^2 + 62.84^2} = \sqrt{3600 + 3939} = 86.9\,\Omega$

If $PF = \frac{R}{Z}$ then $PF = \frac{60}{86.9}$ and therefore **PF = 0.69**

Resistance and inductance in series (RL)

Consider Figure 3.171.

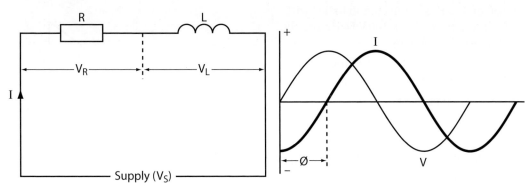

Figure 3.171: Resistor and inductor in series

Here we have a resistor connected in series with an inductor and fed from an AC supply. In a series circuit, the current (I) will be common to both the resistor and the inductor, causing a voltage drop V_R across the resistor and V_L across the inductor.

The sum of these voltages must equal the supply voltage. Here's how to construct a phasor diagram for this circuit.

In a series circuit we know that current will be common to both the resistor and the inductor. It therefore makes sense to use current as our reference phasor. We also know that voltage and current will be in phase for a resistor. Therefore, the volt drop (p.d.) V_R across the resistor must be in phase with the current. Also, in an inductive circuit, the current lags the voltage by 90°.

If the current is lagging voltage, then we must be right in saying that voltage is leading the current.

This means in this case that the volt drop across the inductor (V_L) will lead the current by 90°. We can then find the value of the supply voltage (V_S), by completing the parallelogram that was discussed on page 357, Figure 3.170. When we draw phasors, we always assume that they rotate anticlockwise and the symbol Ø represents the phase angle.

There are two ways of doing the drawing, as shown in Figure 3.172.

We can see that in the second example, the phasors produce a right-angled triangle. We can therefore use Pythagoras' Theorem to give us the formula:

$$V_S^2 = V_R^2 + V_L^2$$

We can then use trigonometry to give us the different formulae, dependent on the values that we have been given:

$$\cos \varnothing = \frac{V_R}{V_S} \quad \sin \varnothing = \frac{V_L}{V_S} \quad \tan \varnothing = \frac{V_L}{V_R}$$

JTL tip

Remember – because this is an AC circuit, you cannot just add the voltages together as you would have done for a DC circuit. You need to construct a phasor diagram to work it out.

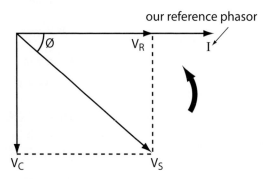

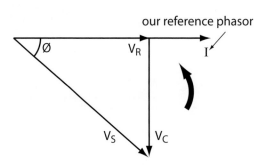

Figure 3.172: Two ways of drawing a phasor diagram

Example 1

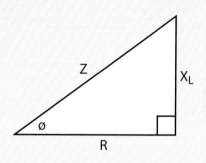

A coil of 0.15 H is connected in series with a 50 Ω resistor across a 100 V 50 Hz supply. Calculate the following:

(a) The inductive reactance of the coil

(b) The impedance of the circuit

(c) The circuit current

(a) Inductive reactance (X_L)

For inductive reactance, we use the formula:

$X_L = 2\pi fL$ (Ω)

Figure 3.173: Impedance triangle

Inserting the values, this would give us

$X_L = 2 \times 3.142 \times 50 \times 0.15$ therefore $X_L = \textbf{47.13 Ω}$

(b) Circuit impedance (Z)

When we have resistance and inductance in series, we calculate the impedance using the following formula:

$Z^2 = R^2 + X_L^2$

which becomes

$Z = \sqrt{R^2 + X_L^2}$

In the case of the first formula, isn't this the same as Pythagoras' Theorem for a right-angled triangle ($A^2 = B^2 + C^2$)? We therefore sometimes refer to this as the impedance triangle and it can be drawn for this type of circuit, as shown. Here, the angle (Ø) between sides R and Z is the same as the phase angle between sides R and Z, is the same as the phase angle between current and voltage.

If we therefore apply some trigonometry, the following applies:

$$\cos Ø = \frac{R}{Z} \qquad \sin Ø = \frac{X_L}{Z} \qquad \tan Ø = \frac{X_L}{R}$$

However, using our formula

$Z = \sqrt{R^2 + X_L^2}$

Then $Z = \sqrt{50^2 + 47.1^2}$ therefore $Z = \textbf{68.69 Ω}$

(c) Circuit current (I)

As we are referring to the total opposition to current, we use the formula

$$I = \frac{V}{R} = \frac{100}{68.69} = \textbf{1.46 A}$$

Example 2

A coil of 0.159 H is connected in series with a 100 Ω resistor across a 230 V 50 Hz supply. Calculate the following:

(a) The inductive reactance of the coil
(b) The circuit impedance
(c) The circuit current
(d) The p.d. across each component
(e) The circuit phase angle

(a) Inductive reactance (X_L)
$X_L = 2\pi fL$ therefore $X_L = 2 \times 3.142 \times 50 \times 0.159 = \textbf{50 Ω}$

(b) Circuit impedance (Z)
$Z = \sqrt{R^2 + X_L^2}$ therefore $Z = \sqrt{100^2 + 50^2} = \textbf{111.8 Ω}$

(c) Circuit current (I)
$I = \dfrac{V}{Z}$ therefore $I = \dfrac{230}{111.8} = \textbf{2.06 A}$

(d) The p.d. across each component (V)

$V_R = I \times R$ therefore $V = 2.06 \times 100 = \textbf{206 V}$
$V_L = I \times X_L$ therefore $V = 2.06 \times 50 = \textbf{103 V}$

(e) Circuit phase angle (Ø)
Using our right-angled triangle:
$\tan Ø = \dfrac{V_L}{V_R}$ therefore $\tan Ø = \dfrac{103}{206} = \textbf{0.5}$

If you then key ⒤ⓃⓋ ⓉⒶⓃ ⓪ • ⑤ ⩵ into your calculator you should get the number 26.6.

Therefore, the current is lagging voltage by **26.6°**

Resistance and capacitance in series (RC)

Figure 3.174 shows a resistor connected in series with a capacitor and fed from an AC supply. Once again, in a series circuit the current (I) will be common to both the resistor and the capacitor, causing voltage to drop (p.d.) V_R across the resistor and V_C across the capacitor.

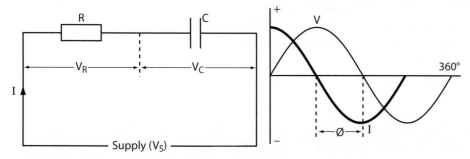

Figure 3.174: A resistor connected in series with a capacitor, fed from an AC supply

As with the resistance/inductance (RL) circuit previously, we can take current as the reference phasor. The voltage across the resistor will be in phase with that current. In a capacitive circuit the current leads the voltage by 90° so the voltage across the

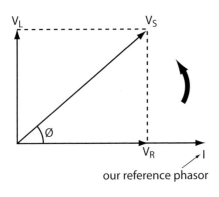
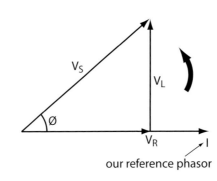

our reference phasor   our reference phasor

Figure 3.175: Phasor diagrams

capacitor will be lagging the current. Now calculate the supply voltage (V_S) by completion of the parallelograms (see Figure 3.175). As with the inductor, we can apply Pythagoras' Theorem and trigonometry to give us the following formulae:

$$V_S{}^2 = V_R{}^2 + V_C{}^2$$

$$\cos \emptyset = \frac{V_R}{V_S} \quad \sin \emptyset = \frac{V_C}{V_S} \quad \tan \emptyset = \frac{V_C}{V_R}$$

Example

A capacitor of 15.9 μF and a 100 Ω resistor are connected in series across a 230 V 50 Hz supply. Calculate:

(a) The circuit impedance

(b) The circuit current

(c) The p.d. across each component

(d) The circuit phase angle

(a) Circuit impedance (Z)

To be able to find the impedance we must first find the capacitive reactance.

$$X_C = \frac{1}{2\pi fC}$$

However, as the capacitor value is given in μF, we use $X_C = \frac{10^6}{2\pi fC}$

This gives us $X_C = \dfrac{10^6}{2 \times 3.142 \times 50 \times 15.9} = \dfrac{10^6}{4995.76} = \mathbf{200\,\Omega}$

When we have resistance and capacitance in series, we use the following formula:

$Z^2 = R^2 + X_C^2$ which becomes $Z = \sqrt{R^2 + X_C^2}$

Therefore $Z = \sqrt{100^2 + 200^2} = \sqrt{50\,000} = \mathbf{224\,\Omega}$

(b) Circuit current (I)

$I = \dfrac{V}{Z}$ therefore $I = \dfrac{230}{224} = \mathbf{1.03\,A}$

(c) The p.d. across each component (V)

$V_R = I \times R$ therefore $V_R = 1.03 \times 100 = \mathbf{103\,V}$

$V_C = I \times X_L$ therefore $V_C = 1.03 \times 200 = \mathbf{206\,V}$

(d) Circuit phase angle ($\emptyset$)

Using our right-angled triangle: $\tan \emptyset = \dfrac{X_C}{V_R}$ therefore $\tan \emptyset = \dfrac{206}{103} = \mathbf{2}$

If you then key (INV)(TAN)(2)(=) into your calculator you should get the number 63.4. Therefore, the current is leading voltage by **63.4°**.

Resistance, inductance and capacitance in series (RLC)

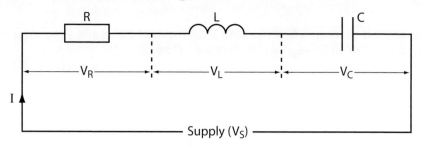

Figure 3.176: Resistor connected in series with an inductor and capacitor, fed from an AC supply

Figure 3.176 shows a resistor connected in series with an inductor and a capacitor then fed from an AC supply. This is often referred to as an RLC circuit or a **general series circuit**. Again, as we have a series circuit, the current (I) will be common to all three components, causing a voltage drop (p.d.) V_R across the resistor, V_L across the inductor and V_C across the capacitor.

Here V_R will be in phase with the current, V_L will lead the current by 90° (because the current lags the voltage) and V_C will lag the current by 90° (because current leads the voltage in a capacitive circuit). Because V_L and V_C are in opposition to each other (one leads and one lags), the actual effect will be the difference between their values, subtracting the smaller from the larger. We can once again calculate V_S by completing a parallelogram as shown in Figure 3.177.

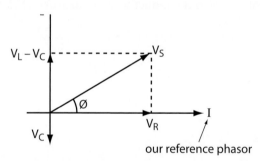

our reference phasor

Figure 3.177: Phasor parallelogram

As before, we can now apply Pythagoras' Theorem and trigonometry to give us the following formulae depending on whether V_L or V_C is the larger:

$$V_S^2 = V_R^2 + (V_L - V_C)^2 \quad \text{or} \quad V_S^2 = V_R^2 + (V_C - V_L)^2$$

and because I is the same for each component we get:

$$Z = \sqrt{R^2 + (X_L - X_C)^2} \quad \text{or} \quad Z = \sqrt{R^2 + (X_C - X_L)^2}$$

and finally: $\cos \varnothing = \dfrac{V_R}{V_S}$ $\sin \varnothing = \dfrac{V_R - V_C}{V_S}$ $\tan \varnothing = \dfrac{V_L - V_C}{V_R}$

Example

A resistor of 5 Ω is connected in series with an inductor of 0.02 H and a capacitor of 150 μF across a 250 V 50 Hz supply. Calculate the following:

(a) The impedance   (b) The supply current   (c) The power factor

(a) Impedance (Z)

In order to find the impedance, we must first find out the relevant values of reactance.

Therefore: $X_L = 2\pi fL = 2 \times 3.142 \times 50 \times 0.02 = \textbf{6.28 Ω}$

$X_C = \dfrac{1}{2\pi fC}$ which allowing for microfarads becomes $X_C = \dfrac{10^6}{2 \times 3.142 \times 50 \times 150} = \textbf{21.2 Ω}$

If you remember, we said that the effect of inductance and capacitance together in series would be the difference between their values. Consequently, this means that the resulting reactance (X) will be found as follows:

$X = X_L - X_C$ or, in this case because X_C is the larger: $X = X_C - X_L$

and therefore: $X = 21.2 - 6.28 = \textbf{14.92 Ω}$

We can now use the impedance formula as follows:

$Z = \sqrt{R^2 + (X_L - X_C)^2}$ or $Z = \sqrt{R^2 + (X_C - X_L)^2}$

which gives us

$Z = \sqrt{5^2 + 14.92^2} = \textbf{15.74 Ω}$

Note: X_C is greater than X_L. Therefore we subtract X_L from X_C. Had X_L been the higher, then the reverse would be true. Also, as capacitive reactance is highest, the circuit current will lead the voltage. Had the inductive reactance been the higher, then the current would lag the voltage.

(b) Supply current (I)

$I = \dfrac{V}{Z} = \dfrac{230}{15.74} = \textbf{14.6 A}$

(c) Power factor (Ø)

$\cos Ø = \dfrac{R}{Z} = \dfrac{5}{15.74} = \textbf{0.32}$

Therefore PF = **0.32 leading**

Resistance, inductance and capacitance in parallel

Consider Figure 3.178.

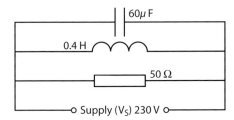

Figure 3.178: Resistor, capacitor and inductor in parallel connected to an AC supply

There can obviously be any combination of the above components in parallel. However, to demonstrate the principles involved, we will look at all three connected across an AC supply.

As we have a parallel circuit, the voltage (V_s) will be common to all branches of the circuit. Consequently, when we draw our parallelogram we will use voltage as the reference phasor.

In this type of circuit, the current through the resistor will be in phase with the voltage, the current through the inductor will lag the voltage by 90° and the current through the capacitor will lead the voltage by 90°.

Normally, when we carry out calculations for parallel circuits, it is easier to treat each branch as being a separate series circuit. We then draw to scale each of the respective currents and their relationships to our reference phasor, which is voltage.

As with voltage V_L and V_S in the RLC series circuit, the current through the inductor (I_L) and the current through the capacitor (I_C) are in complete opposition to each other. Therefore, the actual effect will be the difference between their two values. We calculate this value by the completion of our parallelogram. But, bear in mind that the bigger value (I_C or I_L) will determine whether the current ends up leading or lagging.

If we use the diagram as the basis for our example, calculate the circuit current and its phase angle relative to the voltage.

To calculate the circuit current and its phase angle relative to the voltage, we must first find the current through each branch:

$I_R = \dfrac{V}{R} = \dfrac{230}{50} = \textbf{4.6 A}$

$X_L = 2\pi fL = 2 \times 3.142 \times 50 \times 0.4 = \textbf{126 } \Omega$

Therefore $I_L = \dfrac{V}{X_L} = \dfrac{230}{126} = \textbf{1.8 A}$

$X_C = \dfrac{10^6}{2\pi fC} = \dfrac{10^6}{2 \times 3.142 \times 50 \times 60} = \textbf{53 } \Omega$

Therefore $I_C = \dfrac{V}{X_C} = \dfrac{230}{53} = \textbf{4.3 A}$

The actual effect will be $I_C - I_L$ which gives $4.3 - 1.8 = \textbf{2.5 A}$

Now add this to I_R by completing the scale drawing in Figure 3.179. This gives a current of 5.2 A that is leading voltage by an angle of 28°.

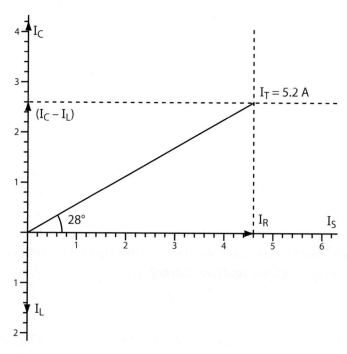

Figure 3.179: Scale drawing

Power in an AC circuit

If we were to try to push something against a resistance, we would get hot and bothered as we use up energy in completing the task. When current flows through a resistor, a similar thing happens in that power is the rate of using up energy – in other words, the amount of energy that was used in a certain time.

If a resistor (R) has a current (I) flowing through it for a certain time (t), then the power (energy being used per second) given in watts, can be calculated by the formula:

$P = I^2 \times R$

This power will be dissipated in the resistor as heat and reflects the average power in terms of the r.m.s. values of voltage and current.

What we are effectively saying here is that power is only dissipated by the resistance of a circuit and that the average power in a resistive circuit (one which is non-reactive, i.e. doesn't possess inductance or capacitance) can be found by the product of the readings of an ammeter and a voltmeter.

In other words, in the resistive circuit, the power (energy used per second) is associated with that energy being transferred from the medium of electricity into another medium, such as light (filament lamp) or heat (electric fire/kettle). We call this type of power the active power. When we look at the capacitive circuit, we find that current flows to the capacitor, but we have no power.

Look at this wave diagram for voltage in Figure 3.180.

During the first period of the cycle, the voltage is increasing and this provides the energy to charge the capacitor. However, in the second period of the cycle, the voltage is decreasing and therefore the capacitor discharges, returning its energy back to the circuit as it does so. The same is also true of the third and fourth periods.

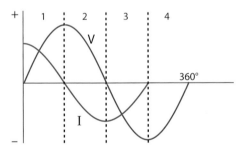

Figure 3.180: Sine wave diagram

This exchange of energy means that we have voltage and current, but no average power and therefore no heating effect. This means that our previous formula ($P = I^2 \times R$) is no longer useful.

We therefore say that the result of voltage and current in this type of circuit is called **reactive power** and we express this in reactive voltamperes (VAr). Equally, we say that the current in a capacitive circuit, where there is no resistance and no dissipation of energy, is called **reactive current**.

When we come to the inductive circuit we have a similar position. This time, as voltage increases during the first period of the cycle, the energy is stored as a magnetic field in the inductor. This energy will then be fed back into the circuit during the second period of the cycle as the voltage decreases and the magnetic field collapses. In other words, once again the exchange of energy produces no average power (energy used per second).

Circuits are likely to comprise combinations of resistance, inductance and capacitance. In a circuit, which has resistance and reactance, there will be a phase angle between the voltage and current. This relationship has relevance, as power will only be expended in the resistive part of the circuit.

Let's now look at this relationship via a phasor diagram (see Figure 3.181), for a circuit containing resistance and capacitance, remembering that for this type of circuit the current will lead the voltage. This circuit has two components (resistance and capacitance), so we've drawn two current phasors. In reality, as we already know, these are not currents that will actually flow, but their phasor sum will be the actual current in the circuit I_p (actual).

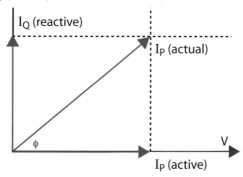

Figure 3.181: Phasor diagram

We also said that in a resistive circuit the voltage and current are in phase, and therefore this section of the current has been represented by the phasor I_p (active). This part of the current is in the active section and we therefore refer to this as the active current.

We then show that part of the current in the reactive section (capacitor) as leading the voltage by 90° and this has been represented by the phasor I_Q (reactive). As stated previously, we refer to this as the reactive current.

We also know that for a resistive circuit, we calculate the power by multiplying together the r.m.s. values of voltage and current (V × I).

Logically, as we know that no power is consumed in the reactive section of the circuit, we can therefore calculate the power in the circuit by multiplying together the r.m.s. value of voltage and the value of current, which is in phase with it (I_p(active)). This would give us the formula:

$P = V \times I_p$

But as the actual current will be affected by the reactive current and therefore the phase angle (cos Ø), our formula becomes:

$P = V \times I_p$ (active) × cos Ø

If I_p (active) is zero then Ø = 90° and cos Ø = 0. Therefore P = 0.

We have now established that it is possible in an AC circuit for current to flow, but no power to exist.

We also say that the product of voltage and current is power given in watts. However, it would be fair to say that this is not the actual power of the circuit.

The actual (true) power of the circuit has to take on board the effect of the phase angle (cos Ø), the ratio of these two statements being the power factor. In other words:

$$\text{Power Factor (cos Ø)} = \frac{\text{True power (P)}}{\text{Apparent power (S)}}$$

$$= \frac{V \times I_p \text{ (actual)} \times \cos Ø}{V \times I_p \text{ (actual)}} = \frac{\text{watts}}{\text{volts-amperes}}$$

To summarise, what we perceive to be the power of a circuit (the apparent power) can also be the true power, as long as we have a unity power factor (1.0). However, as long as we have a phase angle, then we have a difference between apparent power and reality (true power). This difference is the power factor (a value less than unity).

In reality we will use a wattmeter to measure the true power and a voltmeter and ammeter to measure the apparent power.

The power triangle

We can use Pythagoras' Theorem to help us calculate the different power components within a circuit.

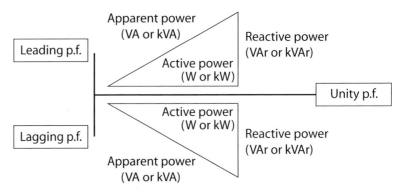

Figure 3.182: Power triangle

We do so by using Pythagoras' formula as follows: $(VA)^2 = (W)^2 + (VAr)^2$

This is then applied in Figure 3.182, where we have shown both inductive and capacitive conditions.

Example

A resistor of 15 Ω has been connected in series with a capacitor of reactance 30 Ω. If they are connected across a 230 V supply, establish both by calculation and by drawing a scaled power triangle, the following:

(a) the apparent power

(b) the true power

(c) the reactive power

(d) the power factor.

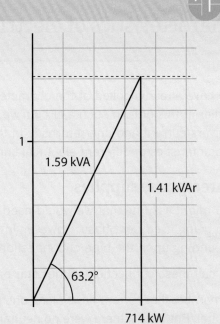

In order to establish the elements of power, we must first find the current. To do this we need to find the impedance of the circuit.

Therefore:

$$Z = \sqrt{R^2 + X_C^2} = \sqrt{15^2 + 30^2} = \sqrt{225 + 900} = \sqrt{1125}$$

Therefore $Z = 33.5 \, \Omega$

$$I = \frac{V}{Z} = \frac{230}{35.5} = 6.9 \, A$$

$$Pf \, (\cos \varnothing) = \frac{R}{Z} = \frac{15}{35.5} = 0.45$$

True power $= I \times V \times Pf$

$\qquad\qquad = 6.9 \times 230 \times 0.45$

$\qquad\qquad = 714.15 \, W \quad$ or $\quad 0.714 \, kW$

Apparent power $= I \times V$

$\qquad\qquad = 6.9 \times 230$

$\qquad\qquad = 1587 \, VA \quad$ or $\quad 1.587 \, kVA$

Reactive power $= \sin \varnothing \times$ apparent power

However, we do not know the value of sin Ø, we must therefore convert cos Ø to an angle and then find the sine of that angle.

$\cos \varnothing = 0.45 \quad$ INV cos of 0.45 = 63.2

sine of 63.2° = 0.89

Therefore reactive power $= \sin \varnothing \times$ apparent power

$\qquad\qquad\qquad = 0.89 \times 1587$

$\qquad\qquad\qquad = \textbf{1412.43 VAr} \quad$ or $\quad \textbf{1.412 kVAr}$

Summary

1. What factors make up the total opposition to current referred to an impedance?

2. How would impedance be graphically shown?

Characteristics of electrical supplies

We have already looked at the characteristics of single-phase electrical supplies earlier in this unit. In such a circuit, we normally use two conductors, where one delivers current and one returns it. In this section we will look at some of the characteristics of different electrical supplies.

Three-phase supplies

You might assume that we would need six conductors for a three-phase system, with two being used per phase. However, in reality we only use three or four conductors, depending upon the type of connection that is being used.

We call these connections either **star** or **delta**.

Remember that current flows along one conductor and returns along another called the neutral. But what if there were no neutral? And what exactly is the neutral conductor for?

Keeping things simple, when we generate an e.m.f., we do so by spinning a loop of wire inside a magnetic field. To get three phases, we just spin three loops inside the magnetic field. Each loop will be mounted on the same rotating shaft, but they'll be 120° apart.

Figure 3.183: Three-phase generation

In Figure 3.183, each loop will create an identical sinusoidal waveform, or in other words, three identical voltages, each 120° apart.

Whether or not we need a neutral will now depend upon the load. If we accept that the e.m.f. being generated by each loop pushes current down the conductors (lines), then we would find that where we have a balanced three-phase system, i.e. one where the current in each of the phases (lines) is the same, then by phasor addition, we would find that the resultant current is zero.

If the current is zero then we do not need a neutral, because the neutral is used to carry the current in an out-of-balance system. Let us now look at the different types of connection.

Delta connection

We tend to use the delta connection when we have a balanced load. This is because there is no need for a neutral connection and therefore only three wires are needed. We tend to find that this configuration is used for power transmission from power stations or to connect the windings of a three-phase motor.

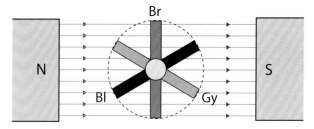

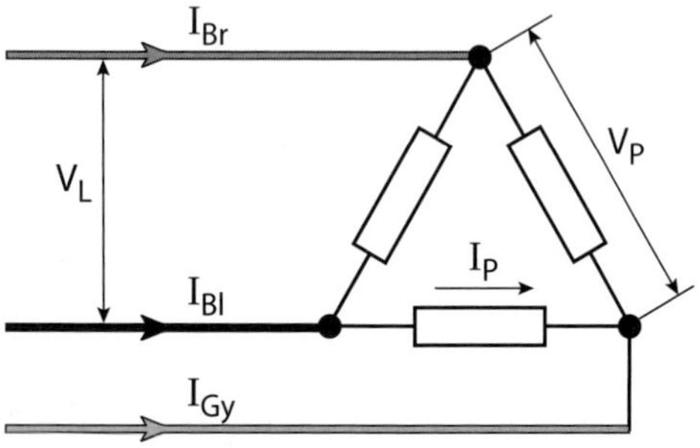

Figure 3.184: Delta connection

In Figure 3.184 we have shown a three-phase load, which has been delta connected. You can see that each leg of the load is connected across two of the lines, e.g. Br–Gy, Gy–Bl and Bl–Br. We refer to the connection between phases as being the line voltage and have shown this on the drawing as V_L.

Equally, if each line voltage is pushing current along, we refer to these currents as being line currents, which are represented on the drawing as I_{Br}, I_{Gy} or I_{Bl}. These line currents are calculated as being the phasor sum of two phase currents, which are shown on the drawing as I_P and represent the current in each leg of the load. Similarly, the voltage across each leg of the load is referred to as the phase voltage (V_P).

In a delta connected balanced three-phase load, we are then able to state the following formulae: $V_L = V_P$ $I_L = \sqrt{3} \times I_P$

Note that a load connected in delta would draw three times the line current and consequently three times as much power as the same load connected in star. For this reason, induction motors are sometimes connected in **star–delta**.

This means they start off in a star connection (with a reduced starting current) and are then switched to delta. In doing so we reduce the heat that would otherwise be generated in the windings.

Star connection

Although we can have a balanced load connected in star (three-wire), we tend to use the star connection when we have an unbalanced load, i.e. one where the current in each of the phases is different. In this circumstance, one end of each of the three star connected loops is connected to a central point and it is then from this point that we take our neutral connection, which in turn is normally connected to earth. This is the three-phase four-wire system.

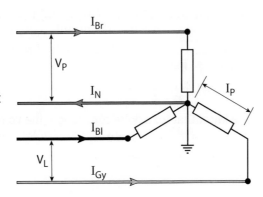

Figure 3.185: Star connection

Another advantage of the star connected system is that it allows us to have two voltages – one when we connect between any two phases (400 V) and another when we connect between any phase and neutral (230 V). You should note that we will also have 230 V between any phase and earth.

In Figure 3.185 we have shown a three-phase load that has been star connected.

As with delta, we refer to the connection made between phases as the line voltage and have shown this on the drawing as V_L. However, unlike delta, the **phase voltage** exists between any phase conductor and the neutral conductor and we have shown this as V_P. Our line currents have been represented by I_{Br}, I_{Gy} and I_{Bl} with the phase currents being represented by I_P.

In a star connected load, the line currents and phase currents are the same, but the line voltage (400 V) is greater than the phase voltage (230 V).

In a star connected load, we are therefore able to state the following formulae:

$I_L = I_P$ $V_L = \sqrt{3} \times V_P$

Using the star connected load we have access to a 230 V supply, which we use in most domestic and low load situations.

Example 1

A three-phase star connected supply feeds a delta-connected load as shown in the diagram below. If the star-connected phase voltage is 230 V and the phase current is 20 A, calculate the following:

- the line voltages and line currents in the star connection
- the line and phase voltages and currents in the delta connection.

The star connection

In a star system the line current (I_L) is equal to the phase current (I_P). Therefore if we have been given I_P as 20 A, then I_L must also be 20 A.

We find line voltage in a star connection using the formula:

$$V_L = \sqrt{3} \times V_P$$

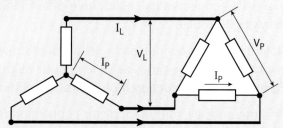

$\sqrt{3}$, the square root of 3, is a constant having the value of 1.732. Therefore if we substitute our values, we get:

$V_L = 1.732 \times 230 =$ **398 V**

The delta connection

In a delta system, the line current (I_L) is 1.732 times greater than the phase current (I_P). We calculate this using the formula: $I_L = \sqrt{3} \times I_P$

However, we know that I_L is 20 A, so if we transpose our formula and substitute our values, we get:

$$I_P = \frac{I_L}{\sqrt{3}} = \frac{20}{1.732} = 11.5 \text{ A}$$

We know that for a delta connection line voltage and phase voltage have the same values. Therefore: $V_L = V_P =$ **398 V**

Example 2

Three identical loads of 30 Ω resistance are connected to a 400 V three-phase supply. Calculate the phase and line currents if the loads were connected:

(a) in star   (b) in delta.

Star connection

First we need to establish the phase voltage. If $V_L = \sqrt{3} \times V_P$ and $\sqrt{3} = 1.732$ then by transposition:

$$V_P = \frac{V_L}{\sqrt{3}} = \frac{400}{1.732} = 230.9 \text{ A}$$

Using Ohm's Law: $I_P = \frac{V_P}{Z} = \frac{230.9}{30} =$ **7.7 A**

However, in a star-connected load, $I_P = I_L$, therefore I_L will also = 7.7 A.

Delta connection

In a delta connection $V_L = V_P$ and therefore we know the phase voltage will be 400 V.

Using Ohm's Law: $I_P = \frac{V_P}{Z} = \frac{400}{30} =$ **13.3 A**

However, the line current:

$I_L = \sqrt{3} \times I_P = 1.732 \times 8 =$ **23.09 A**

As can be seen from this example, the current drawn from a delta connected load (23.09A) is three times that of a star-connected load (7.7 A).

Neutral currents

As we have already discussed, where we have a balanced load, we can have a three-phase system with three wires. However, in truth it is more likely that we will find an unbalanced system and will therefore need to use a three-phase four-wire system.

In such a system, we are saying that each line (Br, Gy, Bl) will have an unequal load and therefore the current in each line can be different. It therefore becomes the job of the neutral conductor to carry the out of balance current. If we used **Kirchhoff's Law** in this situation, we would find that the current in the neutral is normally found by the phasor addition of the currents in the three lines.

Key term

Kirchhoff's Law – the sum of the voltage drops around a closed loop in the network must equal zero

Example 3

For a three-phase four-wire system, the line currents are found to be $I_R = 30$ A and in phase with V_{Br}, $I_{Gy} = 20$ A and leading V_{Gy} by 20° and $I_{Bl} = 25$ A and lagging V_{Bl} by 10°. Calculate the current in the neutral by phasor addition.

The phasor diagram for this example has been provided. However, you should note that in order to establish the current in the neutral (I_N), you would need to draw two parallelograms. The first should represent the resultant currents I_{Br} and I_{Gy}. The second, I_N, should be drawn between this resultant and the current in I_{Bl}.

When this has been done to scale, we should find a current in the neutral of 18 A.

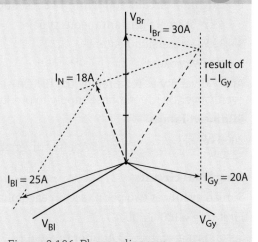

Figure 3.186: Phasor diagram

Load balancing

The regional electricity companies (now commonly known as District Network Operators – DNO) also require load balancing as a condition of their electricity supply, because it is important to try to achieve balanced currents in the mains distribution system.

In order to design a three-phase four-wire electrical installation for both efficiency and economy, it needs to be subdivided into load categories. By doing this, the maximum demand can be assessed and items of equipment can be spread over all three phases of the supply to achieve a balanced system. This section looks at load balancing on three-phase systems. The designer needs to make a careful assessment of the various installed loads, which in turn leads to the proper sizing of the main cable and associated switchgear.

Standard circuit arrangements exist for many final circuits operating at 230 V. For example, a ring final circuit is rated at 30–32 A, a lighting circuit at 5–6 A, and a cooking appliance is rated at 30–45 A. Where more than one standard circuit arrangement is present, such as three ring final circuits and/or two cooking appliances, then a diversity allowance can be applied.

Once the designer has made these allowances for diversity, the single-phase loads can be evenly spread over all three phases of the supply so that each phase takes approximately the same amount of current. If this is done carefully, minimum current will flow along the neutral conductor; the sizes of cables and switchgear can be kept to a minimum, thus reducing costs, and the system is therefore said to be reasonably well balanced.

Example

A small guesthouse with 10 bedrooms is supplied with a 400/230 V, three-phase four-wire supply. It has the following installed loads:

20 × filament lighting points each rated at 100 W

6 × ring final circuits supplying 13 socket outlets

6 × 4 kW showers (instantaneous type)

3 × 3 kW immersion heaters

2 × 10 kW cookers.

Apply diversity as required by the IET On-site Guide, Appendix A and 'spread' the loads evenly over the three-phase supply to produce the most effective load-balanced situation.

Filament lamps

$$\frac{2000\ W}{230\ V} = 8.69\ A\ @\ 75\% = 6.5\ A\ (\text{after diversity})$$

Ring final circuits

Spread evenly at two per phase on each phase:

First ring = 100% = 30 A

Second ring = 50% = 15 A (after diversity)

Total = 45 A

Showers

Spread evenly at two per phase both at 100%:

$$\frac{4000\ W}{230\ V} = 17.4\ A \times 2 = 34.8\ A$$

Immersion heaters

Spread as required over the phases (no diversity):

$$\frac{3000\ W}{230\ V} = 13\ A$$

Cookers

If both cookers are on the same phase then:

$$100\%\ \text{and}\ 80\% = \frac{10\,000\ W}{230\ V} = 43\ A\ \text{for}\ 100\%$$

$$= 35\ A\ \text{for}\ 80\%\ (\text{after diversity})$$

	Brown	Grey	Black
Ring circuits	45 A	45 A	45 A
Shower	34.8 A	34.8 A	34.8 A
Immersion			13 A
			13 A
			13 A
Cooker	43 A	43 A	
Lighting			6.5 A
Totals	122.8 A	122.8 A	125.3 A

Or if both on different phases both are at 100% (this is what will be used).

Based on these calculations, a suggested load balancing is shown in the table above. Note the immersion heaters have all been allocated to the Blue phase.

Also, should one phase be 'lost', only a portion of the lighting will fail. If this is the case then care must be taken, as there could be three-phase voltage values present in multi-gang switches. It is also advisable to position distribution boards in large factories and commercial premises as near to the load centre as possible. This will help reduce voltage drop and make the installation more cost-effective.

The load balancing shown above provides satisfactory balancing over three phases, but it may be recommended that if discharge lighting is to be used, then it should be spread over all three phases because of the stroboscopic effect.

Power in three-phase supplies

As we have seen in the previous section, we can find the power in a single-phase AC circuit by using the following formula:

Power $= V \times I \times \cos \emptyset$

Logically, you might assume that for three-phase we could multiply this formula by three. Although this is not far from the truth we must remember that this could only apply where we have a balanced three-phase load. We can therefore say, that for any three-phase balanced load, the formula to establish power is:

Power $= \sqrt{3} \times (V_L \times I_L \times \cos \emptyset)$

However, in the case of an unbalanced load, we need to calculate the power for each separate section and then add them together to get total power (see pages 366–368 for calculating power).

Example 1

A balanced load of $10\,\Omega$ per phase is star connected and supplied with 400 V 50 Hz at unity power factor. Calculate the following:

(a) Phase voltage

(b) Line current

(c) Total power consumed

(a) Phase voltage

$V_L = \sqrt{3} \times V_P$

Therefore by transposition

$V_P = \dfrac{V_L}{\sqrt{3}} = \dfrac{400}{1.732} = \mathbf{231\ V}$

(b) Line current

$I_L = I_P$

and therefore

$I_P = \dfrac{V_P}{R_P} = \dfrac{231}{10} = \mathbf{23.1\ A}$

(c) Total power consumed

In a balanced system

Power $= \sqrt{3} \times V_L \times I_L \times \cos \emptyset$

Power $= 1.732 \times 400 \times 23.1 \times 1 = \mathbf{16\ kW}$

Example 2

Three coils of resistance 40 Ω and inductive reactance 30 Ω are connected in delta to a 400 V 50 Hz three-phase supply. Calculate the following:

(a) Current in each coil

(b) Line current

(c) Total power

(a) Current in each coil

We must first find the impedance of each coil:

$$Z = \sqrt{R^2 + X_L^2} = \sqrt{40^2 + 30^2} = \sqrt{2500} = 50 \, \Omega$$

The current in each coil (I_P) can then be found by applying Ohm's Law:

This gives $I_P = \dfrac{V}{Z} = \dfrac{400}{50} = \mathbf{8\,A}$

(b) Line current

For a delta connected system

$I_L = \sqrt{3} \times I_P$

Therefore $I_L = 1.732 \times 8 = \mathbf{13.86\,A}$

(c) Total power

We must first find the power factor using the formula:

$\cos \emptyset = \dfrac{R}{Z}$

This gives us $\cos \emptyset = \dfrac{40}{50} = 0.8$

And for a delta system $V_L = V_P$

Therefore we can now use the power formula of:

$P = \sqrt{3} \times V_L \times I_L \times \cos \emptyset$

$P = 1.732 \times 400 \times 13.86 \times 0.8$

$P = \mathbf{7682\,W}$ **or**   **7.682 kW**

Example 3

A small industrial estate is fed by a 400 V, three-phase, 4-wire TN-S system. On the estate there are three factories connected to the system as follows:

Factory A taking 50 kW at unity power factor

Factory B taking 80 kVA at 0.6 lagging power factor

Factory C taking 40 kVA at 0.7 leading power factor

Calculate the overall kW, kVA, kVar and power factor for the system.

To clarify, we are trying to find values of P (true power), S (apparent power) and Q (reactive power). First, we need to work out the situations for each factory.

Factory A

We know that power factor

$$\cos \varnothing = \frac{\text{True power (P)}}{\text{Apparent power (S)}}$$

We also know that the power factor is 1.0 and that P = 50 kW. Therefore, by transposition:

$$S = \frac{P}{\cos \varnothing} = \frac{50}{1} = 50 \text{ kVA}$$

And with unity power factor for Factory A, Q = 0

Factory B

Using the same logic, we need to find true power and reactive power.

Therefore P = cos Ø × S = 0.6 × 80 kW = 48 kW

Reactive component (Q) = S × sin Ø = 80 × 0.8 = 64 kVAr

Factory C

P = S × cos Ø = 40 kW × 0.7 = 28 kW

Q = S × sin Ø = 40 × 0.714 = 28.6 kVAr

We can now find the **total kW** by addition: 50 + 48 + 28 = **126 kW**

We can find the **total kVAr** as the difference between the reactive power components, the larger one, Factory B, lagging and the smaller one, Factory C, leading:

64 kVAr – 28.6 kVAr = **35.4 kVAr**

We can use Pythagoras' Theorem to find the total kVA

$$S = \sqrt{P^2 + Q^2} = \sqrt{126^2 + 35.4^2} = \textbf{131 kVA}$$

Consequently, the overall power factor will be:

$$\cos \varnothing = \frac{P}{S} = \frac{126}{131} = \textbf{0.96 lagging}$$

Power factor correction (PFC)

As we have seen throughout this section, in the eyes of the suppliers it is desirable to have the power factor of a system as close to perfection (1.0) as possible.

Power factor is adjusted by supplying reactive power of the opposite form. For example, if power factor is being dragged down below 1.0 due to the inductive effect of motors, we can add capacitors locally to control the effect. If the load has a capacitive value, then we add inductors to correct the power factor.

We can therefore generalise to say that inductors remove reactive power from a system and capacitors add reactive power to the system.

Power factor correction may be applied by an electrical distributor to improve the stability and efficiency of the transmission network; a high power factor is generally required in a transmission system to reduce transmission losses and improve voltage regulation at the load.

However, in some installations, an automatic power factor correction unit is used to improve power factor. These normally consist of a bank of capacitors switched in via contactors when the power factor is detected as being higher than a pre-set value.

A power factor correction unit usually consists of a number of capacitors that are switched by contactors. These contactors are controlled by a regulator that measures power factor in an electrical network. To be able to measure power factor, the regulator uses a current transformer to measure the current in one phase.

Large industrial plants also use the effect of the synchronous motor to cancel out the effect of the induction motor, as it provides a leading power factor. Taken one step further, a synchronous condenser is a synchronous motor without a load, which when introduced into the system can compensate either a leading or lagging power factor, by absorbing or supplying reactive power to the system, which in turn enhances voltage regulation.

Summary

1. Power factor is usually a number less than what?
2. What is power factor used to represent?

9. The operating principles and applications of DC machines and AC motors

In essence there are two categories of motor: those that run on direct current (DC) and those that run on alternating current (AC).

The basic concept of the motor was actually explained in our electromagnetism section. As lines of flux cannot cross, Figure 3.187 shows what the result would be if we actually placed a current-carrying conductor in a magnetic field.

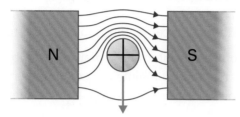

Figure 3.187: Force on a current-carrying conductor in a magnetic field

In Figure 3.187 the main field now becomes distorted. As the two fields above the conductor are in the same direction, the amount of flux is high and therefore the force will move the conductor downwards. It is this basic principle of a force being exerted on a current-carrying conductor in a magnetic field that is used in the construction of motors and moving coil instruments.

Basic types, applications and operating principles of DC machines

The operating principle of a DC motor is fairly straightforward. Looking at Figure 3.188, if we take a conductor, form it into a loop that is pivoted at its centre, place it within a magnetic field and then apply a DC supply to it, a current will pass around the loop. This will cause a magnetic field to be produced around the conductor, and this magnetic field will interact with the magnetic field between the two poles (**pole pair**) of the magnet.

Key term

Pole pair – any system consisting of a north and south pole

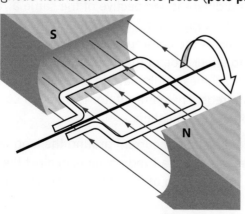

Figure 3.188: Single current-carrying loop in a magnetic field

The magnetic field between the two poles (pole pair) becomes distorted and, as mentioned earlier, this interaction between the two magnetic fields causes a bending or stretching of the lines of force. The lines of force behave a bit like an elastic band and consequently are always trying to find the shortest distance between the pole pair. These stretched lines, in their attempt to return to their shortest length, therefore exert a force on the conductor that tries to push it out of the magnetic field, and thus they cause the loop to rotate.

In reality we don't have just one loop, we have many, with them being wound on to a central rotating part of the DC motor known as the **armature**. When the armature is positioned so that the loop sides are at right angles to the magnetic field, a turning force is exerted. But we have a problem when the coil has rotated 180°, as the magnetic field in the loop is now opposite to that of the field, and this will tend to push the armature back the way it came, thus stopping the rotating motion.

The solution is to reverse the current in the armature every half rotation so that the magnetic fields will work together to maintain a continuous rotating motion. The device that we use to achieve this switching of polarity is known as the **commutator**.

The commutator

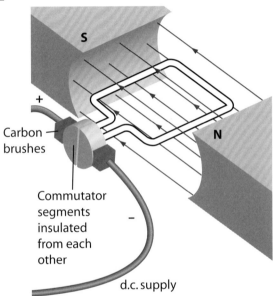

Figure 3.189: Single loop with commutator

Figure 3.189 now gives a different perspective of the same arrangement, showing the device that enables the supply to be connected to the loop, enabling the loop to rotate continuously. This is the commutator. This simplified version has only two segments, connecting to either side of the loop, but in actual machines there may be any number. Large machines would have in excess of 50, and the numbers of loops can be in the hundreds. The commutator is made of copper, with the segments separated from each other by insulation.

Figure 3.190 shows the direction of current around the loop when connected to a DC supply. The brushes remain in a fixed position, against the copper segments of the commutator. Note the direction of current in those sections indicated by X and Y in the diagram.

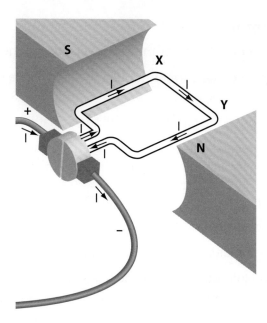

Figure 3.190: Single loop with DC flowing

Figure 3.191 shows the wire loop having rotated 180°. X and Y have changed positions but, as can be seen from the arrows, current flow remains as it was for the previous diagram. As the poles of the armature electromagnet pass the poles of the permanent magnets, the commutator reverses the polarity of the armature electromagnet. In that instant of switching polarity, inertia keeps the motor going in the proper direction and thus the motor continues to rotate in one direction.

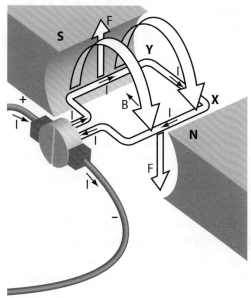

Figure 3.191: Single loop rotated 180°

In the previous drawings, we have shown the armature rotating between a pair of magnetic poles. Practical DC motors do not use permanent magnets, but use electromagnets instead. The electromagnet has two advantages over the permanent magnet:

1. By adjusting the amount of current flowing through the wire the strength of the electromagnet can be controlled.
2. By changing the direction of current flow the poles of the electromagnet can be reversed.

Reversing a DC motor

The direction of rotation of a DC motor may be reversed by either:

- reversing the direction of the current through the field hence changing the field polarity

- reversing the direction of the current through the armature.

Common practice is to reverse the current through the armature, and this is normally achieved by reversing the armature connections only.

Types of DC motor

There are three basic forms of DC motor:

- series
- shunt
- compound.

They are very similar to look at, the difference being the way in which the field coil and armature coil circuits are wired.

The series motor

As the name suggests, this motor has the field winding wired in series with the armature. It is also called a 'universal motor' as it can run in both DC and AC situations.

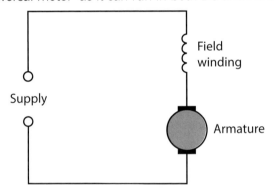

Figure 3.192: Series motor

The large conductors used in the field windings and armature allow the series motor to develop a large magnetic field and consequently a high starting **torque** (rotational force). This means that it is able to move a large load connected to the shaft when first switched on.

As the armature begins to rotate and gather speed the current and torque reduces. However, should the motor ever lose its load (e.g. the shaft breaks or the drive belt breaks) then the load current falls, which reduces the amount of back e.m.f. produced by the armature. As the armature is no longer producing sufficient back e.m.f. and the load is no longer exerting a force on the shaft, the armature will continue to 'runaway'. In other words, it will increase in speed until it self-destructs. We therefore tend to use sensors to disconnect the machine should the **revolutions per minute** (rpm) exceed a set level.

As these motors have a very high starting current, they are started using an external resistance placed in series with the armature. As we saw earlier, the speed of the motor is inversely proportional to the strength of the magnetic field and therefore we can control speed by connecting a variable resistor in the field circuit.

The shunt motor

Electrically, a shunt is something connected in parallel. In the shunt motor it is the field winding that is connected in parallel with the armature.

This motor has a low starting torque and therefore the load on the shaft has to be quite small. The armature's torque increases as the motor gains speed due to the fact that the torque is directly proportional to the armature current. Consequently, when the motor is starting and speed is very low, the motor has very little torque.

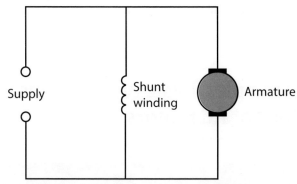

Figure 3.193: Shunt motor

Once the motor reaches full rpm, its torque is at its highest level.

The shunt motor's speed can be controlled by varying the amount of current supplied to the shunt field winding, which will allow the rpm to be changed by up to 20%. We can reverse the direction of rotation by changing the polarity of either the armature coil or the field coil.

The compound motor

A compound is when we produce something by combining two or more parts. The compound motor therefore gets its name by combining the characteristics of the series and shunt motors. There are actually two main types of compound motor – the most commonly used cumulative compound and the rarely used differential compound.

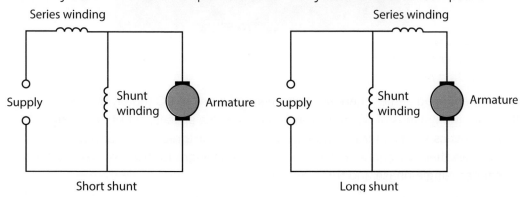

Figure 3.194: Compound motor

Figure 3.194 shows the short and long shunt version of the cumulative compound motor. This is called cumulative because the polarity of the shunt field is the same as that of the armature and thus the shunt field aids the magnetic fields of the series field and armature. The shunt winding can be wired as a long shunt or as a short shunt.

In the case of the differential compound motor, the polarity of the shunt field is reversed with the negative terminal of the shunt field being connected to the positive terminal of the armature and as a result it opposes the flux of the armature and series field.

The cumulative compound motor is probably the most common DC motor because it provides high starting torque and good speed regulation. As a result it tends to be used in situations where a constant speed is needed with varying loads.

Speed control is achieved by voltage regulation of the shunt field and reversal of shaft rotation can be achieved by changing the polarity of the armature winding.

Operating principles, basic types, applications and limitations of AC motors

Figure 3.195: A simple AC motor

As we mentioned earlier, there are three general types of DC motor. However, there are many types of AC motor, each one having a specific set of operating characteristics such as torque, speed, single-phase or three-phase, and this determines their selection for use. We can essentially group them in to two categories: single-phase and three-phase.

In a DC motor, electrical power is conducted directly to the armature through brushes and a commutator. Due to the nature of an alternating current, an AC motor doesn't need a commutator to reverse the polarity of the current. Whereas a DC motor works by changing the polarity of the current running through the armature (the rotating part of the motor), the AC motor works by changing the polarity of the current running through the stator (the stationary part of the motor).

The series-wound (universal) motor

We will begin the discussion of AC motors by looking at the series-wound (universal) motor because it is different in its construction and operation from the other AC motors considered here, and also because it is constructed as we have just discussed in the DC motor section, having field windings, brushes, commutator and an armature.

As can be seen in Figure 3.196, because of its series connection, current passing through the field windings also passes through the armature. The turning motion (torque) is produced as a result of the interaction between the magnetic field in the field windings and the magnetic field produced in the armature.

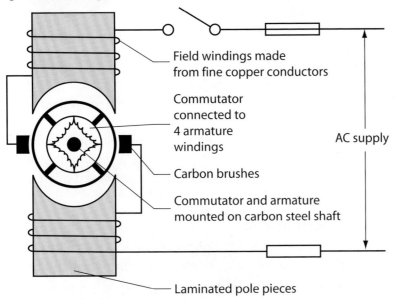

Field windings made from fine copper conductors

Commutator connected to 4 armature windings

AC supply

Carbon brushes

Commutator and armature mounted on carbon steel shaft

Laminated pole pieces

Figure 3.196: Series universal motor

For this motor to be able to run on an AC supply, modifications are made both to the field windings and armature formers. These are heavily laminated to reduce eddy currents and I^2R losses, which reduces the heat generated by the normal working of the motor, thus making the motor more efficient.

This type of motor is generally small (less than a kilowatt) and is used to drive small hand tools such as drills, vacuum cleaners and washing machines.

A disadvantage of this motor is that it relies on contact with the armature via a system of carbon brushes and a commutator. It is this point that is the machine's weakness, as much heat is generated through the arcing that appears across the gap between the brushes and the commutator. The brushes are spring-loaded to keep this gap to a minimum, but even so the heat and friction eventually cause the brushes to wear down and the gap to increase. These then need to be replaced, otherwise the heat generated as the gap gets larger will eventually cause the motor to fail.

The advantages of this machine are:

- more power for a given size than any other normal AC motor
- high starting torque
- relative cheapness to produce.

Three-phase AC induction motors

Figure 3.197: Three-phase induction motor showing component parts

Induction motors operate because a moving magnetic field induces a current to flow in the rotor. This current in the rotor then creates a second magnetic field, which combines with the field from the stator windings to exert a force on the rotor conductors, thus turning the rotor.

Production of the rotating field

Figure 3.198 shows the stator of a three-phase motor to which a three-phase supply is connected. The windings in the diagram are in star formation and two windings of each phase are wound in the same direction.

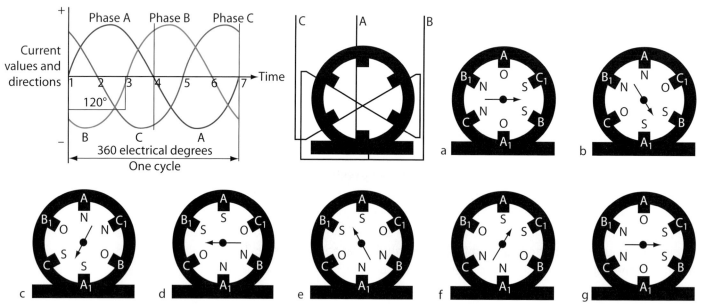

Figure 3.198: Stator of three-phase motor with three-phase supply connection

Each pair of windings will produce a magnetic field, the strength of which will depend upon the current in that particular phase at any instant of time. When the current is zero, the magnetic field will be zero. Maximum current will produce the maximum magnetic field.

As the currents in the three phases are 120° out of phase (see graph in Figure 3.198) the magnetic fields produced will also be 120° out of phase. The magnetic field set up by the three-phase currents will therefore give the appearance of rotating clockwise around the stator.

The resultant magnetic field produced by the three phases is at any instant of time in the direction shown by the arrow in the diagram, where diagrams (1) to (7) in Figure 3.198 show how the direction of the magnetic field changes at intervals of 60° through one complete cycle. The speed of rotation of the magnetic field depends upon the supply frequency and the number of 'pole pairs', and is referred to as the **synchronous** speed. We will discuss **synchronous** speed later in this chapter.

The direction in which the magnetic field rotates is dependent on the sequence in which the phases are connected to the windings. Reversing the connection of any two incoming phases can therefore reverse rotation of the magnetic field.

Stator construction

As shown in Figure 3.199, the stator (stationary component) comprises the field windings, which are many turns of very fine copper wire wound on to formers, which are then fixed to the inside of the stator steel frame (sometimes called the yoke).

The formers have two roles:

1. to contain the conductors of the winding
2. to concentrate the magnetic lines of flux to improve the flux linkage.

The formers are made of laminated silicon steel sections to reduce eddy currents, thereby reducing the I^2R losses and reducing heat. The number of poles fitted will determine the speed of the motor.

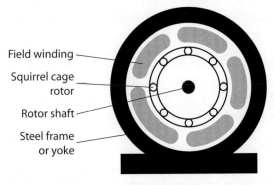

Field winding

Squirrel cage rotor

Rotor shaft

Steel frame or yoke

Figure 3.199: Stator construction

Figure 3.200: Stator field winding

Squirrel-cage rotor

In the squirrel cage (see Figure 3.201), the bars of the rotor are shorted out at each end by 'end rings' to form the shape of a cage. This shape creates numerous circuits within it for the induced e.m.f. and resultant current to flow and thus produce the required magnetic field.

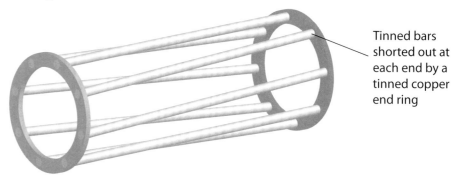

Tinned bars shorted out at each end by a tinned copper end ring

Figure 3.201: Squirrel-cage rotor

Figure 3.202 shows the cage fitted to the shaft of the motor. The rotor bars are encased within many hundreds of very thin laminated (insulated) segments of silicon steel and are skewed to increase the rotor resistance.

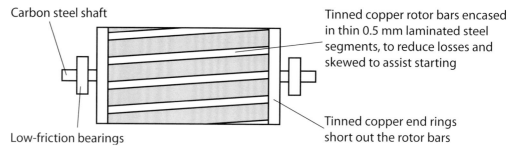

Carbon steel shaft

Tinned copper rotor bars encased in thin 0.5 mm laminated steel segments, to reduce losses and skewed to assist starting

Low-friction bearings

Tinned copper end rings short out the rotor bars

Figure 3.202: Cage fitted to shaft and motor

On the shaft will be two low-friction bearings which enable the rotor to spin freely. The bearings and the rotor will be held in place within the yoke of the stator by two end caps which are normally secured in place by long nuts and bolts that pass completely through the stator.

When a three-phase supply is connected to the field windings, the lines of magnetic flux produced in the stator, rotating at 50 revolutions per second, cut through the bars of the rotor, inducing an e.m.f. into the bars.

Faraday's Law states that 'when a conductor cuts, or is cut, by a magnetic field, then an e.m.f. is induced in that conductor the magnitude of which is proportional to the rate at which the conductor cuts or is cut by the magnetic flux'.

The e.m.f. produces circulatory currents within the rotor bars, which in turn result in the production of a magnetic field around the bars. This leads to the distortion of the magnetic field as shown in Figure 3.203. The interaction of these two magnetic fields results in a force being

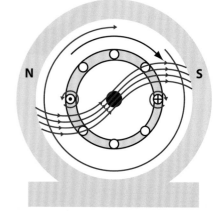

Figure 3.203: Rotating field

applied to the rotor bars, and the rotor begins to turn. This turning force is known as a torque, the direction of which is always as Fleming's left-hand rule indicates.

Wound rotor

In the wound rotor type of motor, the rotor conductors form a three-phase winding, which is starred internally. The other three ends of the windings are brought out to slip rings mounted on the shaft. Thus it is possible through brush connections to introduce resistance into the rotor circuit, albeit this is normally done on starting only to increase the starting torque. This type of motor is commonly referred to as a slip-ring motor.

Figure 3.204 shows a completed wound-rotor motor assembly. Although it looks like a squirrel-cage motor, the difference is that the rotor bars are exchanged for heavy conductors that run through the laminated steel rotor, the ends then being brought out through the shaft to the slip rings on the end.

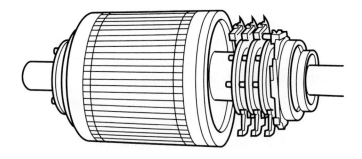

Figure 3.204: Wound-rotor motor assembly

The wound-rotor motor is particularly effective in applications where using a squirrel-cage motor may result in a starting current that is too high for the capacity of the power system. The wound-rotor motor is also appropriate for high-inertia loads having a long acceleration time. This is because you can control the speed, torque and resulting heating of the wound-rotor motor. This control can be automatic or manual. It's also effective with high-slip loads as well as adjustable-speed installations that do not require precise speed control or regulation. Typical applications include conveyor belts, hoists and elevators.

Single-phase induction motors

If we were to construct an induction motor as shown in Figure 3.205, we would find that, on connecting a supply to it, it would not run. However, if we were then to spin the shaft with our fingers, we would find that the motor would continue to run. Why is this?

When an AC supply is connected to the motor, the resulting current flow, and therefore the magnetic fields produced in the field windings, changes polarity, backwards and forwards, 100 times per second. Therefore no lines of flux cut through the rotor bars. If no lines of flux cut through the rotor bars then there is no e.m.f. being produced in them and there is therefore no magnetic field for the stator winding to interact with.

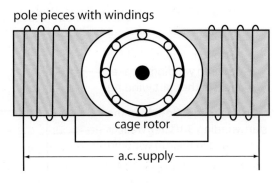

Figure 3.205: Single-phase induction motor

However, if we were to manually spin the rotor, we'd create the effect of the rotor bars cutting through the lines of force, hence the process begins; the motor would start and run up to speed and keep on running. However, if we were to stop the motor and then connect the supply again, the motor would still not run automatically. This time, if we manually spin the rotor in the opposite direction, the motor will again start and run up to speed, but in this new direction. So how can we get the rotor to turn on its own (i.e. self-starting)?

If we think back to the three-phase motor we discussed previously, we did not have this problem, because the connection of a three-phase supply to the stator automatically produced a rotating magnetic field. This is what is missing from the motor in Figure 3.205: we have no rotating field.

The split-phase motor (induction start/induction run)

We can overcome this problem if we add another set of poles, positioned 90° around the stator from our original wiring, as shown in Figure 3.206.

Now when the supply is connected, both sets of windings are energised, both windings having resistive and reactive components to them – resistance as every conductor has and also inductive reactance because the conductors form a coil. These are known as the 'start' and 'run' windings.

The start winding is wound with fewer turns of smaller wire than the main winding, so it has a higher resistance. This extra resistance creates a small phase shift that results in the current in the start winding lagging that in the run winding by approximately 30°, as shown in Figure 3.207.

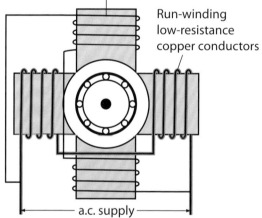

Figure 3.206: Split-phase induction motor

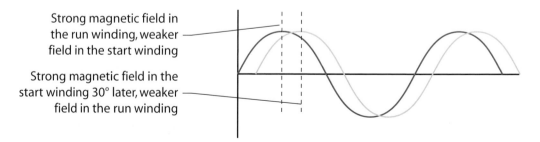

Figure 3.207: Run and start winding phases

Therefore the magnetic flux in each of the windings is growing and collapsing at different periods in time, so that for example as the run winding is having a strong north/south on the face of its pole pieces, the start winding will only have a weak magnetic field.

In the next instance, the run winding's magnetic field has started to fade, but the start winding's magnetic field is now strong, presenting to the rotor an apparent shift in the lines of magnetic flux.

In the next half of the supply cycle, the polarity is reversed and the process repeated, so there now appears to be a rotating magnetic field. The lines of force cutting through the rotor bars induce an e.m.f. into them, and the resulting current flow now produces a magnetic field around the rotor bars: the interaction between the magnetic fields of the rotor and stator takes place and the motor begins to turn.

It is because the start and run windings carry currents that are out of phase with each other that this type of motor is called the 'split-phase'.

Once the motor is rotating at about 75 per cent of its full load speed, the start winding is disconnected by the use of a device called a centrifugal switch, which is attached to the shaft; see Figure 3.208.

This switch works by centrifugal action, in that sets of contacts are held closed by a spring, and this completes the circuit to the start winding. When the motor starts to turn, a little weight gets progressively thrown away from the shaft, forcing the contacts to open and thus disconnecting the start winding. It's a bit like the fairground ride known as 'the Rotor', in which you are eventually held against the sides of the ride by the increasing speed of the spinning wheel. Once the machine has disconnected the start winding, the machine continues to operate from the run winding.

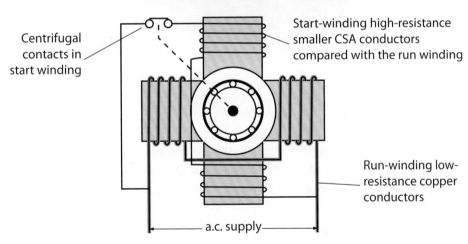

Figure 3.208: Split-phase induction motor with centrifugal switch

The split-phase motor's simple design makes it typically less expensive than other single-phase motors. However, it also limits performance. Starting torque is low at about 150 to 175 per cent of the rated load. Also, the motor develops high starting currents of about six to nine times the full load current. A lengthy starting time can cause the start winding to overheat and fail, and therefore this type of motor shouldn't be used when a high starting torque is needed. Consequently it is used on light-load applications such as small hand tools, small grinders and fans, where there are frequent stop/starts and the full load is applied after the motor has reached its operating speed.

Reversal of direction

If you think back to the start of this section, we talked about starting the motor by spinning the shaft. We also said that we were able to spin it in either direction and the motor would run in that direction. It therefore seems logical that in order to change the direction of the motor, all we have to concern ourselves with is the start winding. We therefore need only to reverse the connections to the start winding to change its polarity, although you may choose to reverse the polarity of the run winding instead. The important thing to remember is that if you change the polarity through both the run and start windings, the motor will continue to revolve in the same direction.

The capacitor-start motor (capacitor start/induction run)

Normally perceived as being a wide-ranging industrial motor, the capacitor-start motor is very similar to the split-phase motor discussed previously. Indeed, it probably helps to think of this motor as being a split-phase motor but with an enhanced start winding that includes a capacitor in the circuit to help out with the start process. If we look at Figure 3.209 we can see the capacitor mounted on top of the motor case.

Figure 3.209: Capacitor-start motor

In this motor the start winding has a capacitor connected in series with it, and since this gives a phase difference of nearly 90° between the two currents in the windings, the starting performance is improved. We can see this represented in the sine waves shown in Figure 3.210.

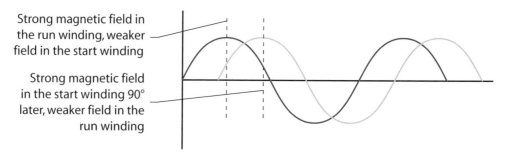

Strong magnetic field in the run winding, weaker field in the start winding

Strong magnetic field in the start winding 90° later, weaker field in the run winding

Figure 3.210: Magnetic field in capacitor-start motor

In this motor the current through the run winding lags the supply voltage due to the high inductive reactance of this winding, and the current through the start winding leads the supply voltage due to the capacitive reactance of the capacitor. The phase displacement in the currents of the two windings is now approximately 90°. Figure 3.211 shows the winding connections for a capacitor-start motor.

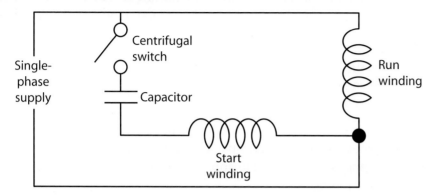

Figure 3.211: Winding connections for capacitor-start split-phase motor

The magnetic flux set up by the two windings is much greater at starting than in the standard split-phase motor, and this produces a greater starting torque. The typical starting torque for this type of motor is about 300% of full-load torque, and a typical starting current is about five to nine times the full-load current.

The capacitor-start motor is more expensive than a comparable split-phase design because of the additional cost of the capacitor. But the application range is much wider because of higher starting torque and lower starting current. Therefore, because of its improved starting ability, this type of motor is recommended for loads that are hard to start, so we see this type of motor used to drive equipment such as lathes, compressors and small conveyor systems.

As with the standard split-phase motor, the start windings and the capacitor are disconnected from the circuit by an automatic centrifugal switch when the motor reaches about 75% of its rated full-load speed.

Reversal of direction

Reversing the connections to the start winding will only change its polarity, although we may choose to reverse the polarity of the run winding instead.

Permanent split capacitor (PSC) motors

Permanent split capacitor (PSC) motors look exactly the same as capacitor-start motors. However, a PSC motor doesn't have either a starting switch or a capacitor that is strictly used for starting. Instead, it has a run-type capacitor permanently connected in series with the start winding, and the second winding is permanently connected to the power source. This makes the start winding an auxiliary winding once the motor reaches running speed. However, because the run capacitor must be designed for continuous use, it cannot provide the starting boost of a starting capacitor.

Typical starting torques for this type of motor are low, from 30% to 150% of rated load, so these motors are not used in difficult starting applications. However, unlike the split-phase motor, PSC motors have low starting currents, usually less than 200% of rated load current, making them excellent for applications with high cycle rates.

PSC motors have several advantages. They need no starting mechanism and so can be reversed easily, and designs can easily be altered for use with speed controllers. They can also be designed for optimum efficiency and high power factor at rated load.

Permanent split capacitor motors have a wide variety of applications depending on the design. These include fans, blowers with low starting torque and intermittent cycling uses such as adjusting mechanisms, gate operators and garage-door openers, many of which also need instant reversing.

Capacitor start-capacitor run motors

In appearance we can distinguish this motor because of the two capacitors that are mounted on the motor case.

This type of motor is widely held to be the most efficient single-phase induction motor, as it combines the best of the capacitor-start and the permanent split capacitor designs and is able to handle applications too demanding for any other kind of single-phase motor.

As shown in Figure 3.212, it has a start capacitor in series with the auxiliary winding like the capacitor-start motor, and this allows for high starting torque. However, like the PSC motor, it also has a run capacitor that remains in series with the auxiliary winding after the start capacitor is switched out of the circuit.

Figure 3.212: Capacitor-start, capacitor -run

Another advantage of this type of motor is that it can be designed for lower full-load currents and higher efficiency, which means that it operates at a lower temperature than other single-phase motor types of comparable horsepower. Typical uses include woodworking machinery, air compressors, high pressure water pumps, vacuum pumps and other high-torque applications.

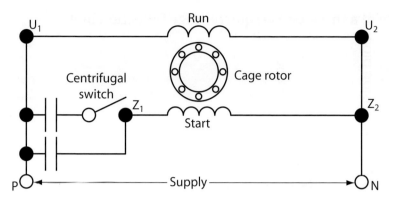

Figure 3.213: Capacitor start-capacitor run 'split-phase' motor

Shaded-pole motors

One final type of single-phase induction motor that is worthy of mention is the shaded-pole type. We cover this last as, unlike all of the previous single-phase motors we have discussed, shaded-pole motors have only one main winding and no start winding.

Starting is by means of a continuous copper loop wound around a small section of each motor pole. This 'shades' that portion of the pole, causing the magnetic field in the ringed area to lag the field in the non-ringed section. The reaction of the two fields then starts the shaft rotating.

Because the shaded pole motor lacks a start winding, starting switch or capacitor, it is electrically simple and inexpensive. In addition, speed can be controlled merely by varying voltage or through a multi-tap winding.

The shaded pole motor has many positive features, but it also has several disadvantages. As the phase displacement is very small, it has a low starting torque, typically in the region of 25 to 75 per cent of full-load torque. Also, it is very inefficient, usually below 20 per cent.

Low initial costs make shaded pole motors suitable for light-duty applications such as multi-speed fans for household use and record turntables.

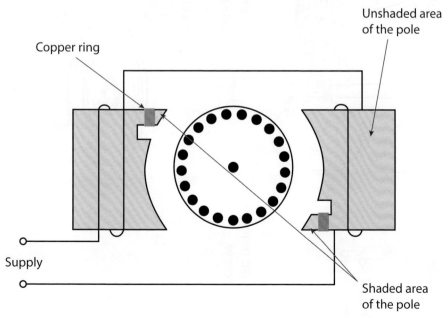

Figure 3.214: Shaded pole motor

Construction of a three-phase squirrel-cage induction motor

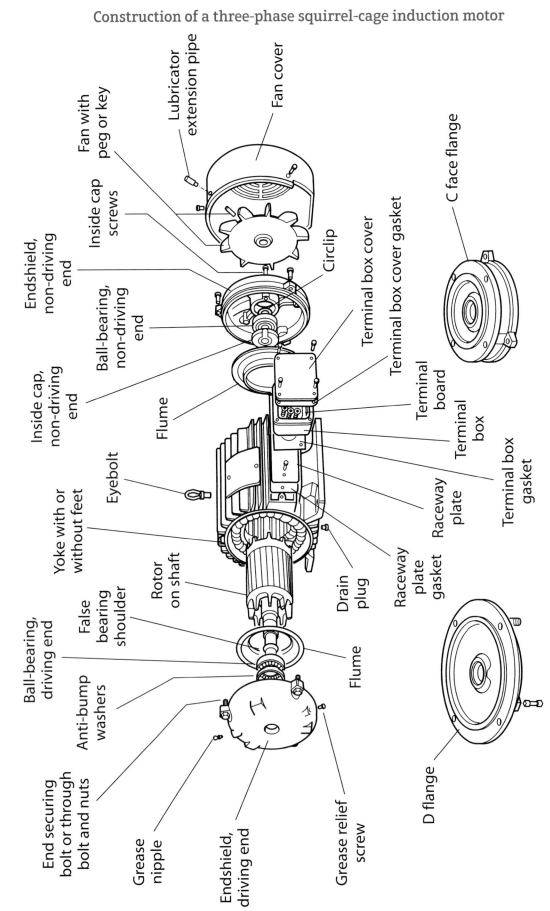

Figure 3.215: Construction of a three-phase squirrel-cage induction motor

Construction of a single-phase, capacitor-start, induction motor

This motor consists of a laminated stator wound with single-phase windings arranged for split-phase starting, and a cage rotor. The cage rotor is a laminated framework with lightly insulated longitudinal slots into which copper or aluminium bars are fitted.

The bars are then connected together at their ends by metal end-rings. No electrical connections are made to the rotor.

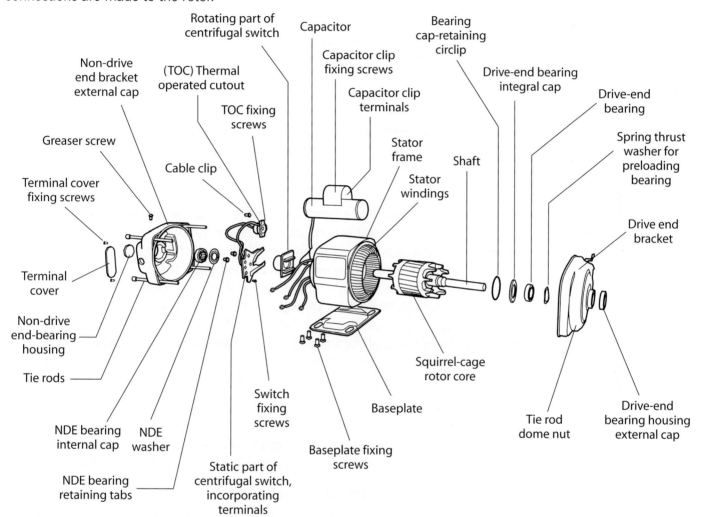

Figure 3.216: Construction of a single-phase induction motor

Motor speed and slip calculation

There are essentially two ways to express the speed of a motor.

- **Synchronous speed.** For an AC motor this is the speed of rotation of the stator's magnetic field. Consequently, this is really only a theoretical speed, as the rotor will always turn at a slightly slower rate.

- **Actual speed**. This is the speed at which the shaft rotates. The nameplate on most AC motors will give the actual motor speed rather than the synchronous speed.

The difference between the speed of the rotor and the synchronous speed of the rotating magnetic field is known as the **slip**, which can be expressed either as a unit or in percentage terms. Because of this, we often refer to the induction motor as being an asynchronous motor.

Remember, the speed of the rotating magnetic field is known as the synchronous speed, and this will be determined by the frequency of the supply and the number of pairs of poles within the machine. The speed at which the rotor turns will be between 2 and 5 per cent slower, with an average of 4 per cent being common.

The reduced speed of the rotor is due to it having to overcome friction, as during the turning movement there is friction from the bearings in addition to any friction deriving from the load that the motor is connected to. Another factor that comes into play in determining the speed of a motor is **windage**. This means that within the enclosure there is a certain amount of air, and as the rotor rotates it has to move the air, which in turn contributes to the slowing down of the rotor. Of course there are no moving parts involved with the rotating magnetic field, so the rotor will never catch up. However, were some miracle to happen and the rotor reached the synchronous speed, we would have a different problem.

We already know that when a conductor passes at right angles through a magnetic field current is induced in the conductor. The direction of the induced current is dependent on the direction of movement of the conductor, and the strength of the current is determined by the speed at which the conductor moves. If the rotating magnetic field and the rotor are now revolving at the same speed, there will be no lines of magnetic flux cutting through the rotor bars, no induced e.m.f. and consequently no resultant magnetic field around the rotor bars to interact with the rotating magnetic field of the stator. The motor will immediately slow down and, having slowed down, will then start to speed up as the lines of magnetic flux start to cut through the rotor bars again – and so the process would continue.

Standard AC induction motors therefore depend on the rotor trying, but never quite managing, to catch up with the stator's magnetic field. The rotor speed is just slow enough to cause the proper amount of rotor current to flow, so that the resulting torque is sufficient to overcome windage and friction losses and drive the load.

Determining synchronous speed and slip

All AC motors are designed with various numbers of magnetic poles. Standard motors have two, four, six or eight poles, and these poles play an important role in determining the synchronous speed of an AC motor.

As we said before, the synchronous speed can be determined by the frequency of the supply and the number of pairs of poles within the machine. We can express this relationship with the following formula:

Synchronous speed (n_s) in revolutions per second = $\dfrac{\text{Frequency (f) in Hz}}{\text{The number of pole pairs (p)}}$

Key term

Windage – the air resistance of a moving object or the force of the wind on a stationary object

Example 1

Calculate the synchronous speed of a four-pole machine connected to a 50 Hz supply.

$$n_s = \frac{f}{p}$$

As we know the motor has four poles, this means it has two pole pairs. We can therefore complete the calculation as:

$$n_s = \frac{50}{2} \quad \text{therefore, } n_s = 25 \text{ revolutions per second (rps)}$$

To convert revolutions per second into the more commonly used revolutions per minute (rpm), simply multiply n_s by 60. This new value is referred to as N_s, which in this example will become 25×60, giving 1500 rpm.

We also said that we refer to the difference between the speed of the rotor and the synchronous speed of the rotating magnetic field as the slip, which can be expressed either as a unit (S) or in percentage terms (S per cent). We express this relationship with the following formula:

$$\text{per cent slip} = \frac{\text{Synchronous speed } (n_s) - \text{Rotor speed } (n_r)}{\text{Synchronous speed } (n_s)} \times 100$$

Example 2

In this example numbers have been rounded up for ease.

A six-pole cage-induction motor runs at 4% slip.

Calculate the motor speed if the supply frequency is 50 Hz.

$$S \text{ (per cent)} = \frac{(n_s) - (n_r)}{(n_s)} \times 100$$

We therefore need first to establish the synchronous speed; as the motor has six poles it will have three pole pairs. Consequently:

$$\text{Synchronous speed } n_s = \frac{f}{p} \text{ giving us } \frac{50}{3} \text{ and therefore } n_s = 16.7 \text{ revs/sec}$$

We can now put this value into our formula and then, by transposition, rearrange the formula to make n_r the subject. Consequently:

$$S \text{ (per cent)} = \frac{(n_s) - (n_r)}{(n_s)} \times 100 \text{ giving us } 4 = \frac{(16.7 - n_r)}{16.7} \times 100$$

Therefore by transposition:

$$4 = \frac{(16.7 - n_r)}{16.7} \times 100 \text{ gives us } (16.7 - n_s) = \frac{4 \times 16.7}{100}$$

When calculated:

$$(16.7 - n_r) = \frac{4 \times 16.7}{100} \text{ becomes } (16.7 - n_r) = 0.668$$

Therefore by further transposition:

$$(16.7 - n_r) = 0.668 \text{ becomes } 16.7 - 0.668 = n_r$$

Therefore **n_r = 16.032 rps or N_r = 962 rpm**

Working life

You are called out to check a split-phase motor reported as not turning and making a humming sound.

1. What steps would you take to diagnose the problem?
2. What are the likely causes of this problem?

Synchronous motors

A synchronous motor, as the name suggests, runs at synchronous speed. Because of the problems discussed earlier, this type of motor is not self-starting and instead must be brought up to almost synchronous speed by some other means.

Three-phase AC synchronous motors

To understand how the synchronous motor works, assume that we have supplied three-phase AC power to the stator, which in turn causes a rotating magnetic field to be set up around the rotor. The rotor is then supplied via a field winding with DC and consequently acts a bit like a bar magnet, having north and south poles. The rotating magnetic field now attracts the rotor field that was activated by the DC. This results in a strong turning force on the rotor shaft, and the rotor is therefore able to turn a load as it rotates in step with the rotating magnetic field.

It works this way once it's started. However, one of the disadvantages of a synchronous motor is that it cannot be started from a standstill by just applying a three-phase AC supply to the stator. When AC is applied to the stator, a high-speed rotating magnetic field appears immediately. This rotating field rushes past the rotor poles so quickly that the rotor does not have a chance to get started. In effect, the rotor is repelled first in one direction and then the other.

An induction winding (squirrel-cage type) is therefore added to the rotor of a synchronous motor to cause it to start, effectively meaning that the motor is started as an induction motor. Once the motor reaches synchronous speed, no current is induced in the squirrel-cage winding, so it has little effect on the synchronous operation of the motor.

Synchronous motors are commonly driven by transistorised variable-frequency drives.

Single-phase AC synchronous motors

Small single-phase AC motors can be designed with magnetised rotors. The rotors in these motors do not require any induced current so they do not slip backwards against the mains frequency. Instead, they rotate synchronously with the mains frequency. Because of their highly accurate speed, such motors are usually used to power mechanical clocks, audio turntables and tape drives; formerly they were also widely used in accurate timing instruments such as strip-chart recorders or telescope drive mechanisms. The shaded-pole synchronous motor is one version.

As with the three-phase version, inertia makes it difficult to accelerate the rotor instantly from stopped to synchronous speed, and the motors normally require some sort of special feature to get started. Various designs use a small induction motor (which may share the same field coils and rotor as the synchronous motor) or a very light rotor with a one-way mechanism (to ensure that the rotor starts in the 'forward' direction).

Motor windings

A motor can be manufactured with the windings internally connected. If this is the case and there are three terminal connections in the terminal block labelled U, V and W, you would expect the motor windings to be connected in a delta configuration. This is shown in Figure 3.217.

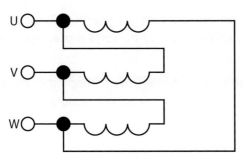

Figure 3.217: Motor windings with delta connection

However, there may be four connections in the terminal box labelled U, V, W and N. If this is the case, the windings would be arranged to give a star configuration, as shown in Figure 3.218.

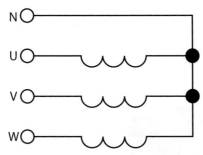

Figure 3.218: Motor windings with four connections

Alternatively the terminal block may contain six connections: U1, U2, V1, V2, W1 and W2. This is used where both star and delta configurations are required. The terminal connections can then be reconfigured for either star or delta, starting within the terminal block. Figure 3.219 illustrates the connections that would come out to the terminal block.

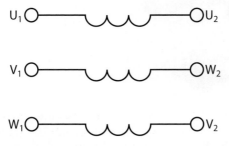

Figure 3.219: Motor windings with six connections

Operating principles, limitations and applications of motor control

A practical motor starter has to do more than just switch on the supply. It also has to have provision for automatically disconnecting the motor in the event of overloads or other faults. The overload protective device monitors the current consumption of the motor and is set to a predetermined value that the motor can safely handle. When a condition occurs that exceeds the set value, the overload device opens the motor starter control circuit and the motor is turned off. The overload protection can come in a variety of types, including solid-state electronic devices.

The starter should also prevent automatic restarting should the motor stop because of supply failure. This is called **no-volts protection** and will be discussed later in this section.

The starter must also provide for the efficient stopping of the motor by the user. Provision for this is made by the connection of remote stop buttons and safety interlock switches where required.

The Direct-On-Line (DOL) starter

This is the simplest and cheapest method of starting squirrel-cage (induction) motors.

The expression 'Direct-On-Line' starting means that the full supply voltage is directly connected to the stator of the motor by means of a contactor-starter, as shown in Figure 3.220.

Figure 3.220: DOL starter

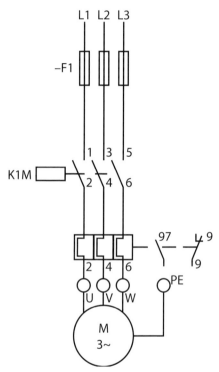

Figure 3.221: DOL starter

Since the motor is at a standstill when the supply is first switched on, the initial starting current is heavy. This 'inrush' of current can be as high as 6 to 10 times the full load current, i.e. a motor rated at 10 A could have a starting current inrush as high as 60 A, and the initial starting torque can be about 150 per cent of the full-load torque. Thus you may observe motors 'jumping' on starting if their mountings are not secure. As a result, Direct-On-Line starting is usually restricted to comparatively small motors with outputs of up to about 5 kW.

DOL starters should also incorporate a means of overload protection, which can be operated by either magnetic or thermal overload trips. These activate when there is a sustained increase in current flow.

To reverse the motor you need to interchange any two of the incoming three-phase supply leads. If a further two leads are interchanged then the motor will rotate in the original direction.

Operating principle of a DOL starter

A three-pole switch controls the three-phase supply to the starter. This switch normally includes fuses, which provide a means of electrical isolation and also short-circuit protection. We shall look at the operation of the DOL starter in stages.

Let's start by looking at the one-way switch again. In this circuit (Figure 3.222), the switch is operated by your finger and the contacts are then held in place mechanically.

We could decide that we don't want to operate the switch this way and instead use a relay. In this system (Figure 3.223), when the coil is energised it creates a magnetic field. Everything in the magnetic field will be pulled in the direction of the arrow and the metal strip will be pulled onto the contacts. As long as the coil remains energised and is a magnet, the light will stay on.

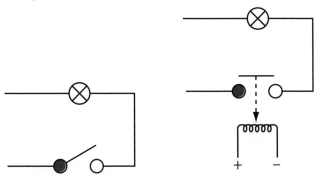

Figure 3.222: One-way switch   Figure 3.223: Switch relay

Looking at Figures 3.222 and 3.223, we can see that the first option works well enough for its intended purpose. However, it couldn't be used in a three-phase system as we would need one for each phase and would have to trust to luck each time we tried to hit all three switches at the same time. However, the second option does provide us with an effective method of controlling more than one thing from one switch, as long as they are all in the same magnetic field.

Let's apply this knowledge to a DOL starter. We know that we can't have three one-way switches in the starter. But it helps to try to think of the contacts as such: where the switches aren't operated by your fingers but instead are pulled in the direction of the arrow by the magnetic effect of the coil (see Figure 3.224), and where items affected by the same magnetic effect are normally shown linked by a dotted line. For ease of explanation we'll use a 230 V coil.

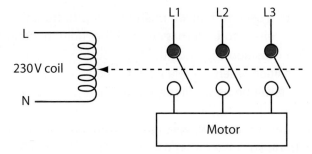

Figure 3.224: Three-switch relay

From this we can see that as soon as we put a supply onto the coil it energises, becomes a magnet and pulls the contacts in. Obviously, this would be no good for our starter, as every time the power is put on, the starter will become active and start operating whatever is connected to it. In the case of machinery this could be very dangerous. The starter design therefore goes one step further to include what we call no-volt protection. The simple addition of a 'normally open' Start button gives this facility, as shown in Figure 3.225.

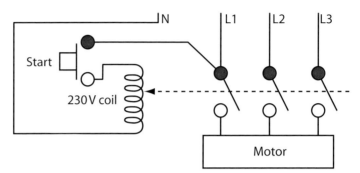

Figure 3.225: DOL with inclusion of 'normally open' start button

So far so good. We now have to make a conscious decision to start the motor.

Our next problem though, is that every time we take our finger off the Start button, the button springs back out, the supply to the coil is lost and the motor stops. This is the 'no volt' protection element in operation.

What we need for normal operation is a device called the 'hold in' or 'retaining' contact, as shown in Figure 3.226. This is a 'normally closed' contact (position 1) which is also placed in the magnetic field of the coil. Consequently, when the coil is energised, it is also pulled in the direction shown, and in this case, across and onto the terminals of the Start button (position 2).

We can now take our finger off the Start button, as the supply will continue to feed the coil by running through the 'hold in' contact that is linking out the Start button terminals (position 2).

This now means that we can only break the coil supply and stop the motor by fitting a Stop button. In the case of starters fitted with a 230 V coil, this will be a normally closed button placed in the neutral wire.

Now, for the fraction of a second that we push the Stop button, the supply to the coil is broken, the coil ceases to be a magnet and the 'hold in' contact returns to its original position (position 1). Since the Start button had already returned to its original open position when we released it, when we take our finger off the Stop button everything will be as we first started. Therefore any loss of supply will immediately break the supply to the coil and stop the motor: if a supply failure was restored, the equipment could not restart itself – someone would have to take the conscious decision to do so.

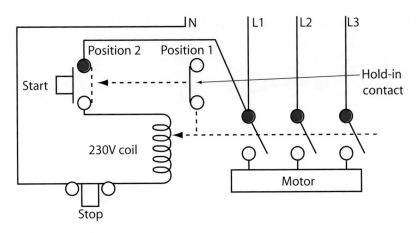

Figure 3.226: DOL 'hold in' contact operation

This system is basically the same as that of a contactor. In fact, many people refer to this item as the contactor starter. Such starters are also available with a 400 V coil, which is therefore connected across two of the phases.

Remote stop/start control

In the DOL starter just described, we have the means of stopping and starting the motor from the buttons provided on the starter enclosure. However, there are situations where the control of the motor needs to take place from some remote location. This could be, for example, in a college workshop where, in the case of an emergency, emergency stop buttons located throughout the workshop can be activated to break the supply to a motor. Equally, because of the immediate environment around the motor, it may be necessary to operate it from a different location.

Commonly known as a remote stop/start station, the enclosure usually houses a start and a stop button connected in series. However, depending on the circumstances it is also possible to have an additional button included to give 'inch' control of a motor.

If we use the example of our DOL starter as described in the previous diagrams, but now include the remote stop/start station, the circuit would look as in Figure 3.227, where for ease the additional circuitry has been shown in red.

As can be seen, the remote start button is effectively in parallel with the start button on the main enclosure with the supply to both of these buttons being routed via the stop button of the remote station.

If the intention is to provide only emergency stops, omit the remote station shown so that these are all connected in series with the stop button on the main enclosure.

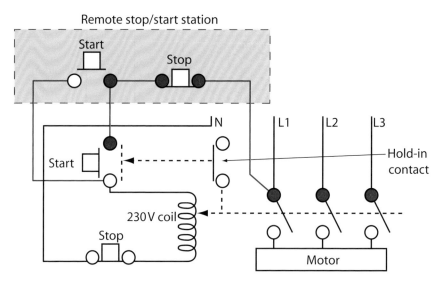

Figure 3.227: Remote stop/start control

Hand-operated star–delta starter

This is a two-position method of starting a three-phase squirrel-cage motor, in which the windings are connected firstly in star for acceleration of the rotor from standstill, and then secondly in delta for normal running.

The connections of the motor must be arranged for star–delta, starting with both ends of each phase winding – six in all – brought out to the motor terminal block. The starter itself, in its simplest form, is in effect a changeover switch. Figure 3.228 gives the elementary connections for both star and delta.

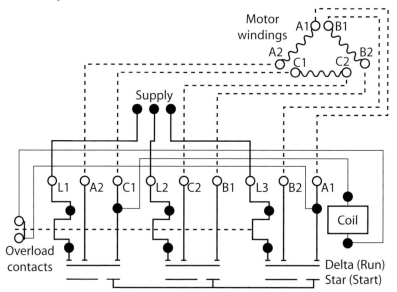

Figure 3.228: Hand-operated star–delta connections

When the motor windings are connected in star, the voltage applied to each phase winding is reduced to 58% of the line voltage, thus the current in the winding is correspondingly reduced to 58% of the normal starting value.

Applying these reduced values to the typical three-phase squirrel-cage induction motor, we would have: initial starting current from two to three-and-a-half times full-load current and initial starting torque of about 50% of the full-load value.

The changeover from star to delta should be made when the motor has reached a steady speed on star connection, at which point the windings will now receive full line voltage and draw full-rated current.

If the operator does not move the handle quickly from the start to run position, the motor may be disconnected from the supply long enough for thc motor speed to fall considerably. When the handle is eventually put into the run position, the motor will therefore take a large current before accelerating up to speed again. This surge current could be large enough to cause a noticeable voltage dip. To prevent this, a mechanical interlock is fitted to the operating handle. However, in reality the handle must be moved quickly from start to run position, otherwise the interlock jams the handle in the start position.

The advantage of this type of starter is that it is relatively cheap. It is best suited for motors against no load or light loads, and it also incorporates no-volts protection and overload protection.

Automatic star-delta starter

Bearing in mind the user actions required of the previous hand-operated starter, the fully automatic star-delta contactor starter (as shown in Figures 3.229 and 3.230) is the most satisfactory method of starting a three-phase cage-induction motor. The starter consists of three triple-pole contactors, one employing thermal overload protection, the second having a built-in time-delay device, and the third providing the star points.

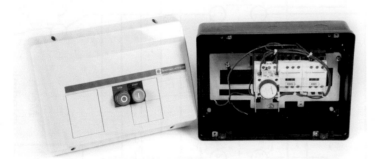

Figure 3.229: Star–delta starter

The changeover from star to delta is carried out automatically by the timing device, which can be adjusted to achieve the best results for a particular situation.

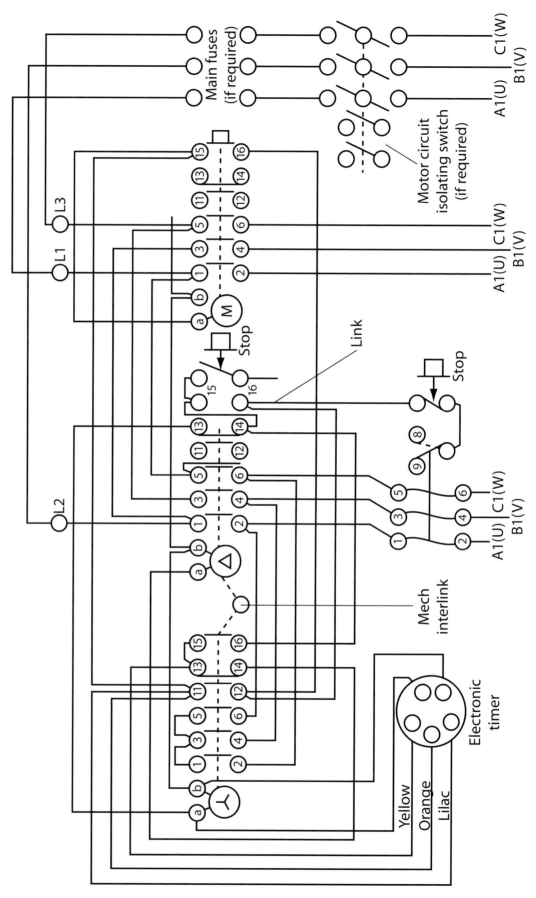

Figure 3.230: Automatic star–delta contactor starter

Soft starters

A soft starter is a type of reduced-voltage starter that reduces the starting torque for AC induction motors. The soft starter is in series with the supply to the motor, and uses solid-state devices to control the current flow and therefore the voltage applied to the motor. In theory, soft starters can be connected in series with the line voltage applied to the motor, or can be connected inside the delta loop of a delta-connected motor, controlling the voltage applied to each winding. Soft starters can also have a soft-stop function, which is the exact opposite to soft start, and sees the voltage gradually reduced and thus a reduction in the torque capacity of the motor.

The auto-transformer starter

This method of starting is used when star–delta starting is unsuitable, either because the starting torque would not be sufficiently high using that type of starter, or because only three terminals have been provided at the motor terminal box – a practice commonly found within the UK water industry.

This again is a two-stage method of starting three-phase squirrel-cage induction motors, in which a reduced voltage is applied to the stator windings to give a reduced current at start. The reduced voltage is obtained by means of a three-phase auto transformer, the tapped windings of which are designed to give 40, 60 and 75 per cent of the line voltage respectively.

Although there are a number of tappings, only one tapping is used for the initial starting, as the reduced voltage will also result in reduced torque. Once this has been selected for the particular situation in which the motor is operating, it is left at that position and the motor is started in stages – much like the star-delta starter in that once the motor has reached sufficient speed the changeover switch moves onto the run connections, thus connecting the motor directly to the three-phase supply. Figure 3.231 illustrates the connections for an auto-transformer starter.

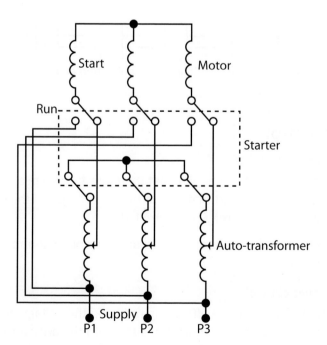

Figure 3.231: Connections for an auto-transformer starter

The rotor-resistance starter

This type of starter is used with a slip-ring wound-rotor motor. These motors and starters are primarily used where the motor will start against full load, as an external resistance is connected to the rotor windings through slip rings and brushes, which serves to increase the starting torque.

When the motor is first switched on, the external rotor resistance is at a maximum. As the motor speed increases, the resistance is reduced until at full speed, when the external resistance is completely eliminated and the machine runs as a squirrel-cage induction motor.

The starter is provided with no-volts and overload protection and an interlock to prevent the machine being switched on with no rotor resistance connected. (For clarity these are not shown in Figure 3.232, since the purpose of the diagram is to show the principle of operation.)

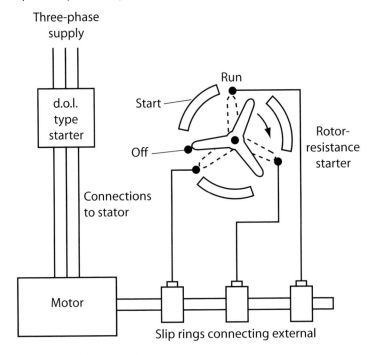

Figure 3.232: Rotor-resistance starter

Motor speed control

Speed control of DC machines

We said at the beginning of this chapter that there are three types of DC motor: series, shunt and compound, and that one of the advantages of the DC machine is the ease with which the speed may be controlled.

Some of the more common methods used to achieve speed control on a DC machine are described below.

Armature resistance control

With this system of control we are effectively reducing the voltage across the armature terminals by inserting a variable resistor into the armature circuit of the motor. In effect we are creating the illusion of applying a lower-than-rated voltage across the armature terminals.

The disadvantages of this method of control are that we see much of the input energy dissipated in the variable resistor, a loss of efficiency in the motor and poor speed regulation in the shunt and compound motors.

Although not fully discussed in this book, the principle of applying a lower-than-rated voltage across the armature terminals forms the basis of the Ward-Leonard system of speed control, which in essence provides a variable voltage to the armature terminals by controlling the field winding of a separate generator. Although expensive, this method gives excellent speed control and therefore finds use in situations such as passenger lifts.

Field control

This method works on the principle of controlling the magnetic flux in the field winding. This can be controlled by the field current and as a result controls the motor speed. As the field current is small, the power dissipated by the variable resistor is reasonably small. We can control the field current in the various types of motor as follows:

- **Series motor** – Place a variable resistor in parallel with the series field winding.

- **Shunt motor** – Place a variable resistor in series with the field shunt winding.

This method of speed control is not felt to be suitable for compound machines, as any reduction in the flux of the shunt is offset by an increase in flux from the series field because of an increase in armature current.

Pulse width modulation (PWM)

We know all about the problem with the variable resistor: although it works well, it generates heat and hence wastes power. PWM DC motor control uses electronics to eliminate this problem. It controls the motor speed by driving the motor with short pulses. These vary in duration to change the speed of the motor. The longer the pulses, the faster the motor turns, and vice versa. The main disadvantages of PWM circuits are their added complexity and the possibility of generating radio frequency interference (RFI), although this can be minimised by the use of short leads or additional filtering on the power supply leads.

Speed control of AC induction motors

We have already established that synchronous speed is directly proportional to the frequency of the supply and inversely proportional to the number of pole pairs. Therefore the speed of an induction motor can be changed by varying the frequency and/or the number of poles. We can also control the speed by changing the applied voltage and the armature resistance.

For adjustable speed applications, variable speed drives (VSD) use these principles by controlling the voltage and frequency delivered to the motor. This gives control over motor torque and reduces the current level during starting. Such drives can control the speed of the motor at any time during operation.

The phrase 'AC drive' has different meanings to different people. To some it means a collection of mechanical and electromechanical components (the variable frequency inverter and motor combination), which, when connected together, will move a load. More commonly – and also for our purposes – an AC drive should be considered as being a variable-frequency inverter unit (the drive) with the motor as a separate component. Manufacturers of variable-frequency inverters will normally refer to these units as being a variable-frequency drive (VFD).

A variable-frequency drive is a piece of equipment that has an input section – the converter – which contains diodes (see page 297–302 for more information on diodes) arranged in a bridge configuration. This converts the AC supply to DC. The next section of the VFD, known as the constant-voltage DC bus, takes the DC voltage and filters and smoothes out the wave form. The smoother the DC wave form is, the cleaner the output wave form from the drive.

The DC bus then feeds the final section of the drive, the inverter. This section of the drive will invert the DC back to AC using Insulated Gate Bipolar Transistors (IGBT), which create a variable AC voltage and frequency output.

Working life

You are asked to investigate a problem in the plant room of a hospital. The estates, maintenance manager has reported a noisy motor on the air-conditioning system. When you look at the motor, you find that as well as it being noisy there is a vibration. Do you think this is a real problem? If so, what actions would you recommend?

Summary

1. Name three advantages of a series-wound motor.
2. What four main parts make up the stator construction?
3. Why are the squirrel cage rotor bars encased in 0.5 mm thin laminated steel segments?

10. Understand the operating principles of electrical components

There are many electrical components that you will need to become familiar with when working on electrical installations. Many are covered in the content of Book A and Book B of this series. Table 3.17 indicates where you can find the related information.

Topic	Book	Chapter	Page
Contactors	B	Fault Diagnosis and rectification	
Relays	A	Scientific principles and technologies	258–259
Solenoids	A	Scientific principles and technologies	263
Circuit protective devices	B	Design and Installation Practices and Procedures	
Motors	A	Scientific principles and technologies	379–412
Transformers	A	Scientific principles and technologies	341–348

Table 3.17 Mapping grid for information about electrical components

11. The principles and applications of electrical lighting systems

Illumination by means of electricity has been available for over 100 years. In that time it has changed in many ways, though many of the same ideas are still in use. The first type of electric lamp was the 'arc lamp', which used electrodes to draw an electrode through the air, this is now known as discharge lighting. This was quite an unsophisticated use of electricity, and many accidents and fires resulted from it. Regulations had to be developed to control discharge lighting installations, and the use of electrical lighting systems has changed dramatically over the centuries.

This section will look at the basic principles of illumination and the applications of the different methods used to calculate lighting requirements, after introducing the key operating principles, types and applications of common luminaires you will use.

Operating principles, types, limitations and applications of luminaires

Before we look at the types of lamp available, we should look at lamp caps. The cap is that part of the lamp that allows an electrical connection to be made with the supply. There are many different types, some of which are shown below.

Light emitting diodes are also types of luminaires. More information can be found about these later in this unit on pages 426–428.

The bayonet cap

The bayonet cap (BC) is probably the lamp you have come across most often. It is 22 mm diameter and has two locating lugs, the electrical contact made over two pins on the base of the cap. Two popular variations of this are the SBC cap which is 15 mm in diameter and the SCC cap. The SCC cap only has one contact on the base, the other contact being the cap itself.

Figure 3.233: Bayonet cap

The Edison Screw cap

Most Edison Screw (ES) lamps are represented as the letter 'E' followed by a number. This number denotes the diameter of the cap. The most popular types for domestic use in the UK are E14 (14 mm and also known as SES) and E27. There is also a version used in street lighting and industrial situations with mercury fluorescent lamps, the E40 or GES (Giant Edison Screw).

Figure 3.234: Edison Screw cap

Halogen lamp caps

There are three common types of halogen lamp camp:

- **Halogen capsule lamps** are generally designated by the distance in millimetres between the pins of the lamp. The most common of these, G4 (2 pins – 4 mm apart) is used in low voltage applications such as desk lamps.

Figure 3.235: Halogen capsule lamp

- **Linear tungsten halogen lamps** are mains voltage and normally seen in security lights, floodlights and some up-lighters. They have what is known as an R7 cap at each end of a thin gas-filled quartz tube.

Figure 3.236: Linear tungsten halogen capsule lamp

- **Halogen spotlights** have become ever more popular and are seen in many domestic applications such as bathrooms, dining rooms and kitchens or commercially in display applications. The most common is the GU10 version shown in Figure 3.237.

Figure 3.237: Halogen spotlights

Low pressure mercury (fluorescent) caps

Using their common name, fluorescent tubes have a bi-pin cap at both ends of the gas-filled tube. Diameters of the tube range from T5 (16 mm) through T8 (25 mm) to T12 (38 mm). T8 and T12 tubes normally have pins that are 13 mm apart, whereas the T5 tube has pins that are 5 mm apart.

Figure 3.238: Low pressure mercury (fluorescent) caps

Incandescent lamps – GLS and tungsten halogen

In this method of creating light a fine filament of wire is connected across an electrical supply, which makes the filament wire heat up until it is white-hot and gives out light. The filament wire reaches a temperature of 2500–2900°C. These lamps are very inefficient and only a small proportion of the available electricity is converted into light; most of the electricity is converted into heat as infrared energy. The light output of this type of lamp is mainly found at the red end of the visual spectrum, which gives an overall warm appearance.

Operation of GLS lamps

The General Lighting Service (GLS) lamp is one type of incandescent lamp and is commonly referred to as the 'light bulb'. It has at its 'core' a very thin tungsten wire that is formed into a small coil and then coiled again.

A current is passed through the tungsten filament, which causes it to reach a temperature of 2500°C or more so that it glows brightly. At these temperatures, the oxygen in the atmosphere would combine with the filament to cause failure, so all the air is removed from the glass bulb and replaced by gases such as nitrogen and argon. Nitrogen is used to minimise the risk of arcing and argon is used to reduce the evaporation process. On low-power lamps such as 15 and 25 watt, the area inside the bulb remains a vacuum. The efficiency of a lamp is known as the efficacy. It is expressed in lumen per watt, lm/w. For this type of lamp the efficacy is between 10 and 18 lumens per watt. This is low compared with other types of lamp, and its use is limited. However, although now being phased out, it is the most familiar type of light source used and has many advantages including:

- comparatively low initial costs

- immediate light when switched on

- no control gear

- it can easily be dimmed.

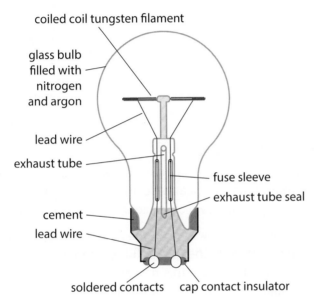

Figure 3.239: GLS lamp

When a bulb filament finally fails it can cause a very high current to flow for a fraction of a second – often sufficient enough to operate a 5 or 6 amp miniature circuit breaker which protects the lighting circuit. High-wattage lamps, however, are provided with a tiny integral fuse within the body of the lamp to prevent damage occurring when the filament fails.

If the lamp is run at a lower voltage than that of its rating this results in the light output of the lamp being reduced at a greater rate than the electricity used by the lamp, and the lamp's efficacy is poor. This reduction in voltage, however, increases the lifespan and can be useful where lamps are difficult to replace or light output is not the main consideration.

It has been calculated that an increase in 5% of the supply voltage can reduce the lamp life by half. However, if the input voltage is increased by just 1% this will produce an increase of 3.5% in lamp output (lumens). When you consider that the Electricity Supply Authority is allowed to vary its voltage up to and including 6% it is easy to see that if this was carried on for any length of time the lamps would not last very long.

Tungsten halogen lamps

These types of lamps were introduced in the 1950s. For their operation the tungsten filament is enclosed in a gas-filled quartz tube together with a carefully controlled amount of halogen such as iodine. Figure 3.240 illustrates the linear tungsten halogen lamp.

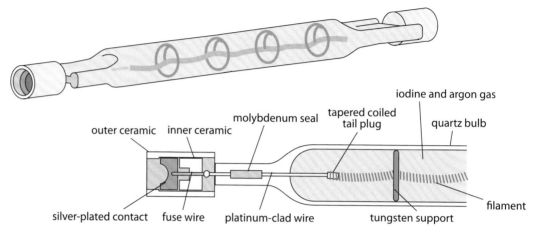

Figure 3.240: Linear tungsten lamp

Operation of tungsten halogen lamps

The inclusion of argon and iodine in the quartz tube allows the filament to burn at a much higher temperature than the incandescent lamp. The inclusion of the halogen gas produces a regeneration effect which prolongs the life of the lamp.

As small particles of tungsten fall away from the filament, they combine with the iodine passing over the face of the quartz tube, forming a new compound. Convection currents in the tube cause this new compound to rise, passing over the filament. The intense heat of the filament causes the compound to separate into its component parts, and the tungsten is deposited back on the filament.

The lamp should not be touched with bare fingers as this would deposit grease on the quartz glass tube; this would lead to small cracks and fissures in the tube when the lamp heats rapidly, causing the lamp to fail. If accidentally touched on installation, the lamp should be cleaned with methylated spirit before being used.

The linear type of lamp must be installed within 4° of the horizontal to prevent the halogen vapour migrating to one end of the tube, causing early failure. These types of lamps have many advantages, which include:

- increased lamp life (up to 2000 hours)
- increase in efficacy (up to 23 lumens per watt)
- reduction in lamp size.

There are two basic designs that have been produced: the double-ended linear lamp and the single-ended lamp, which has both contacts embedded in the seal at one end (see Figure 3.241). This type of lamp has been produced to work on extra-low voltages; they are used extensively in the automobile industry for vehicle headlamps. They may also be used for display spotlights where extra-low voltage is desirable. They may be supplied from an in-built 230 V/12 V transformer.

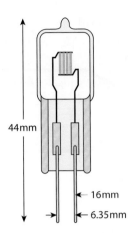

44mm

16mm

6.35mm

Figure 3.241: Single-ended tungsten halogen lamp

Discharge lighting

This is a term that refers to illumination derived from the ionisation of gas.
This section looks at:

- low pressure mercury vapour lamps

- the glow-type starter circuit

- semi-resonant starting

- high frequency

- stroboscopic effect

- other methods of starting the fluorescent tube

- other discharge lamps.

Low pressure mercury vapour lamps

The fluorescent lamp, or, more correctly, the low pressure mercury vapour lamp, consists of a glass tube filled with a gas such as krypton or argon and a measured amount of mercury vapour. The inside of the glass tube has a phosphor coating, and at each end there is a sealed set of oxide-coated electrodes, known as cathodes.

When a voltage is applied across the ends of a fluorescent tube the cathodes heat up, and this forms a cloud of electrons, which ionise the gas around them. The voltage to carry out this ionisation must be much higher than the voltage required to maintain the actual discharge across the lamp. Manufacturers use several methods to achieve this high voltage, usually based on a transformer or choke. This ionisation is then extended to the whole length of the tube so that the arc strikes and is then maintained in the mercury, which evaporates and takes over the discharge. The mercury arc, being at low pressure, emits little visible light but a great deal of ultraviolet, which is absorbed by the phosphor coating and transformed into visible light.

The cathodes are sealed into each end of the tube and consist of tungsten filaments coated with an electron-emitting material. Larger tubes incorporate cathode shields – iron strips bent into an oval shape to surround the cathode. The shield traps material given off by the cathodes during the tube life and thereby prevents the lamp-ends blackening.

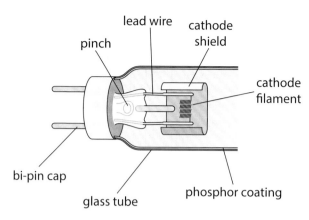

Figure 3.242: Detail of one end of a fluorescent tube

The gas in standard tubes is a mercury and argon mix, although some lamps (the smaller ones and the new slim energy-saving lamps) have krypton gas in them. The phosphor coating is a very important factor affecting the quantity and quality of light output. When choosing different lamps there are three main areas to be considered:

- lamp efficacy
- colour rendering
- colour appearance.

Lamp efficacy

This refers to the lumen output for a given wattage. For fluorescent lamps this varies between 40 and 90 lumens per watt.

Colour rendering

This describes a lamp's ability to show colours as they truly are. This can be important depending on the building usage. For example, it would be important in a paint shop but less so in a corridor of a building. The rendering of colour can affect people's attitude to work etc. – quite apart from the fact that in some jobs true colour may be essential. By restoring or providing a full colour range the light may also appear to be better or brighter than it really is.

Colour appearance

This is the actual look of the lamp, and the two ends of the scale are warm and cold. These extremes are related to temperatures: the higher the temperature, the cooler the lamp. This is important for the overall effect, and generally warm lamps are used to give a relaxed atmosphere while cold lamps are used where efficiency and businesslike attitudes are the priorities. The subject of lamp choice has become very complicated, and a programme of lamp rationalisation has begun. The intention is that the whole range currently available will be reduced. Also, new work has resulted in lamps with high lumen outputs and good colour rendering possibilities.

Starting using the glow-type starter circuit

In the starter (the small plastic cannister that we see plugged in to the side of the fitting), a set of normally open contacts is mounted on bi-metal strips and enclosed in an atmosphere of helium gas. When switched on, a glow discharge takes place around the open contacts in the starter, which heats up the bi-metal strips, causing them to bend and touch each other. This puts the electrodes at either end of the fluorescent tube in circuit and they warm up, giving off a cloud of electrons; simultaneously an intense magnetic field is building up in the choke, which is also in circuit.

The glow in the starter ceases once the contacts are touching so that the bi-metal strips now cool down and they spring apart again. This momentarily breaks the circuit, causing the magnetic field in the choke to rapidly collapse. The high back-e.m.f. produced provides the high voltage required for ionisation of the gas and enables the main discharge across the lamp to take place. The voltage across the tube under running conditions is not sufficient to operate the starter and so the contacts remain open.

The resistance of the ionised gas gets lower and lower as it warms up and conducts more current. This could lead to disintegration of the tube. However, the choke has a secondary function as a current-limiting device: the impedance of the choke limits the current through the lamp, keeping it in balance. This is one reason why it is often referred to as ballast.

This type of starting may not succeed first time and can result in the characteristic flashing on/off, when initially switching it on.

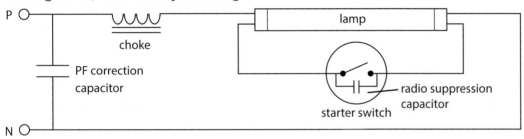

Figure 3.343: Glow-type starter circuit

Starting using semi-resonant starting

In this circuit the place of the choke is taken by a specially wound transformer. Current flows through the primary coils to one cathode of the lamp and then through the secondary coil, which is wound in opposition to the primary coil. A fairly large capacitor is connected between the secondary coil and the second cathode of the lamp (the other end of which is connected to the neutral).

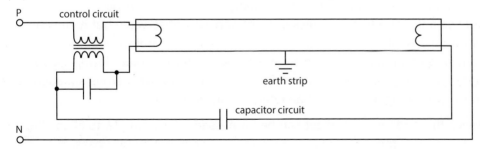

Figure 3.344: Semi-resonant circuit

The current that flows through this circuit heats the cathodes and, as the circuit is predominantly capacitive, the pre-start current leads the main voltage. Owing to the primary and secondary windings being in opposition, the voltages developed across them are 180° out of phase, so that the voltage across the tube is increased, causing the arc to strike. The primary windings then behave as a choke, thus stabilising the current in the arc. The circuit has the advantage of high power factor and easy starting at low temperatures.

High frequency

Standard fluorescent circuits operate on a mains supply frequency of 50 Hz; however, high-frequency circuits operate on about 30 000 Hz. There are a number of advantages to high frequency:

*   higher lamp efficacy

*   first-time starting

*   noise free

*   the ballast shuts down automatically on lamp failure.

The higher efficacy for this type of circuit can lead to savings of at least 10%, and in some large installations they may be as high as 30%. Many high-frequency electronic ballasts will operate on a wide range of standard fluorescent lamps. The high-frequency circuit will switch on the lamp within 0.4 of a second and there should be no flicker (unlike glow-type starter circuits).

Stroboscopic effect is not a problem as this light does not flicker on/off due to its high frequency.

However, a disadvantage of this type of circuit is that supply cables installed within the luminaire must not run adjacent to the leads connected to the ballast output terminals as interference may occur. Also, the initial cost of these luminaires is greater than traditional glow-type switch starts.

Stroboscopic effect

A simple example of this effect is that, when watching the wheels rotate on a horse-drawn cart on television, it appears that the wheels are stationary or even going backwards. This phenomenon is brought about by the fact that the spokes on the wheels are being rotated at about the same number of revolutions per second as the frames per second of the film being shot. This effect is known as the 'stroboscopic effect' and can also be produced by fluorescent lighting.

The discharge across the electrodes is extinguished 100 times per second, producing a flicker effect. This flicker is not normally observable but it can cause the stroboscopic effect, which can be dangerous. For example, if rotating machinery is illuminated from a single source it will appear to have slowed down, changed direction of rotation or even stopped. This is a potentially dangerous situation to any operator of rotating machines in an engineering workshop.

However, this stroboscopic effect can be harnessed – for example, to check the speed of a CD player or the speed of a motor vehicle for calibration purposes.

By using one of the following methods, the stroboscopic effect can be overcome or reduced. The first three maintain the light falling on the rotating machine. The fourth makes the falling light flicker at a different frequency from the operating frequency of the machines.

1. Tungsten filament lamps can be fitted locally to lathes, pillar-drilling machines, etc. This will lessen the effect but will not eliminate it completely.

2. Adjacent fluorescent fittings can be connected to different phases of the supply. Because in a three-phase supply the phases are 120° out of phase with each other, the light falling on the machine will arrive from two different sources.

Safety

Certain frequencies of stroboscopic flash can induce degrees of drowsiness, headaches, eye fatigue and, in extreme cases, disorientation. Some television shows have warnings about stroboscopic lights before their transmission.

3. Each of these will be flickering at a different time and will interfere with each other, reducing the stroboscopic effect.

4. Twin lamps can be wired on lead-lag circuits, thus counteracting each other. The lead-lag circuit, as the name implies, is a circuit that contains one lamp in which the power factor leads the other – hence the other lags. Using the leading current effect of a capacitor and the lagging current effect of an inductor produces the lead-lag effect. The lagging effect is produced naturally when an inductor is used in the circuit as shown in Figure 3.345. The leading effect uses a series capacitor, which has a greater effect than the inductor in the circuit. When these two circuits are combined as shown there is no need for further power factor correction as one circuit will correct the other.

5. The use of high-frequency fluorescent lighting reduces the effect by about 60%.

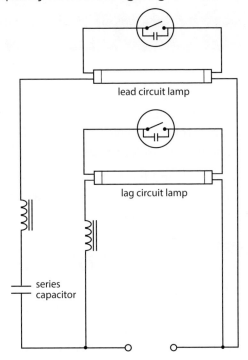

Figure 3.345: Lead lag circuit

Other methods of starting the fluorescent tube

Quick start

The electrodes of this type of circuit are rapidly pre-heated by the end windings of an autotransformer so that a quick start is possible. The method of ionisation of the gas is the same as in the semi-resonant circuit. Difficulties may occur in starting if the voltage is low.

Thermal starter circuit

This type of circuit has waned in popularity over the years. However, there are still thousands of these fittings in service, so it is worth describing them. In this starter, the normally closed contacts are mounted on a bi-metal strip. A small heater coil heats one of these when the supply is switched on. This causes the strip to bend and the contacts to open, creating the momentary high voltage and starting the circuit discharge. The starter is easily recognised as it has four pins instead of the usual two, the extra pins being for the heater connection.

Other discharge lamps

Low pressure sodium vapour

Low pressure sodium lamps have a gas discharge tube containing solid sodium and a small amount of neon and argon gas mixture to start the gas discharge. When the lamp is initially turned on it emits a dull red light as the sodium metal is warmed before becoming a bright orangey-yellow once the sodium has vaporised.

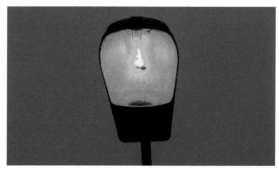

Figure 3.346: Low pressure sodium vapour lamp

These lamps have an outer glass vacuum envelope around the inner discharge tube for thermal insulation, which improves their efficiency along with coating the glass envelope with an infrared reflecting layer of metal oxide, thus resulting in their common name of SOX (sodium and oxide) lamps.

As a result of their colour when lit and the fact that they glow rather than glare, you will most commonly find them used on street or motorway lighting where accurate colour rendition of objects is not important.

High pressure sodium vapour

High pressure sodium lamps are smaller than SOX lamps and use low pressure xenon as the starter gas required to begin the sodium and mercury vaporisation.

When the lamp is initially turned on it emits a dull red light as the sodium metal is warmed before becoming a blue-white light once the sodium and mercury have vaporised. Because of this they are used where good colour rendering is considered important. As they are reasonably efficient, they are also used in street and security lighting.

As they were felt to be replicating sunlight, they are commonly referred to as SON lamps.

Figure 3.347: High pressure sodium vapour lamp

High pressure mercury vapour

When a mercury vapour lamp is first turned on, the voltage initiates an argon glow discharge between the main and the auxiliary electrode pair(s), causing a sufficient number of mercury atoms to be ionised. This in turn initiates a low pressure discharge between the two main electrodes and it will produce a dark blue glow because only a small amount of the mercury is ionised and the gas pressure in the arc tube is very low. As the main arc strikes and the gas heats up and increases in pressure, the light appears nearly white to the human eye.

Metal halide

By adding rare earth metal salts to the mercury vapour lamp, metal halide lamps produce high light-output for their size, making them a powerful and efficient light source.

Since the lamp is small compared to a fluorescent or incandescent lamp of the same light level, relatively small reflective luminaires can be used to direct the light for different applications (flood lighting outdoors, or lighting for warehouses or industrial buildings).

Metal halide lamps are used both for general lighting purposes, and for very specific applications that require specific UV or blue-frequency light. Because of their wide spectrum, they are used for indoor growing applications.

Like all discharge lamps, metal halide lamps produce light by passing an electric arc through a mixture of gases. In a metal halide lamp, the compact arc tube contains a high-pressure mixture of argon, mercury, and a variety of metal halides. The argon gas in the lamp is easily ionised and facilitates striking the arc across the two electrodes when voltage is first applied to the lamp. The heat generated by the arc then vaporises the mercury and metal halides, which produce light as the temperature and pressure increases.

Compact (energy saving) fluorescent lamps

The incandescent lamp is simply a very hot piece of wire inside a glass container. It is the heat that created the light, thus making it an inefficient device. In fact, it wastes about 90% of the electricity it uses. The problem is, just about every domestic property in the UK uses them in pendant or table light fittings. The typical incandescent lamp used in the home is either 60 watts or 100 watts, which means that if 10 × 100 watt lamps are on then you are using 1 kW of power.

Figure 3.348: Energy-saving light bulbs

Energy-saving lights are simply a compact version of the fluorescent tube mentioned earlier; in other words they are a low pressure mercury vapour lamp. The compact design is necessary to allow domestic users to replace their old incandescent lamps without having to replace shades or fittings.

Additionally, these low energy equivalents typically use only 9 or 11 watts each even though they give the same amount of light. So, using our same example, instead of using 1 kW of power our demand would be 10 × 11 watt or 110 watts in total – quite an energy saving. There are two types of compact fluorescent lamp:

- Integrated lamps combine a tube, an electronic ballast and either an Edison screw or a bayonet fitting in a single unit. Most domestic users will be familiar with these.

- Non-integrated lamps have the ballast permanently installed in the luminaire, and therefore only the lamp bulb has to be changed when it fails. Since the ballast is in the fitting itself, they tend to be larger but last longer when compared to the integrated lamp.

Standard compact fluorescents are not suitable for dimming applications and special lamps are required instead.

Working life

Your customer has installed glow-type fluorescents in the kitchen area of a large house. They have reported that one of them continues to flicker as though trying to start but doesn't.

1. What should you do to determine the facts?
2. What are the most likely causes of this fault?
3. How would you proceed?

LED lighting

Light emitting diodes (LEDs) have been around for many years and are used for a range of items, from lighting digital clocks to Christmas tree lights.

As with the compact fluorescent, the LED lamp saves energy against traditional incandescent lamps and they are likely to last about 30 000 hours. An LED in this context could be called 'solid-state lighting' technology as it emits its light from a piece of solid matter, namely a semiconductor.

Regulations concerning lighting circuits

Chapter 55 of BS.7671 contains section 559, which applies to the selection and erection of luminaires and lighting installations intended to be part of the fixed installation.

Outdoor lighting installations comprising one or more luminaires, a wiring system and accessories, and highway power supplies and street furniture are covered in Part 7, Section 714 - Outdoor lighting installations, where the following are included in outdoor lighting installations:

- lighting installations such as those for roads, parks, car parks, gardens, places open to the public, sporting areas, illumination of monuments and floodlighting

- other lighting arrangements in places such as telephone kiosks, bus shelters, advertising panels and town plans

- road signs.

The following are excluded from Section 714:

- temporary festoon lighting
- luminaires fixed to the outside of a building and supplied directly from the internal wiring of that building (they are covered by section 559)
- road traffic signal systems.

The most relevant regulations of section 559 are as follows:

- **559.3.1** – Every luminaire shall comply with the relevant standard for manufacture and test of that luminaire, and shall be selected and erected to take account of the manufacturer's instructions.

- **559.4.1** – In the selection and erection of a luminaire, the thermal effects of radiant and convected energy on the surroundings shall be taken into account, including:
  - the maximum permissible power dissipated by the lamps
  - the fire-resistance of adjacent material at the point of installation and in the thermally affected areas
  - the minimum distance to combustible materials, including material in the path of a spotlight beam
  - the relevant markings on the luminaire.

- **559.5.1** – At each fixed lighting point one of the following shall be used for the termination of the wiring system:

1. a ceiling rose complying with BS 67
2. a luminaire supporting coupler (LSC) complying with BS 6972 or BS 7001
3. a batten lamp-holder or a pendant set complying with BS EN 60598
4. a luminaire complying with BS EN 60598
5. a suitable socket-outlet complying with BS 1363-2, BS 546 or BS EN 60309-2
6. a plug-in lighting distribution unit complying with BS 5733
7. a connection unit complying with BS 1363-4
8. appropriate terminals enclosed in a box complying with the relevant part of BS EN 60670 series or BS 4662
9. a device for connecting a luminaire (DCL) outlet complying with BS IEC 61995-1
10. an installation coupler complying with BS EN 61535.

- **559.5.1.201** – A ceiling rose or lamp-holder shall not be installed in any circuit operating at a voltage normally exceeding 250 volts.

- **559.5.1.204** – Lighting circuits incorporating B15 (SBC), B22 (BC), E14 (SES), E27 (ES) or E40 (Giant ES) lamp-holders shall be protected by an overcurrent protective device of maximum rating 16 A.

- **559.5.1.207** – A lighting installation shall be appropriately controlled.

- **559.5.1.208** – Consideration shall be given to the provision of the neutral conductor, at each switch position, to facilitate the installation of electronic switching devices.

- **559.5.2** – Adequate means to fix luminaires shall be provided. The fixing means may be mechanical accessories (e.g. hooks or screws), boxes or enclosures which are able to support luminaires or supporting devices for connecting a luminaire. However, where the fixing means is intended to support a luminaire, the fixing means shall be capable of carrying a mass of not less than 5 kg. If the mass of the luminaire is greater than 5 kg, a fixing means capable of supporting the mass of the luminaire shall be installed.

- **559.5.5** – Groups of luminaires divided between the line conductors of a polyphase circuit with only one common neutral conductor shall be provided with at least one device that simultaneously disconnects all the line conductors.

- **559.9** – In the case of lighting for premises where machines with moving parts are in operation, consideration shall be given to stroboscopic effects which can give a misleading impression of moving parts being stationary. Such effects may be avoided by selecting luminaires with suitable lamp control-gear, such as high frequency control-gear, or by distributing lighting loads across all the phases of a polyphase supply.

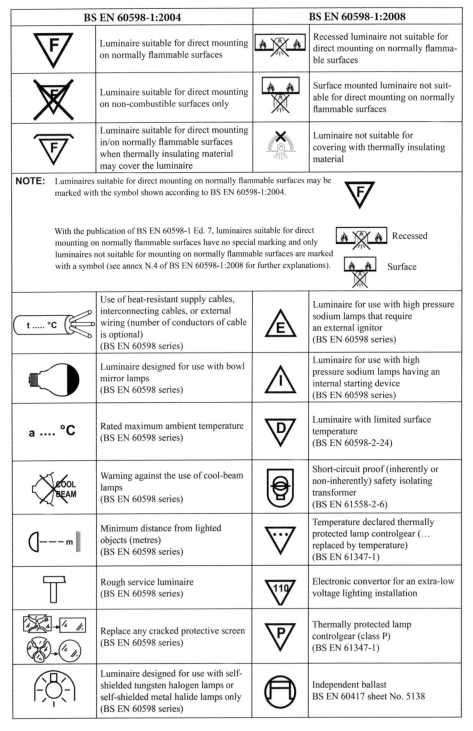

Figure 3.349: Explanations of symbols used in luminaires in control gear for luminaires and in installation of luminaires (Table 55.2)

Basic principles of illumination

Before we can perform any calculations, it is probably a good idea to know what we are trying to calculate and what we can use to achieve it.

Simply, two early things to consider are:

- How powerful is something at source? (How bright is the light?)
- How much light has landed on an object a certain distance away from the light?

Measuring light

We refer to the 'brightness' of a source (the power of the light) as **luminous intensity** and this is given the symbol I and is measured in candelas (cd).

Luminous flux is the measure of the flow (or amount) of light being emitted from that source and one of the factors used when designing lighting systems is **illuminance**.

Formerly called illumination, illuminance is our measure of the amount of light falling on a surface. This is defined as 'the density of the luminous flux striking a surface'.

Using the symbol E, illuminance has the unit of measurement (Lux), with one Lux being the illuminance at a point on a surface that is one metre from, and perpendicular to, a uniform point source of one candela.

Let's explore that a bit more. Take a ruler 1 metre long and place it flat on the floor with one end touching a 1 m² wall. Fix a candle to the other end of it and then light the candle. If we assume that the candle has a luminous intensity of one candela, then the amount of light hitting the wall is one Lux. In other words, one lumen uniformly distributed over one square metre of wall surface provides an illuminance of 1 Lux (1 Lux = 1 lumen/square metre).

If we were now to move the ruler and candle further away from the wall, then the wall will appear less brightly lit. However, the amount coming from the candle has remained the same. This is inversely proportional.

As a concept what we are saying is the closer you are to a luminaire, the brighter that luminaire is. Or, put another way, if we can't change how much light comes out of the luminaire, to make more light land on an object we either have to move the luminaire closer, or add more luminaires.

Other factors that affect illuminance

Whatever type of luminaires we eventually decide to install will be affected by age, collection dust etc. All of these factors will affect our level of illuminance and are grouped under an overall title of **Maintenance Factor**.

Maintenance Factor (MF) is the ratio of the illuminance provided by an installation after a period of use against its initial illuminance when it first started use. This is expressed as a number or percentage and has no unit.

As a simple example, let's say that a shift manager's office in a garage workshop has a ceiling luminaire with one 65 W fluorescent lamp inside it installed from new. When first installed the lamp had a lumen output of 1000 lm, but when measured again after six months in operation the output had fallen to 850 lm.

The output has decreased by a ratio of: $\frac{850}{1000} = 0.85$

We therefore have a Maintenance Factor of 0.85.

The Maintenance Factor is based on how often the lights are cleaned and replaced. It takes into account such factors as decreased efficiency with age, accumulation of dust within the fitting itself and the depreciation of reflectance as walls and ceiling age. It is fully represented by the following formula:

MF = LLMF × LSF × LMF × RSMF

Where:

- LLMF (lamp lumen maintenance factor) – the reduction in lumen output after specific burning hours
- LSF (lamp survival factor) – the percentage of lamp failures after specific burning hours
- LMF (luminaire maintenance factor) – the reduction in light output due to dirt deposited on or in the luminaire
- RSMF (room surface maintenance factor) – the reduction in reflectance due to dirt deposition in the room surfaces.

As a rough guide, for convenience, MF is usually taken as being around the following values:

- Good = 0.70
- Medium = 0.65
- Poor = 0.55

One other consideration is the **utilisation factor** (UF), once referred to as the coefficient of utilisation (CU). Using tables available from manufacturers, it is possible to determine the utilisation factor for different lighting fittings if the reflectance of both the walls and ceiling is known, the room index has been determined and the type of luminaire is known.

In other words, UF is a number used to represent the amount of luminous flux emitted by a lamp that reaches a working surface.

Factors that make up the UF include:

- the light output of luminaire
- the flux distribution of the luminaire
- Room Index (room dimensions and spacing and mounting height of luminaires)
- room reflectances.

When checking existing light levels in a building, you should be aware that, as the light output of lamps varies depending on their operating temperature, it is essential that the luminaires have been operating under normal thermal conditions before checking. This may require, for example, both lighting and heating or air conditioning systems to be switched on for long enough to achieve steady conditions.

Where lamps are known to be new, they should be run for about 100 hours under normal operating conditions. Also, where possible the line voltage supply to the lighting circuit should also be monitored, as fluctuations in lumen output are caused by variations in supply voltage.

Let's now look at the calculations.

The lumen method

This method of calculation is only applicable in square or rectangular rooms with a uniform array of luminaires as shown in Figure 3.350.

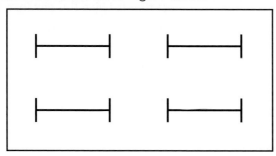

Figure 3.350: A uniform array of luminaires in a room

Using the factors mentioned previously, it is the simplest method of calculating the overall illumination level for such areas. It is accurate enough for the majority of purposes, and is the calculation most used by lighting engineers when determining the number of luminaires for a given lighting level. The formula is as follows:

$$E = \frac{F \times n \times N \times MF \times UF}{A}$$

Where:

E = average illuminance (lux)

F = initial lamp lumens

n = number of lamps in each luminaire

N = number of luminaires

MF = maintenance factor

UF = utilisation factor

A = area

Example

You have been given the following information and asked to calculate how many luminaires we need to give 300 lux at desk level within a room in a primary school.

UF = 0.44

MF = 0.85 (as the building is clean and without any air conditioning system)

n = 4 lamps per luminaire

F = 2350 lumens for the fluorescent tube

E = 300 lux at the level of the table (good for such a school)

A = 9 m × 4 m = 36 m²

By transposition of the formula:

$$N = \frac{A \times E}{F \times n \times MF \times UF}$$

Therefore:

$$N = \frac{300 \times 36}{2350 \times 4 \times 0.85 \times 0.44} = \frac{10\,800}{3515} = 3.07$$

Therefore 3 × 4 tube luminaires are required.

The inverse square law

In physics, an inverse square law is any physical law stating that some physical quantity or strength is inversely proportional to the square of the distance from the source of that physical quantity.

Simply, what this means is that an object that is twice the distance from a point source of light will receive only a quarter of the illumination. Or put another way, if you moved an object from 3 m to 6 m (**twice** the distance) away from a light source, you would need four times (2^2) the amount of light to maintain the same level of illumination.

We can see this in real life very easily. Consider a campfire at night – a pool of light surrounded by darkness. Or a torch being shone into the night sky – a bright beam of light that rapidly fades to nothing. You might think that when you double the distance from a light source you are now getting half as much light, but it doesn't work like that – you actually get just a quarter as much light. Figure 3.351 shows how the inverse square law works.

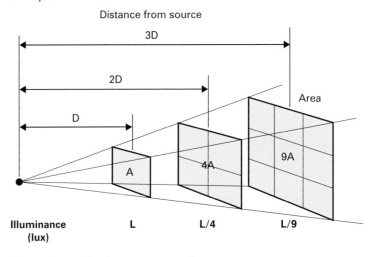

Figure 3.351: The inverse square law

Notice in Figure 3.351 how as the distance from the source increases to three times the original distance from the light source (3D), that the intensity of illumination at the new distance is nine times less ($3D^2$). This is because the amount of illumination is inversely proportional to the distance from the source.

We express this phenomenon with the following formula and apply it when the light source is directly above a surface:

Illuminance in lux $E = \frac{I}{d^2}$ (luminous intensity in candela)
(distance between source and point of measurement in m²)

Example

A luminaire producing a luminous intensity of 1000 cd is installed 3 m above a surface, what is the illuminance on that surface directly beneath the luminaire?

$$E = \frac{I}{d^2} = \frac{1000}{3^2} = \frac{1000}{9} = \textbf{111.1 lux}$$

If the luminaire was now installed 1 m higher, what would be the new level of illuminance on the surface?

$$E = \frac{I}{d^2} = \frac{1000}{4^2} = \frac{1000}{16} = \textbf{62.5 lux}$$

Lambert's cosine law

Inverse square law applies when the light source is directly above the work surface and the measurement of illumination applied to a straight line beneath that luminaire. Lambert's cosine law (commonly referred to as the cosine rule) allows us to measure the illumination on the work surface but at an angle to the light source.

The law states that the illuminance on any surface varies as the cosine of the angle of incidence (the angle of incidence is the angle between the normal to the surface and the direction of the incident light).

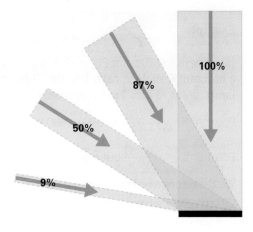

Figure 3.352: Lambert's cosine law

When light strikes a surface normally (perpendicular to the surface), it gives a certain illumination level. As the angle changes from 90°, the same amount of light is spread out over a larger area, so the illumination level goes down.

If we call this angle from the perpendicular x, then the illumination level is proportional to cos x. This is demonstrated in Figure 3.352.

In the environmental context, this is why it's cold in winter and warm during the summer. During the winter the Sun's rays hit the Earth at a steep angle. The light does not spread out as much, thus increasing the amount of energy hitting any given spot. But during the winter, the Sun's rays hit the Earth at a shallow angle. The rays are therefore more spread out, which minimises the amount of energy that hits any given spot.

From our lighting perspective, if we use the pendant light in Figure 3.353 below, then we can see that the level of illuminance at point A must be higher than it is at point B, and that this reduced level at point B depends on the cosine of the angle.

JTL tip

Do not confuse Lambert's cosine law with the cosine calculations we looked at earlier in this unit (see page 204–205).

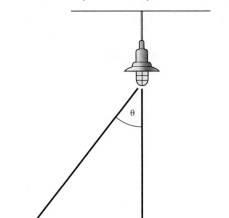

Figure 3.353: Illuminance at a series of points

We express this with the following formula, which is a composite of this and the inverse square law, namely:

$$E = \frac{I \times \cos \emptyset}{d^2}$$

Example

If the pendant light in Figure 3.353 produces 2000 candela and is suspended 2 m above a horizontal surface, calculate the illuminance on the surface both directly beneath the lamp (point A) and 3 m away from the lamp (point B).

Point A: $E = \dfrac{I}{d^2} = \dfrac{2000}{2^2} = \dfrac{2000}{4} = 500$ lux

Point B: $E = \dfrac{I \times \cos \varnothing}{d^2}$ but we don't know $\cos \varnothing$

We therefore need to use some logic and trigonometry.

Effectively, we have been given the dimensions of two sides of a right-angled triangle:

- the distance from the pendant to point A (2 m)
- the distance between points A and B (3 m).

The right angle 'points' at the hypotenuse (side H) and this is the measurement that we are trying to find as it is the distance from the pendant to point B.

Therefore using Pythagoras' Theorem:

$H^2 = A^2 + B^2$

$H^2 = 2^2 + 3^2$

$H^2 = 4 + 9 = 13$

Therefore $H = \sqrt{13} = 3.6$

In other words, the distance from the pendant to Point B (side H) is 3.6 m.

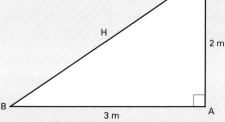

For our illuminance formula we are trying to find $\cos \varnothing$, and a cosine is the ratio between the adjacent side and the hypotenuse. We now know the hypotenuse, and the adjacent side is the one 'next to' the angle we are working with ($\varnothing$), which in this case has a measurement of 2 m.

The cosine formula is:

$\cos \varnothing = \dfrac{\text{Adjacent}}{\text{Hypotenuse}} = \dfrac{2}{3.6} = 0.56$

We can now use this value in our formula

$E = \dfrac{I \times \cos \varnothing}{d^2} = \dfrac{2000 \times 0.56}{12.96} = \dfrac{1120}{12.96} = 86.4$

Therefore the illuminance at point B = 86.4 lux.

Summary

1. Why is it important not to touch (with bare hands) tungsten halogen lamps?
2. What are the two main advantages of LEDs?
3. What is the proper name for the brightness of light and what is it measured in?

12. The principles and applications of electrical heating

It can be argued that there are only two main methods of heating water:

*   storage, where you heat a large amount of water and store it in a tank ready for use
*   instantaneous, where you only heat the water you need, when you need it.

With both of these types, it is important to ensure that the exposed and extraneous conductive parts are adequately bonded to earth, as water and electricity do not mix together well! It is also important to ensure that the cables selected are of the correct size for full load current, since no diversity is allowed for water heaters.

Water heating systems

For storage, large tanks of stored water (typically 137+ litres) are heated using an immersion heater and then controlled to be on or off via a timer switch or an on/off switch. The temperature of the water is regulated by a stem-type thermostat, incorporated within the housing of the heating element. This type of heater is normally found in domestic situations, although larger multiple immersion heaters can be used in commercial/industrial situations.

The heater in a domestic situation must be fed from its own fuse/MCB (Miniature circuit breaker) in the consumer unit and have a double-pole isolator fitted next to the storage tank. The final connection to the heating element must be made with heatproof flexible cable due to the high ambient temperatures where the water tank is normally located.

This type of system can sometimes have two elements: one element is controlled via a separate supply, which only operates at night time (Economy 7 or white-meter supply) when cheap electricity is available, heating a full tank of water ready for use the next day; the other is switched on as and when needed during the day to boost the amount of hot water available.

There are many variations of water system available. Here are some of the factors to consider:

*   how much hot water is needed and where
*   whether the water heating system needs to be part of the central heating system
*   speed of hot water delivery
*   flow rate of water (for a shower, for example)
*   what space is available.

Each system can be powered from the boiler/combi-boiler, but electrically there are several options.

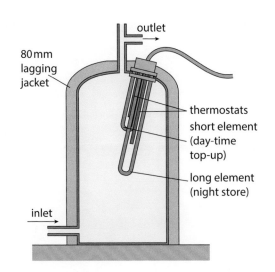

Figure 3.354: Dual-element immersion heater, hot water

Cistern-type (storage)

Where larger volumes of hot water are needed (for example, in a large guest house), a cistern-type water heater (9 kW+) is used which is capable of supplying enough hot water to several outlets at the same time.

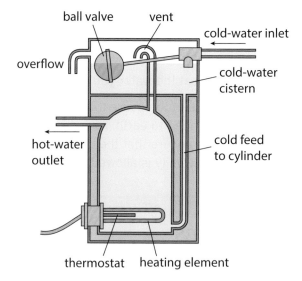

Figure 3.355: Cistern-type storage

Non-pressure (storage)

Non-pressure water heaters, which are typically rated at less than 3 kW and contain less than 15 litres of water, heat and then store water ready for use and are usually situated directly over the sink. Typically they can be seen in a small shop or hairdresser's salon, but are sometimes used in toilet blocks in offices or factories.

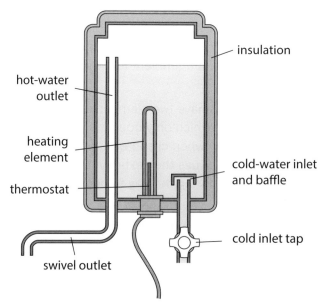

Figure 3.356: Non-pressure water heater

Instantaneous

Instantaneous water heaters heat only the water that is needed. This is done by controlling the rate of flow of water through a small internal water tank, which has heating elements inside it; the slower the flow of the water, the hotter the water will become. The temperature of the water can be continuously altered or stabilised locally at whatever temperature is selected.

This is exactly how an electric shower works, and showers in excess of 10 kW are currently available.

The shower-type water heater must be supplied via its own fuse/MCB in the consumer unit and have a double-pole isolator located near the shower.

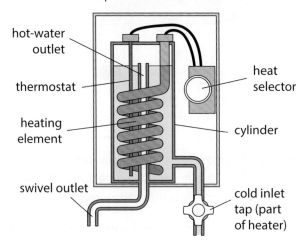

Figure 3.357: Instantaneous water heater

Electric heating

The type of electric heating available falls into two main categories: direct-acting heaters and thermal storage devices.

Direct acting heaters are usually just switched on and off when needed, although some of them can be thermostatically controlled. They fall into two basic categories: radiant and convection.

Radiant heaters

Radiant fires work on the simple principle of an element being heated to high temperature and heat then radiating away from the device. Radiant type heaters reflect heat and come in a variety of shapes, sizes and constructions.

The 'traditional' electric fire

This has a heating element supported on insulated blocks, with a highly polished reflective surface behind it; these range in size from about 750 W to 3 kW.

Infrared heater

This consists of an iconel™-sheathed element or a nickel-chrome spiral element housed in a glass silica tube, which is mounted in front of a highly polished surface. Sizes vary from about 500 W to 3 kW; the smaller versions are usually suitable for use in bathrooms and may be incorporated with a bulb to form a combined heating and lighting unit.

Figure 3.358: Infrared heater

Oil-filled radiator

This consists of a pressed-steel casing in which heating elements are housed; the whole unit is filled with oil. Oil has a lower specific gravity than water, so heats up and cools down more quickly. Surface temperature reaches about 70°C, and power sizes range from about 500 W to 3 kW.

Figure 3.359: Oil-filled raditator

Tubular heater

This is a low-temperature unit designed to supplement the main heating in the building. It consists of a mild steel or aluminium tube of about 50 mm diameter, in which a heater element is mounted. The elements are rated at 200 W to 260 W per metre length, and can range in length from about 300 mm to 4.5 m. The surface temperature is approximately 88°C.

Figure 3.360: Tubular heater

Underfloor heating

This consists of heating elements embedded under the floor that heat up the floor surface. The floor becomes a large, low-temperature radiant heater. A room thermostat controls the temperature within the room; the floor temperature does not normally exceed 24°C.

For laminate flooring, a carbon-heating film roll has heating elements rated at between 130 W/m^2 and 160 W/m^2. The roll is supplied in 1000 mm width and standard lengths between 2 and 6 metres. Each heating element is supplied with standard 5 m leads for connection to the control unit.

Convection heaters

When heated, air decreases in density. This makes the surrounding air cooler and denser. This in turn makes it heavier, so it falls beneath the hot air, forcing it upwards. This is convection.

In a convection heater, the heating element heats the air next to it. By convection, this sets up a constant current of hot air that leaves the appliance through vent holes and heats up the surrounding space.

Convection heaters consist of a heating element housed inside a metal cabinet that is insulated both thermally and electrically from the case, so that the heat produced warms the surrounding air inside the cabinet. Cool air enters the bottom of the cabinet and warm air is passed out at the top of the unit, at a temperature of between 80 and 90°C. A thermostatic control is usually fitted to this type of heater.

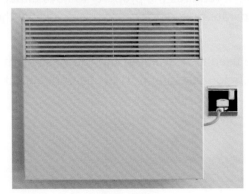

Figure 3.361: Convection heater

Fan heaters

These operate in the same way as a convector heater, but use a fan to force the warm air into the room. Fan heaters usually have a two-speed fan incorporated into the casing and up to 3 kW of heating elements.

Thermal storage devices

Electric storage heaters consist of several heating elements mounted inside firebricks, which in turn are surrounded by thermal insulation such as fibreglass, all housed inside a metal cabinet. The firebricks are made from clay, olivine, chrome and magnesite, which have very good heat retaining properties.

Connected to a special tariff meter in the property, the bricks are heated up during 'off peak' hours (normally overnight, usually Economy 7 tariff) and the heat is stored within the bricks. The outlet vent is then opened the following day and allows the warm air to escape and hence heat up the room.

Economy 7

Because of the costs and process of electricity generation, large power stations need to run 24 hours a day and are therefore producing electricity overnight when most of us have little need for it.

To encourage overnight energy usage, particularly for storage heating, the industry came up with the term Economy (meaning cheap) and 7 (meaning available for 7 hours overnight) to offload the energy that the industry had produced.

Economy 7 electricity is a system introduced in the 1970s that offers cheaper than normal rates between the hours of 12 and 7am (the 7 hours known as off peak), but pricier than normal during the rest of the day (the peak hours). Consequently, they are only really intended for people using storage heaters, as these heaters draw electricity in the evening or night-time, then release their heat during the day when needed.

Current tariffs for 'normal' electricity arrangements are around 12.6p/kWh, irrespective of the time of day, whereas Economy 7 tariffs are around 7.5p/kWh for 'off-peak' usage but around 15.6p/kWh for peak usage. The Economy 7 system also suits the generating companies, as it's better to be able to sell electricity at a cheaper rate rather than have the cost of having to keep powering down and then re-firing their generating plant.

From a user perspective, it requires the property to have either one meter with two readings or two separate meters to record usage against the 'on peak' and 'off peak' tariffs.

Economy 7 can also be used to heat water, and run washing machines and dishwashers using timers to make the most of cheap rate electricity.

Environment and building management control

This section will look at systems intended for the building rather than the individual.

Central heating systems and controls

Before looking at the controls associated with them, perhaps it would be wise to have a very brief overview of what domestic central heating systems are available as installed by plumbing contractors.

Pumped systems

The water is heated by the boiler and sent round the pipework by means of a pump. The water is then directed to either the radiators or the hot water cylinder by means of a motorised valve.

Gravity systems

In gravity-fed hot water systems, heating of domestic hot water relies on convective action to circulate hot water from the boiler to the cylinder. This works because water will expand when heated, will weigh less than cold water (which sinks to the bottom of the system) and therefore cause the hot water to be pushed up. The hot water cylinder will be fed from the cold water tank in the loft, which flows by gravity down to the hot water cylinder and forces hot water out to the hot water taps.

The gravity system therefore doesn't have a pump, but does need larger pipework.

This system usually has a water tank in the loft to keep the system topped up when water is lost by evaporation or leakage.

Sealed systems

This is a closed system and it is common for the boiler to be a combination type rather than connected individual components. A pressure vessel handles expansion and contraction of the water and there is a safety valve to relieve excess pressure instead of the vent pipe found in gravity systems.

As these systems run at higher temperatures than other systems, radiators can be a little smaller.

Hot water

When using a standard boiler, the hot water supply is provided by a pipe which runs from the boiler, coils through the hot water cylinder, and returns to the boiler. The water in the cylinder is completely separate from that which goes through the boiler.

The temperature of the hot water is controlled by a cylinder thermostat which switches the pump on and off or opens a motorised valve.

In the case of a combination boiler, mains water is only heated on demand when a tap is turned on, effectively acting like an instantaneous electric water heater.

Heating controls

It is probably fair to say that it will be the controls involved in the system that will make it easier to install, easy to use and generally make it is as efficient as possible.

It is probably also fair to say that control systems are many and varied, but that perhaps the most common controls are based around a concept introduced about 30 years ago by Honeywell and known as the 'Sundial' system. The two most common variants being the 'S' and 'Y' plan systems, although the 'C' Plan exists for gravity systems.

'S' Plan

The Sundial 'S' Plan uses two two-port valves (one for heating, one for hot water) to provide independent temperature control of heating and hot water circuits in fully pumped central heating installations. Time control must be provided by a programmer.

In terms of its operation, on demand for heat from either thermostat, the respective zone valve will be energised to open. Just before the valve reaches its fully open position, the auxiliary switch will be closed and switch on both pump and boiler. When both thermostats are satisfied, the valves are closed and the pump and boiler switched off. Figure 3.362 shows a wiring diagram for such a system.

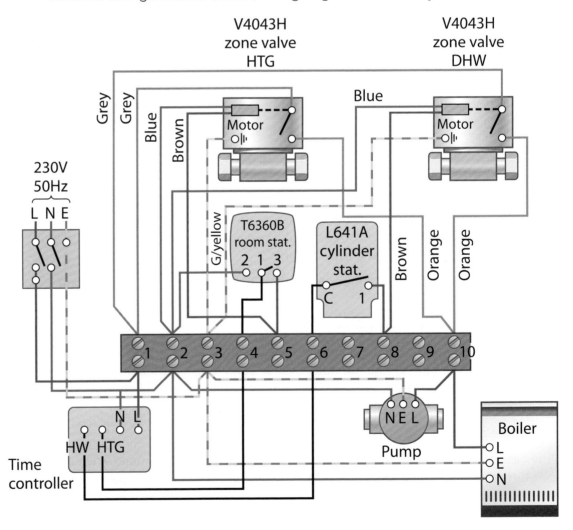

Figure 3.362: Wiring diagram for an 'S' Plan temperature control system

'Y' Plan

The Sundial 'Y' Plan uses one three-port mid position valve (it handles both hot water and heating) to provide independent temperature control of both heating and hot water circuits in fully pumped central heating installations. Time control must be provided by a programmer.

Hot water only requirement

On demand for heat from the cylinder thermostat, the valve remains open to DHW only and the pump and boiler are switched on.

Heating only requirement

On demand for heat from the room thermostat, the valve motor is energised so that the CH port only is opened and the pump and boiler are switched on.

Heating and hot water requirement

When both thermostats demand heat, the valve plug is positioned to allow both ports to be open and the pump and boiler switched on. When neither thermostat is demanding heat, the pump and boiler are off. The valve remains in the last position of operation whilst the time control is in the "on" position. Figure 3.363 shows a wiring diagram for such a system.

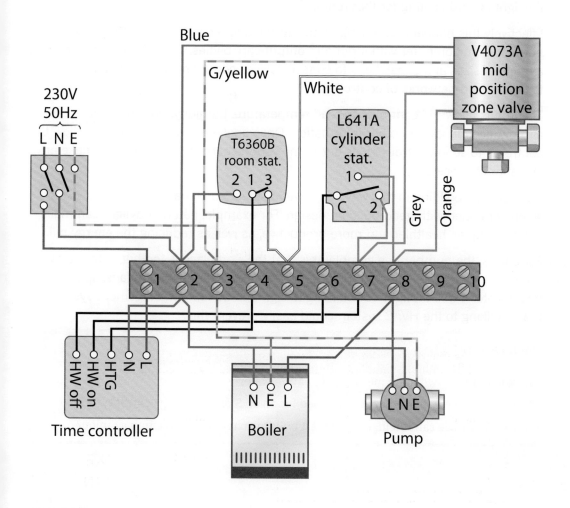

Figure 3.363: Wiring diagram for a 'Y' Plan temperature control system

Heating, ventilating and air conditioning (HVAC)

Although domestic central heating is installed by plumbers, at a commercial and industrial level this tends to become the work of the HVAC contractor.

Some of the technology is similar to that of the plumber, but on a larger scale. For example, in terms of heating, buildings may use boilers and radiators. However, whereas in domestic installations the boiler may be wall mounted as part of the kitchen units, a hospital or university may have a dedicated building to house the boiler.

One system particular to HVAC is the forced air system, which sends heated air through duct work. During warm weather the same duct work can be used for air conditioning and the air can also be filtered or put through air cleaners.

Intelligent (smart) buildings

With developments in technology you can now set up a building to better and more efficiently meet your needs and monitor and adjust its performance against those needs.

The concept of the intelligent building (or, as it is often referred to, the Building Management System) is to get the individual systems in a building – whether it be lighting, audio, heating or ventilation – to 'talk' to each other. For example, if no one is in a room, a PIR detects this, informs the system and the system then switches off the lighting and heating for that room.

Effectively this happens by linking all the systems to a controller, which is basically a purpose-built computer with input and output capabilities. These controllers come in a range of sizes and capabilities to control devices commonly found in buildings, and to control sub-networks of controllers.

The inputs allow the controller to read temperature, humidity, pressure, current flow, air flow, occupancy and other information. Once analysed, the outputs then allow the controller to send control signals out to the various parts of the system to make any adjustments necessary.

Controlling a building in this way can have an effect on climate change, especially when combined with good building design. For example, natural daylight can make people happier, healthier and more productive, as well as reducing the energy bill.

For offices, the number one complaint is that the workplace is too hot, with a close second being that it's too cold! Staff tend to compensate by adding fans, space heaters etc. A well thought-out building design and building management system that is talking to the HVAC system could easily prevent this.

Summary

1. What are the two main methods of heating water?
2. What are the two two-port valves used for on an S plan heating control system?
3. On what issue can intelligent or smart buildings have a positive impact upon?

Getting ready for assessment

EAL	City & Guilds
For this unit you will need to complete the following assessments: • 40 question multiple choice online exam • Practical Task A Transformers • Written exam Task B	For this unit you will need to complete the following assessments: • Multiple choice online exam. • Task A written exam • Task B transformers exam

▶ Preparing for this assessment:

- Most apprentices find this unit the hardest to understand, but don't let this phase you. Take your time with each topic and if you don't understand, ask your tutor or use your initiative and do some research.

- You will also need to know how to use your scientific calculator, so make sure you familiarise yourself with what buttons do what and how to use it for all the calculations in the criteria.

- The written exam is going to be something a little different that you haven't experienced yet in this qualification. Take your time answering the questions and make sure you include all key points and give a full explanation of each answer.

- For the transformers assessment ensure that you know how to use the test instrument and how to test for voltage and current across the transformer. Its also important to know how to calculate the voltage and current across the transformer, as once you start the assessment the assessor will not be able to help.

▶ Worked examples

This section will help you to understand some of the key concepts in this unit.

A. As an electrician what are the SI units you are most likely to come across? (Name at least four.)

Length – useful for things such as measuring the amount of cable you might need in an installation.

Area – could be used to see how many lights are needed for a room.

Volume – used most commonly with heating systems, to calculate how much energy is needed to heat a hot water cylinder.

Mass – this shows how much there is of something. Not the weight!

Weight – related to how gravity influences mass.

Temperature – base unit for temperature is degrees Kelvin but we mostly use Celsius or Fahrenheit.

> Remember it is important to know what each of these SI units are and especially important to not get these mixed up. One example of this would be mass and weight, people may often think these are the same thing however it is important to remember although related, these are not the same.

B. What does the acronym BODMAS stand for?

Brackets – always calculate what is in them first.

Other operations – such as powers or square roots.

Division and multiplication – start on the left and work them out in the order that you find them.

Addition and subtraction – when only addition and subtraction are left in the sum work them out in the order you find them, starting from the left of the sum and working towards the right.

Division and multiplication have the same priority, as do addition and subtraction.

C. The relationship between the angles and sides of triangles is called what?

This is called trigonometry. The long side of a triangle is called the hypotenuse and the right-angle points at it. The names of the other two sides will depend on the angle that you must find or intend to use. The side which is opposite the angle being considered is called the opposite, and the side which is next to the angle under consideration and the right-angle is called the adjacent.

D. Which two ways can three-phase supplies be connected?

Star or Delta connection.

Remember current flows along one conductor and returns along another called the neutral. Whether or not we need a neutral will depend on the load. If we accept that the e.m.f being generated by each loop pushes current down the conductors, then we would find that where we have a balanced three-phase system. If the current size is zero then we do not need a neutral, because the neutral is used to carry the current in an out-of-balance system.

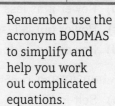

Remember use the acronym BODMAS to simplify and help you work out complicated equations.

Remember SOHCAHTOA can be used to show the ratio between angles and sides.

SOH (Sine = Opposite over Hypotenuse)

CAH (Cosine = Adjacent over Hypotenuse)

TOA (Tangent = Opposite over Adjacent)

Check your knowledge

1. If a transformer has no losses what does this mean?
   a) Power in equals power out
   b) Power in is less than power out
   c) Power out is less than power in
   d) Power out is double the power in

2. A transformer is associated with:
   a) Self-induction
   b) Electromagnetism
   c) Magnetic induction
   d) Mutual induction

3. A fluorescent luminaire emits light due to electricity passing through what?
   a) The starter
   b) The filament
   c) The gas
   d) The choke

4. Which configuration gives us two values of voltage?
   a) Star
   b) Delta
   c) Star two-phase
   d) Delta four-wire

5. In a three-phase system, what is the function of the neutral cable?
   a) Produces 230 V
   b) Carries unbalanced currents
   c) Produces 400 V
   d) Carries balanced currents

6. Which of the following may be defined as 'the capacity for doing work'?
   a) Energy
   b) Work done
   c) Power
   d) Velocity

7. RMS can be defined or seen as:
   a) The useful aspect of a sine wave
   b) The equivalent DC value
   c) 230 V
   d) All the above

8. A relay operates through:
   a) Self-induction
   b) Electromagnetism
   c) Magnetic induction
   d) Mutual induction

9. If a conductor within an alternator cuts the magnetic field at 45 degrees the output will be:
   a) Maximum
   b) Minimum
   c) 50%
   d) 25%

10. An electromagnetic device which controls a large electrical supply by switching a smaller powered circuit is known as:
    a) A transformer
    b) A diode
    c) A relay
    d) An inductor

11. Lines of magnetic field flow from:
    a) North to north
    b) South to south
    c) North to south
    d) South to north

12. A solenoid operates through:
    a) Magnetism
    b) Heat
    c) Chemical reaction
    d) Light

Student Book answers

Chapter 1

Page 26

1. Care for the welfare, health and safety of employees; provide and maintain safe equipment, tools and plant within the workplace; ensure working conditions are safe and hygienic; provide PPE; ensure articles and substances are used/handled/stored/transported safely; provide information/instruction/training/supervision.

2. No, not the same. The employee has a duty to cooperate with the employer to enable the regulations to be complied with. The level of responsibility you hold to make sure the regulations are met depends on the amount of control you have over electrical safety in any situation. Regulation 3(2)(b) of the EAWR repeats the duties placed on employees by HASAWA, equivalent to those placed on employers and the self-employed where these matters are within their control.

3. Properly assessed before use to ensure it is suitable; maintained and stored properly; employees provided with instruction on how to use it safely; employer should ensure it is used correctly by employees.

Page 38

1. Reporting of Injuries, Diseases and Dangerous Occurrences Regulations. RIDDOR places a legal duty on employers, the self-employed and those in control of premises to report work-related accidents, diseases and dangerous occurrences to the relevant enforcing authority, usually HSE.

2. Answers include: fractures (other than to fingers, thumbs and toes); amputations; serious burns covering more than 10% of the body; any injury likely to lead to permanent loss or reduction in sight; any loss of consciousness caused by head injury or asphyxia.

3. There would also need to be a risk of drowning if someone fell from the scaffold.

Page 48

1. A first-aid box, with enough equipment to cope with the number of workers on site. An appointed person to take charge of all first aid arrangements. Information telling workers the name of the appointed person or first aider and where to find them.

2. They should have two first aiders as if there are more than 50 workers on site there should be one additional first aider for every 50 workers.

3. Check for your own safety and make sure you do not put yourself at risk by helping the casualty.

Page 61

1. Waste prevention. This could be achieved by using less product packaging, restricting junk mail, using re-usable shopping bags or sustainability in the building.

2. 10 categories.

3. Check noise, odours and other emissions near the boundary of the site during different operating conditions and make sure there is a good level of housekeeping by regularly checking the site for waste accumulation, evidence of vermin, noise or a smell as applicable.

Page 69

1. Five stages. 1 Identify the hazard. 2 Decide who might be harmed and how. 3 Evaluate the risks and decide on precautions. 4 Record your findings and implement them. 5 Review your assessments and update it if necessary.

2. The young person will most likely have less experience of hazardous substances and situations and may also work at a slower pace than other more experienced employees.

3. Check with an appropriate person before you begin work.

Page 75

1. Your helmet must be replaced.

2. High-visibility jacket, high-visibility waistcoat, overalls and sunscreen.

3. In dusty environments, working with asbestos, where noxious odours are present and where certain gases are present.

Page 77

1. Answers should include:
   • Carry out a risk assessment
   • Step 1 Identify the hazards.
   • Step 2 Decide who might be harmed and how.
   • Step 3 Evaluate the risks and decide on precautions.
   • Step 4 Record your findings and implement them.
   • Step 5 Review your assessment and update it if necessary.

2. Answers should include: hard hat, goggles, safety footwear, overalls, hearing protection, dust mask

   If the material was damaged and you were injured then responsibility would apply to employee for using defective equipment and/or the employer if the faulty equipment had been notified and not replaced.

3. Answer should include:
   • Prohibition – circular, red border and cross, black symbol on white background
   • Mandatory – circular, white symbol on blue background
   • Warning – triangular, yellow background with black border and symbol
   • Information – square or rectangular, white symbols on a green background

4. The accident indicates that there was a breakdown in procedure and the supply was on when work began. Follow the steps for making sure the area is safe, breaking electrical contact, summoning help and then beginning CPR.

Page 87

1. Use the main switch or DB switch disconnector mounted within the DB then use a locking off device with a key or combination that remains in the possession of the person carrying out the work.

2. Phase(s) – CPC, Phase(s) – Neutral, Neutral – CPC

3. Replace/repair device and begin isolation process again.

Page 99

1. Slips, trips and falls.

2. Instruction in the proper use handling and transport of materials, tools and equipment normally by a supervisor during a site toolbox talk or induction.

3. Reduce the need for hazardous manual handling so far as reasonably practicable, assess the risk of injury from any manual handling that cannot be avoided and reduce the risk of injury from hazardous manual handling so far as reasonably practicable.

4. Mechanical handling aids.

Page 111

1. Advance guardrail method and Through the trap method.

2. Anything above or below ground level.

3. 1 Tie the ladder to a suitable point; 2 Use a safe unsecured ladder or a ladder supplemented with an effective ladder stability device; 3 Securely wedge the ladder (e.g. against a wall); 4 As a last resort get someone to foot the ladder.

4. Collapse and burying or injuring people, material falling from the sides into the excavation and people or plant falling into excavations.

Chapter 2

Page 140

1. Motivation, instruction, monitoring and co-operation.

2. Direct observation, written examination, interview and reports or written documents.

3. At the storming stage as the leader is being challenged and other members could become involved in a power struggle and find it hard to reach an agreement.

Page 145

1. Check competency cards, check technical qualifications, ask for written references and by monitoring performance.

2. It will show if they have the relevant experience and if they have the attitude and skills to deal with the work.

3. CSCS and ECS cards.

Page 152

1. The quantity surveyor prepares an initial bill of quantities and an estimator's job is to calculate the total cost that will be given in at the time of tender.

2. Oversee the work of the contract engineers, may also be responsible during the tendering stage for deciding if a tender is to be submitted and the costs and rates to be used in it.

3. An apprentice will actually carry out the electrical work with the guidance of a supervisor whereas an electrical technician will carry out surveys of electrical systems, update electrical drawings, maintain records, obtain costs and assist in the inspection, commissioning, testing and maintenance of electrical systems and services. This means that they have a higher level of responsibility.

Page 166

1. On a small project the electrician may have to produce a work plan, all these skills will be accumulated together to produce a complete work plan. This may include producing drawings and specifications.

2. An example such as the overrun of a previous project or having project Variation Orders.

3. You could study the critical path to see if any changes could be made to make up the time.

Page 176

1. Common Law, UK Legislation and European Legislation/ECJ.

2. The Equality Act 2010.

3. Under the terms of GDPR, not only will organisations have to ensure personal data is gathered legally and under strict conditions, but those who collect and manage it will be obliged to protect it from misuse and exploitation, as well as respecting the rights of data owners – or face penalties for not doing so.

Chapter 3

Page 211

1. BODMAS – Brackets, Other operations, Division, Multiplication, Addition and Subtraction.

2. A fraction.

3. What you do to one side of the equation, you must do to the other side. Transposition.

Page 221

1. Mass is the amount of stuff or matter contained in an object whereas weight is a force and depends on how much gravity pulls on a mass.

2. There are three classes.

3. $MA = \frac{Load}{Effort} = \frac{45}{15} = 3$

4. It does not have limited use. It can still be effective as a small effort can go a long way. For example, lifting a car to change a tyre.

Page 232

1. Solid, liquid, gas, plasma and Bose Einstein.

2. Electrons, protons and neutrons.

3. An insulator does not allow free passage of electrons through them whereas a conductor allows electrons to move freely through.

Page 253

1. $I = \frac{V}{R}$ $I = \frac{230}{23}$ $I = 10\,A$

2. Yes

3. $I = \frac{P}{V}$ $I = \frac{3000}{230}$ $I = 13.04\,A$

Page 268

1. Permanent magnet and electromagnet.

2. Contacts and a coil.

3. Clockwise direction.

Page 271

1. It is when the flow of electrons rises to a maximum value and then falls back to zero before repeating the process in the opposite direction.

2. Higher voltages cannot easily be used with the DC system as transformers don't work with DC. AC allows smaller cables to be used. AC motors are often cheaper and easier to build.

3. 50 Hz.

Page 296

1. Fixed and variable.

2. Band 1 is first figure of value, Band 2 is second figure of value, Band 3 is the number of zeros and Band 4 is the tolerance.

3. A thermistor is temperature sensitive whereas a standard resistor is not.

4. 200 000 000 pF with a tolerance of 10% and a max working voltage of 400 V.

Page 325

1. The base must be very thin, majority carriers in the base must be very few and the base emitter junction must be forward biased, and the base-collector junction reverse biased.

2. Diac.

Page 340

1. Mast mounted and roof mounted.

2. By using a steam turbine.

3. 11 kV.

Page 348

1. Primary windings and secondary windings.

2. A step-up transformer.

Page 369

1. Resistance, inductive reactance and capacitive reactance.

2. By a phasor diagram.

Page 378

1. One.

2. It is used to represent the relationship between the apparent power of a circuit and the true power.

Page 412

1. Has more power for a given size than any other normal AC motor, has high starting torque and relatively cheaper to produce.

2. Field winding, squirrel cage rotor, rotor shaft and the steel frame or yolk.

3. To reduce losses.

Page 434

1. Grease could be deposited on the quartz glass tube causing small cracks and fissures in the tube when the lamp heats rapidly.

2. They save energy and last longer.

3. Luminous intensity and measured in candelas.

Page 444

1. Storage and instantaneous.

2. Provide independent temperature control for heating and hot water.

3. Climate change.

Multiple-choice questions

Chapter 1

1 (b)

2 (a)

3 (d)

4 (c)

5 (a)

6 (d)

7 (d)

8 (b)

9 (a)

10 (a)

11 (d)

12 (c)

Chapter 2

1 (d)

2 (b)

3 (b)

4 (d)

5 (a)

6 (c)

7 (d)

8 (a)

9 (d)

10 (a)

Chapter 3

1 (a)

2 (d)

3 (c)

4 (a)

5 (a) and (b)

6 (a)

7 (d)

8 (b)

9 (c)

10 (c)

11 (c)

12 (a)

Glossary

Acronym – an abbreviation of several words in such a way that the abbreviation itself forms a pronounceable word (e.g. BODMAS); this often helps you to remember a topic.

Alloy – a mixture of two elements.

Apparent power – in an AC circuit the sum of the true or active power and the reactive power.

Arcing – a plasma discharge as a result of current flowing between two terminals through a normally non-conductive media (such as air), producing high light and heat.

Bill of quantities – a list of all the materials required, their specification and the quantities needed; contractors who are tendering for the project use this information to prepare their estimates.

Carbon footprint – the total amount of greenhouse gases produced by an organisation, event, product or person.

Child(ren) – according to the Education Act 1996, persons who are below Minimum School Leaving Age (MSLA); this will be 15 or 16 years old depending on when their birthday falls.

Contract – a legally binding agreement between two or more parties.

Data – factual information and statistics used as a basis for discussion, calculation or analysis.

DB – the abbreviation for decibel, the unit in which noise level is measured.

Dermatitis – inflammation of the skin normally caused by contact with irritating substances.

Detailed visual inspection – a more detailed inspection for visible defects according to the manufacturer's instructions, the results of which should be recorded.

Dielectric – an electrical insulator that can be polarised by an applied electric field.

Disability – a physical or mental impairment that has a substantial and long-term effect on a person's ability to carry out normal everyday activities.

Dual in-line IC – the type of IC with the pins lined up down each side.

Embolism – an obstruction in a blood vessel due to a blood clot in the bloodstream.

Explosive limits – the upper and lower percentages of a gas in a given volume of gas/air mixture at normal atmospheric temperature and pressure that will burn if ignited.

Flash point – the minimum temperature at which a material gives off sufficient vapour to form an explosive atmosphere.

Friction – force that opposes motion.

Genuine Occupational Requirements – where an employer can demonstrate that there is a genuine identified need for someone of a specific race or gender to the exclusion of others (for example, a film company needs an Indian actor for a film set in India, or a modelling agency needs a woman to model female clothes).

Hygroscopic – the ability to absorb water.

Hysteresis – a generic term meaning a lag in the effect of a change of force.

Ignition energy – the spark energy that will ignite the most easily ignited gas/air mixture of the test gas at atmospheric pressure; hydrogen ignites very easily, whereas butane or methane require about ten times the energy.

Ignition temperature or auto-ignition temperature – the minimum temperature at which a material will ignite and sustain combustion when mixed with air at normal pressure, without the ignition being caused by any spark or flame (note: this is not the same as flash point, so don't confuse them).

Impedance – total opposition to current in a circuit.

Isolators – mechanical switching devices that separate an installation from every source of electrical energy.

Kirchhoff's Law – the sum of the voltage drops around a closed loop in the network must equal zero.

Lower explosive limit (LEL) – the concentration below which the gas atmosphere is not explosive.

Noise pollution – excessive noise from any source, but particularly industrial sources, that spoils people's experience of the environment; examples could be noise from machinery, plant or power tools.

Oxidation – a chemical process in which a substance combines with oxygen. During this process, energy is given off, usually in the form of heat.

Pole pair – any system consisting of a north and south pole.

Pre-check – a basic visual check done to spot obvious defects.

Pulping – where paper-based products are dropped into a huge tank and blitzed with water, which separates the paper from any impurities.

Scaled drawing – a drawing on which everything is drawn at a fixed ratio to the size of the actual object; this ratio is called the scale of the drawing, and should be indicated on the drawing itself.

Snagging – a list of omissions, normally prepared by the Consulting Engineer, that require correction before an installation can be classed as complete.

Thermal comfort – an individual's preferred temperature. Environmental factors (such as humidity and sources of heat in the workplace) combine with personal factors (such as the clothing a worker is wearing and how physically demanding their work is) to influence this.

Thesaurus – a type of dictionary that lists words with similar meanings.

Tinnitus – a permanent ringing in the ears.

True or active power – the rate at which energy is used.

Upper explosive limit (UEL) – the concentration of gas above which the gas atmosphere is not explosive.

Valence electrons – the electrons in an atom's outermost orbit.

Wind farm – a large number of wind turbines gathered in one location; there are currently onshore and off-shore wind farms in the UK.

Windage – the air resistance of a moving object or the force of the wind on a stationary object.

Young people – according to the Management of Health and Safety at Work Regulations, people who have not reached the age of 18.

Index